Willard Maclean

66. Walter Road.
Swansea.
19.5.59.

LAW AND ETHICS FOR DOCTORS

LAW AND ETHICS FOR DOCTORS

WITH A SECTION ON GENERAL PRACTICE IN THE NATIONAL HEALTH SERVICE

by

STEPHEN J. HADFIELD

M.A., M.B., B.Chir. (Cantab.)
M.R.C.S., L.R.C.P., D.Obst.R.C.O.G.
Assistant Secretary, British Medical Association

WITH CONTRIBUTED SECTIONS ON

NEGLIGENCE

by W. G. Hawkins and the late W. Mair

SUPERANNUATION

by L. S. Potter, M.B., Ch.B.
Medical Director of the Medical Practices Advisory Bureau and Assistant Secretary, British Medical Association

INCOME TAX

by W. Donald, C.A.
Accountant to the British Dental Association

LONDON
EYRE & SPOTTISWOODE
1958

FIRST PUBLISHED IN 1958

PRINTED IN GREAT BRITAIN
BY BILLING AND SONS LIMITED
GUILDFORD AND LONDON

CATALOGUE NUMBER 6/6052

FOREWORD

by Solomon Wand, D.C.L., M.B., Ch.B.
CHAIRMAN OF COUNCIL, BRITISH MEDICAL ASSOCIATION

Such are the grave responsibilities and obligations that flow from the powers and privileges of a doctor that even two and a half thousand years ago Hippocrates found it necessary to formulate a code of professional conduct. The basic principles of that code still apply, but the complexities of a doctor's life in modern times have led to its elaboration, not only to protect the patient but also the doctor himself.

In the field of legislation, particularly since the advent of the National Health Service, the doctor has to be familiar with the provisions of innumerable Acts of Parliament, Regulations and procedures. Lack of knowledge of these and of the more material aspects of practice can have serious results for him and his family.

How is all this information acquired? Some he learns as a medical student as part of his curriculum, some by precept and the example of his colleagues. Much is contained in a medley of documents, often difficult to understand and easily misplaced. There still remain many problems to which an answer cannot be found in any readily identified publication.

In this book are gathered together for the first time, I believe, those matters touching ethics and law that so frequently present problems to the practising doctor. It will not have a place on the doctor's bookshelf; it will be on his desk, close to his hand.

No longer will the doctor be able to say 'I didn't know'.

PREFACE

The practitioner of medicine today finds that, more than ever before, Acts of Parliament and Regulations impinge daily upon his work. This book has been written in order to make some knowledge of the law easily available to him. More particularly in regard to the National Health Service the book is primarily for general practitioners, but the majority of the material is general and is applicable to practitioners in all fields of medical work.

It became evident in the early stages of composition that there is no real substitute for the wording of Acts and Regulations. In attempting to set out and explain the salient facts regarding legislation relevant to the practice of medicine it has been found necessary to sacrifice minute detail in many places in the cause of clarity. Consequently the pages of the book contain a description of the general meaning of the law and a guide to its application to the conduct of a doctor's practice. The intention is to provide a signpost rather than a detailed map of the journey. Nevertheless it is hoped that most of the possible hazards are clearly indicated.

Certain extracts and quotations from Acts and Regulations are reproduced in the text and appendices and I gratefully acknowledge the permission for this granted by Her Majesty's Stationery Office. I am also grateful to the Registrar of the General Medical Council for permission to reproduce the Warning Notice and the list of registrable qualifications and for helpful advice.

The writing of this book has been greatly facilitated by the fact that, as an official of the British Medical Association and for some time secretary of its Central Ethical Committee, I have enjoyed special opportunities, including access to the Association's files, of studying medico-ethical and medico-legal rulings. I wish to record also my indebtedness to the Association for permission to reproduce the Code contained in Appendix C.

It is a real pleasure to thank Dr L. S. Potter for his co-operation in writing the section on Superannuation, Mr W. Donald for the section on Income Tax and Mr W. G. Hawkins who wrote the section on Negligence; and, with sadness, to record my gratitude to the late Mr W. Mair, who so kindly added a section on negligence in Scotland and gave me useful advice. I count myself fortunate in having had the services of such collaborators and to be able to add that I have also had the benefit of helpful advice and constructive suggestion from my colleagues Dr John Thwaites and Dr J. T. McCutcheon.

At all times during the preparation of the book I have had the kind and wise help of the publishers, Messrs Eyre and Spottiswoode, which help I gratefully acknowledge.

My whole task has been immeasurably lightened by the efficient secretarial assistance given willingly and cheerfully by Mrs David Cairns, to whom I tender my warmest thanks.

CONTENTS

1

THE PRIVY COUNCIL

To begin a book of general guidance for doctors with a description of two bodies from whom the individual doctor must usually feel rather remote might seem, at first sight, inappropriate. Nevertheless much of the ordering of the training and discipline of the profession stems from the seemingly remotely placed General Medical Council, with the even more distant Privy Council placed somewhere above and beyond it. The majority of doctors have little or no contact with the General Medical Council, except at the time of registration in the first instance and, subsequently, of additional qualifications and when they notify, as they should, changes of address. Yet the General Medical Council exercises a continuing interest in the profession as a whole and in every individual doctor as occasion arises.

An outline of the functions and activities of these two bodies as they affect the profession is, therefore, given at the outset of this book before proceeding to the more detailed study of the day-to-day problems of doctors in general and of general practitioners in particular.

The Privy Council is a body whose jurisdiction dates from far back in history. Its Judicial Committee was set up in the early part of the nineteenth century. Its members are mainly the Law Lords and retired English and Scottish Judges. When the Judicial Committee sits a quorum of three is necessary. Since the Medical Act of 1950 a practitioner has a right of appeal to the Judicial Committee from decisions of the Medical Disciplinary Committee of the General Medical Council.

Functions and Powers

The Privy Council has certain duties, responsibilities and supervisory functions in respect of the General Medical

Council. It has an overriding relationship to the General Medical Council regarding a number of its functions, for example the maintenance of a high standard of medical education.

The General Medical Council may report to the Privy Council on the standards of qualification of a licensing body and recommend that, the examinations not being up to the required standard, its graduates may no longer be admitted to the Medical Register and that its representatives may no longer sit on the Council. The Privy Council may, after hearing objection from the licensing body, order that the qualification be no longer accepted for registration. The recommendation, if so endorsed by the Privy Council, must be tabled in Parliament. The General Medical Council itself has no actual powers in this regard. The order may be revoked, and the qualification be restored, when the required improvements have been instituted.

The Privy Council may, if applied to, overrule the General Medical Council in their refusal to recognize any overseas diploma. Any Commonwealth or foreign practitioner refused registration on grounds other than that he does not hold a recognized diploma has a right of appeal to the Privy Council, which may either dismiss the appeal or order the General Medical Council to enter the name of the appellant on the Register.

The Rules of the Medical Disciplinary Committee and also the remuneration for persons performing various services for the Council, for example Assessors to the Medical Disciplinary Committee and visitors to medical schools, are subject to the approval of the Privy Council.

The Privy Council may order an increase or decrease in the limits for the fees to be paid on provisional registration and on registration.

All powers vested in the Privy Council by the Medical Acts may be exercised by any two or more members of the Privy Council. Any Act of the Privy Council is signified by an instrument signed by the Clerk to the Council.

The Privy Council receives copies of reports received by the General Medical Council from the visitors to medical schools and inspectors of examinations.

The Privy Council considers any proposals for revision of the constitution of the General Medical Council and advises Her Majesty accordingly. It also advises the Sovereign with regard to members of the General Medical Council to be nominated by Her Majesty.

2

THE GENERAL MEDICAL COUNCIL

The Medical Acts

The Medical Act, 1858

'Whereas it is expedient that persons requiring medical aid should be enabled to distinguish qualified from unqualified practitioners.' So runs the preamble to The Medical Act of 1858, the first Medical Act, making it clear that the purpose of the Act is to protect the public from being imposed upon by those without proper training and with an imperfect knowledge of medicine.

Through all the centuries of the history of the British Isles before 1858 there could hardly be identified a trained and qualified medical profession as a separate entity.

Thus it was that in the first half of the nineteenth century the people of Great Britain and Ireland were medically treated by both trained professional men and by quacks. The latter were as free to practise medicine as the former and there were no restrictions on their activities, nor were there any simple means by which the patient could distinguish the one from the other.

In 1858 was passed The Medical Act, an Act to regulate the qualifications of practitioners in medicine and surgery.

The Act set up the General Council of Medical Education and Registration of the United Kingdom. This body soon became known as The General Medical Council, a name which was, under Section 13 of the Medical Act, 1950, officially adopted in place of the original but usefully descriptive title. Under the General Council were Branch Councils for Scotland and for Ireland. Wales was not specifically mentioned in the Act but for its purpose has been administered with England by the Branch Council for England. The Registrar of the Council is charged with the duty of compiling and keeping up to date the Medical Register, and with the control of the admission and removal of names to and from the Register.

The Council was by the Act empowered to require information regarding courses of study or examinations conducted by any College of Corporation and was entitled to report any deficiencies to the Privy Council, which might suspend the rights of registration in respect of qualifications achieved by passing such examinations.

The Act severely restricted the activities of non-registered practitioners and prescribed penalties for false registration or for falsely pretending to be registered. By the Act the Council was also charged with the publication and republication of the British Pharmacopoeia and amendments to it, as the Council deems necessary.

The Medical Act, 1886

In the Medical Act of 1886 the powers of the General Medical Council were increased in respect of qualifying examinations. The Council was called upon to secure the maintenance of the standard of proficiency required and to appoint inspectors to report on examinations and could recommend withdrawal of the right to hold qualifying examinations. Provision was made in this Act for the admission of Colonial (later (1950) termed Commonwealth) practitioners and foreign practitioners to the Register under certain conditions. Separate lists are required to be kept for these two categories.

The Medical Act, 1950

The Medical Act, 1950, represented a milestone in the course of the recent history of the profession in that it instituted a further requirement before full registration. This requirement is that of experience after qualifying. It introduced provisional registration and a register of provisionally registered medical practitioners. The experience required for full registration is obtained during the period of provisional registration.

Amendments were made in respect of the members of the General Medical Council nominated by the Sovereign; and the Royal College of Obstetricians and Gynaecologists was added to those bodies permitted to nominate a member of the Council; the number of members elected by the profession was increased for England, Wales and Scotland, with an additional provision to ensure the election of a practitioner from Wales.

The other main provisions were the alteration of the name of the Council to 'The General Medical Council', the establishment of the Disciplinary Committee, increase in registration fees and their subdivision into the fees for provisional registration and for full registration, and the increase of the maximum penalty for falsely pretending to be a registered person from £20 to £500.

The Medical Act, 1956

In 1956 it was considered necessary to prepare a Bill, which subsequently became law, in order to consolidate the Medical Acts and to effect corrections and minor improvements. The effect of this Act was not to alter the laws governing the profession.

The Constitution of the General Medical Council

The General Medical Council consists partly of elected members and partly of appointed members. The normal term of office is five years so that major changes in the composition may normally be expected only once in five years. The body consists of forty-seven members and is made up as follows:

Elected by the Medical Profession:		
Registered medical practitioners for England and Wales	8	
Registered medical practitioners for Scotland	2	
Registered medical practitioners for Northern Ireland and Eire	1	11
Nominated by The Crown:		
Registered medical practitioners (3 for England and Wales; 1 for Scotland; 1 for Northern Ireland)	5	
Not registered or holding any registrable qualification (2 for England and Wales, 1 for Scotland)	3	8
Representatives of Universities, Medical Corporations and Royal Colleges		28
		47

The President is included in the forty-seven and is elected by the members. Membership is open to either sex. The Universities, Medical Corporations and the Royal Colleges each nominate one member, who must be a registered medical practitioner.

Voting

The elected members are elected by postal ballot by fully registered medical practitioners in the three separate electoral areas of (i) England and Wales, (ii) Scotland and (iii) Northern Ireland and Eire.

Each registered medical practitioner has as many votes as there are vacancies in his electoral area. Both English and Welsh constituents vote for all the vacancies in their joint electoral area, with the special proviso that the eight declared elected shall include the candidate resident in Wales (including the county of Monmouth) who obtains more votes than any other candidate resident in Wales.

More than one Welsh resident may in fact be returned but the number of English residents is restricted to seven to make certain the return of at least one Welshman. It is theoretically possible for all eight elected in this constituency to be Welsh residents. The nomination paper of each candidate must bear the signatures of at least twelve registered medical practitioners.

Term of Office

The term of office of an elected member is five years, at the end of which he is eligible for re-election. If he vacates his office before the expiry of his term of office his successor, when elected or appointed, holds office only until the conclusion of the term of office of his predecessor. If the place is vacated less than one year before the normal expiry of the term of office, no election of a successor takes place during that term. An 'appointed' member remains a member for the length of time stated by the appointing body at the time of appointment. This period may be up to five years.

Branch Councils

There are Branch Councils for England and Wales, for Scotland, and for Ireland respectively. Each member of the

General Medical Council is a member of the Branch Council for the area for which he has been elected or appointed.

The addresses of the Branch Councils are:

The Registrar, General Medical Council, 44 Hallam Street, London, W.1. (This office covers the Branch Council for England and Wales.)

The Registrar, Branch Council for Scotland, 8 Queen Street, Edinburgh 2.

The Registrar, Branch Council for Ireland, 68 Fitzwilliam Square, Dublin.

3

THE MEDICAL REGISTER

Although most of the information given in this chapter is applicable only once to each individual doctor, reference to the details of provisional registration and of registration may be required from time to time. Particulars are given here as being descriptive of the essential process of becoming a legally qualified and registered medical practitioner. The onus of completing the various formalities and taking the succession of necessary steps to this end rests with the would-be registered medical practitioner. He will obtain guidance from what follows on all the usual steps that are to be taken. If there is some unusual circumstance regarding his application he should not hesitate to seek the guidance of the Registrar of the General Medical Council over any doubtful point.

It is the duty of the Registrar of the General Medical Council to keep and maintain the Medical Register and to publish it.

The Register must contain the names of all registered medical practitioners in alphabetical order with registered medical titles, degrees and diplomas conferred by any corporation or university. The 1858 Act included 'or by doctorate of the Archbishop of Canterbury', an interesting relic of the past which no longer applies.

Separate sections of the Register are kept for Commonwealth practitioners and for foreign practitioners. These are defined below.

A separate part of the Register is kept for provisionally registered practitioners. This may be published separately at such time as the Council may direct and is called 'The Register of Provisional Medical Registrations'.

The Medical Register and the Register of Provisional Medical Registrations are admitted as evidence in Courts of

Law. Absence of a name from the Medical Register is evidence, until the contrary is proved, that that person is not a registered medical practitioner. A certified true copy of an entry in the Register shall, however, be evidence of medical registration.

Admission to the Register

Before the Appointed Day under the 1950 Medical Act (January 1st, 1953) admission to the Medical Register was achieved by applying with evidence of the holding of a registrable qualification and the payment of the statutory fee.

Provisional Registration

The Medical Act of 1950 introduced the additional requirement, for full registration after January 1st, 1953, of proof of experience. Full registration is no longer granted without proof of experience. The period required for this experience is known as the pre-registration period and its duration is prescribed by Regulations of the General Medical Council (approved by order of the Privy Council). The period prescribed at present is one year and the experience required is six months in employment in a resident* medical capacity as a house officer in medicine and six months in a similar capacity in surgery. One period of six months as a resident house officer in midwifery may be substituted for either the prescribed six months in medicine, or in surgery, but not both. In all cases the periods of six months must be in one or more approved hospitals or approved institutions. In this context an institution includes a health centre provided under Section 21 of N.H.S. Act, 1946, and similar clauses (15 and 17) of the Scottish and N.I. Acts or a health centre provided under the law of the Republic of Ireland.

Employment in a health centre must either be by a registered medical practitioner in the provision of general medical services under the Acts or in the provision of specialist services, as mentioned in paragraph (*e*) of Sub-section (1) of Section 21 of the Act of 1946 and similarly in the Scottish and

* The term 'resident' is interpreted as including residence conveniently near to the hospital (The Medical Act, 1950, Period of Employment as House Officers), Regulations (G.M.C. Regulations, 1951, No. 3) and (Experience before full Registration) Regulations (G.M.C. Regulations, 1951, No. 4).

Irish Acts. By regulation of the General Medical Council the period of such service in an approved health centre is limited to six months.

Commonwealth or foreign practitioners may achieve United Kingdom registration by satisfying the Council that they have undergone comparable experience.

Proof of Experience

The proof of experience required by the General Medical Council takes the form of a certificate to the effect that the body granting the qualifying diploma to the applicant is satisfied that he has engaged in the necessary two periods of six months' service in approved posts and that his service, while so employed, has been satisfactory. The period required for the experience before full registration has come to be known as the pre-registration period and the posts held during this time as pre-registration posts. It is of the utmost importance for a provisionally registered practitioner to realize that it is only the body that has granted him his qualifying diploma that can grant him the certificate of proof of experience necessary for full registration. Such a certificate will only be granted in respect of service in posts in hospitals or institutions that are approved for the time being for the purpose by any university or other corporation empowered to grant a qualifying diploma, Commonwealth or foreign diplomas being excluded. In the Republic of Ireland approval of posts and hospitals is by the Medical Registration Council and not by the universities and diploma granting bodies.

If there should be any doubt in the mind of a provisionally registered practitioner as to whether the post he is about to take will be accepted for the purposes of the certificate he is advised to seek confirmation that it will be so accepted from the responsible officer of the body that will be called upon to grant the certificate.

There is no restriction laid down on the length of time that may elapse between the granting of a qualifying diploma and the application for full registration. That is to say a practitioner may remain provisionally registered for an indefinite period. As examples, progress towards completing experience may be impeded by illness or interrupted for other reasons such as marriage. The experience may be completed in future years. It follows, however, that during the whole of this period he will be subject to the restrictions that apply to the provisionally registered.

The restrictions which apply are that the provisionally registered is only deemed to be registered in so far as it is necessary to enable him to carry out the duties of the pre-registration posts.

The provisionally registered practitioner guilty of offences is liable to removal from the Register of Provisionally Registered Practitioners in a manner similar to that which applies to registered medical practitioners and for similar reasons.

Cases of Physical Disability

A person suffering from 'a lasting disability' which prevents him from undertaking or completing the necessary period of experience in surgery or midwifery, may apply to the General Medical Council for permission to complete his pre-registration year by additional experience in medicine, in lieu of the surgical or midwifery experience that would otherwise be required.

How to become Provisionally Registered

Before applying to the appropriate Registrar for provisional registration, the applicant must satisfy two requirements. He must hold a qualifying diploma (see Appendix A) and he must produce evidence satisfactory to the Registrar that he has been appointed to an approved pre-registration post. If these two conditions are fulfilled he is entitled to be provisionally registered on payment of the statutory fee.* Under The Medical Practitioners Act, 1951, of the Republic of Ireland, however, Irish graduates in Ireland have a right to provisional registration on qualifying and do not have to await appointment to an approved post.

The application should be made to the Registrar of the Branch Council for the country in which the diploma was granted.

In England or Wales the application should be made to the Registrar, The General Medical Council, 44 Hallam

* For fees for Provisional Registration see Appendix F.

Street, London, W.1, in Scotland to the Branch Council for Scotland, 8 Queen Street, Edinburgh, and in Ireland to the Branch Council for Ireland, 68 Fitzwilliam Square, Dublin.

Application for provisional registration may be made by post with the fee and evidence of each qualification in respect of which the applicant requires to be provisionally registered, stating the date on which it was obtained. The 1956 Act expressly permits the Registrar to accept, as evidence of qualification, certified lists of those qualifying (i.e. entitled to be registered) issued from time to time by the body granting the diploma.

Thus for full registration the practitioner must produce the following certificates:

- a certificate of acceptance for each pre-registration appointment;
- a certificate by the employing authority of satisfactory service in each pre-registration appointment. This certificate is issued on evidence provided by the member of the consultant or specialist staff under whom the applicant has worked;
- a certificate of proof of experience, signed by the authorized officer of the licensing body, after the completion of the appointments.

It has been stated in the Minutes of the General Medical Council (November 23rd, 1954) that it is not legally open to a licensing body to grant a certificate of experience until twelve months have elapsed since the date when the applicant, having previously passed his qualifying examination, first became engaged in employment as a house officer in an approved hospital and until six months have passed since the applicant began to be engaged on his second period of employment.

Employment of Provisionally Registered Practitioners

So far as a hospital authority is concerned, any provisionally registered practitioner may be employed either fully in post as a provisionally registered house officer or as locum tenens in an approved post. It does not matter to the employing authority whether or not the practitioner intends to have the period of employment counted towards his proof of experience, so long as the employment falls within the definition in Section 15 (7) of the Medical Act, 1956 (formerly set down in Section 2 (5) of the Medical Act, 1950).

The following Opinion of the legal Assessor to the General Medical Council, quoted by the President in his address to the Council on 19 May, 1953, states also that a provisionally registered practitioner may be so employed in any post in an approved hospital:

> 'A person who is provisionally registered may lawfully be employed, whether as a locum tenens or not, in a resident medical capacity (as defined in section 2 (5)) in any approved Hospital and it is immaterial (to the Hospital) whether he wishes or intends that the period of such employment shall be counted hereafter towards his twelve months' pre-registration intern service or whether or not he intends ever to become fully registered. Nor, so long as the employment falls within the definition given in section 2 (5), does it matter to the Hospital (though it may matter to the employee) that the post itself has not been approved by any Licensing Body. The Act is not concerned with the approving of posts as opposed to the approving of Hospitals.'

Full Registration*

Full registration is not granted except by way of provisional registration.

The exception to this is the case of a person claiming registration by virtue of a Commonwealth or foreign diploma where the Council is satisfied that the applicant has had employment in medicine and surgery similar to that required of persons in the United Kingdom and has given satisfactory service during that time. Alternatively, it will suffice if the Council is satisfied that the applicant has given satisfactory service in an appointment or appointments overseas (whether or not in British Dominions) which confer experience in medicine and surgery, or in medicine, surgery and midwifery not less extensive than that experienced in pre-registration posts in the United Kingdom or has otherwise acquired the necessary experience.

* For fees for Registration see Appendix F.

A person holding a qualifying diploma granted by a licensing body in the Republic of Ireland cannot be provisionally registered unless he is provisionally registered under the similar law of the Republic of Ireland (The Medical Practitioners Act, 1957). If he is so provisionally registered no fee is payable for provisional registration in the United Kingdom. Hospitals and Institutions in the Republic of Ireland require to be approved by the Medical Registration Council or a body acting on its behalf. The certificates of satisfactory service in approved posts are issued by the Medical Registration Council or a body acting on its behalf.

Any person who was, before January 1st, 1953, registered under the Medical Practitioners Act, 1927, of the Republic of Ireland and who is otherwise entitled to be registered under the Medical Acts, does not require to be provisionally registered before registration with the General Medical Council.

Registration by virtue of a qualification or qualifications granted in a Commonwealth country shall be registration as a Commonwealth practitioner, and by virtue of a qualification or qualifications granted in a foreign country shall be registration as a foreign practitioner, and a person entitled to be registered under this section both as a Commonwealth and as a foreign practitioner may be registered in both ways.

A 'Commonwealth practitioner' is a person holding some recognized medical diploma or diplomas granted to him in a Commonwealth country and is by law entitled to practise in that country. The diploma must have been obtained when not resident in the United Kingdom or in a period of not less than five years in the whole of which he resided out of the United Kingdom.

A 'foreign practitioner' is one similarly placed, but in respect of a recognized foreign diploma. For registration he must show either that he is not a British subject or, if he is a British subject, that the same requirements apply regarding domicile.

Before registration a Commonwealth practitioner or a foreign practitioner must statisfy the Registrar regarding the above-mentioned requirements and also that he is of good character.

Refusal to Register

The Registrar cannot enter a name on the Register or append an additional qualification unless he is satisfied that the person claiming is entitled. Any appeal against the decision of the Registrar falls to be decided by the Disciplinary Committee of the Council (see page 31).

Registration of Extra Qualifications

A registered medical practitioner on the Medical Register, or included in one of the separate lists for Commonwealth and foreign practitioners, may have a recognized Commonwealth or foreign diploma which he holds or acquires added to his name in the Medical Register, subject to payment of the appropriate fee. The approved qualifications for this purpose are the same as those approved for registration.

Every registered medical practitioner who obtains a registrable diploma or degree or qualification, other than that in respect of which he is registered, is entitled to have it added to his name on the register in addition to or as substitute for the original registered qualification, on payment of the fee of £1 for every qualification (1957) except for Diplomas of Public Health, Diplomas in State Medicine and Diplomas in Sanitary Science, for which the fee is £2 (1957).

The following are examples of additional qualifications that are registrable:

M.B., Ch.B., B.Chir., M.D., M.Chir., M.R.C.P., F.R.C.P., F.R.C.S., D.P.H., D.S.M. and D.S.Sc.

The following are examples of diplomas which are NOT registrable:

B.A.O., D.Obst.R.C.O.G., M.R.C.O.G., F.R.C.O.G., D.A., F.F.A., F.F.R., D.C.H., D.O., D.L.O., D.O.M.S., D.M.R.D., D.M.R.E., D.P.M., D.T.M. and D.T.H.

4

THE MEDICAL REGISTER

(continued)

The fact of registration, and in some degree of provisional registration, places the doctor in a special position, often responsible, sometimes privileged, in relation to the rest of the community. On the whole the granting of these responsibilities, often to the exclusion of others, and of privileges is to be regarded as being in the public interest rather than the doctors' and bears out one of the original intentions of the Medical Act, 1858, that of enabling the public to distinguish between the qualified and the unqualified.

Rights conferred by Registration

The Act of 1858 gave to a registered person the right to practise medicine as a registered medical practitioner in any part of Her Majesty's dominions. The Act of 1886 repealed this on the institution of the Colonial Register and the Foreign Register, thus confining the right to practice in the British Isles and 'subject to any local law, in any other part of Her Majesty's dominions'.

The right to practise Medicine

The majority of the rights of the registered are best expressed by indicating what an unregistered person may not do. The right to practise medicine is not reserved to those on the Register or Provisional Register. With the exception of midwifery and the treatment of venereal disease anyone, registered or not, trained or not, may practise medicine so long as he does not hold himself out to be a registered medical practitioner (or a provisionally registered medical practitioner).

Appointments

An unregistered person may not practise medicine or hold a medical appointment in Her Majesty's service, in a ship, in any hospital or place for the reception of persons of unsound mind, in a hospital or similar institution not supported wholly by voluntary contributions, in a prison or in any public institution or body; he may not be a Medical Officer of Health nor practise obstetrics or dentistry (Dentists Act, 1921) or treat venereal disease (Venereal Diseases Act, 1917). He may not act as Medical Officer to a friendly society or mutual benefit society.

A foreign unregistered person entitled to practise medicine in his own country may, however, act as resident physician or medical officer in a hospital established exclusively for the relief of foreigners in sickness.

Although no unregistered person may hold a post as a ship's medical officer, a person holding a medical diploma entitling him to practise in a Commonwealth country may hold an appointment as a medical officer in any vessel registered in that part of the Commonwealth.

Certificates

The Act of 1858 rendered invalid any certificate required from a medical practitioner under any Act then in force if signed by an unregistered person. The National Insurance Regulations, however, do not prohibit acceptance of certificates of incapacity from unregistered persons.* Unregistered persons are not employed as doctors in the Health Service, but any decision to accept their certificates in particular cases is continued recognition of the right of the individual to seek medical advice and treatment from whom he will. In the matters of childbirth and dental treatment, however, the right of the individual is restricted (see above).

Dangerous Drugs and Poisons

An unregistered person has no authority under the Dangerous Drugs Act and Poisons Rules such as is given to registered medical practitioners.

* See Appendix D.

Suing for Fees

A registered medical practitioner is entitled to recover fees, expenses and charges in a Court of Law. If he is a Fellow of a College of Physicians which has a bye-law prohibiting this he may not sue. Such a bye-law may be pleaded as a bar to any proceedings instituted by a Fellow for recovery of fees, etc. The unregistered person may not recover in a Court of Law any charge for giving medical or surgical advice, or attendance, or for the performance of any operation or for any medicine which he has prescribed and supplied.

Exemption from Public Duties

All registered medical practitioners actually engaged in practice have the right, if they so desire, to be exempted from serving on all Juries. They should give advance notice to the summoning authority, usually the Town Clerk, claiming exemption. In the original Act of 1858 exemption could be claimed from service in parochial, ward, hundred and township offices and in the Militia. With regard to the latter, however, in these modern times the medical practitioner is required to undergo his National Service unless he is the subject of some special exemption. If fully registered he will serve as a medical officer. He cannot do so if he is only on the provisional register but such persons are usually granted deferment on qualifying in order to enable them to achieve the necessary experience and become fully registered, after which they are called up. A practitioner who has already done his military service in another capacity, for example prior to or during his student days, is not liable to call up for the statutory National Service after registration.

Title and Description

In the early part of this century it used to be common enough to see the general practitioner's brass plate bearing the words 'Physician and Surgeon'—an accurate enough description, for in order to be registered it was necessary, and is so now in even greater degree, to have shown proficiency under both general headings. Such descriptions are still seen, although nowadays it is more common to have inscribed the name and abbreviations of the degrees (M.B., B.Chir., or M.R.C.S.,

L.R.C.P., for example). But whatever the brass plate proclaims it is almost universal to refer to a registered medical practitioner as 'Doctor'. Specialist surgeons are, by custom and their own preference, referred to as 'Mr', even when they have the degree of Doctor of Medicine. All other members of the profession, whether the possessors of a Doctorate or not, are referred to as Doctor. This is generally accepted as a convenient way of indicating the profession of the individual and is believed also to be a mark of respect. So customary has its use become that it does not constitute an offence or a departure from etiquette or any rule. The General Medical Council, however, as is proper in so official a body, confines the use of the term to those who have a registered qualification of Doctorate of Medicine.

While being perfectly proper for a registered practitioner to be so described and addressed the unregistered person is, if he permits such a style, placing himself in danger. He is by law prohibited from holding himself out to be a registered medical practitioner (or a provisionally registered medical practitioner). 'Holding himself out' means using such style or title, or representing himself in any way that might lead a member of the public to believe he is, in fact, a registered medical practitioner. The law is so expressed as to be difficult to evade. Any words meaning 'recognized by law as a medical practitioner or member of the medical profession' must only mean a person registered or provisionally registered under the Medical Acts. As an example one describing himself as a 'duly qualified medical practitioner' might well claim that, by the dictionary, his description was true. He might have passed his qualifying examinations and never registered, or his name might have been struck off the Register. So that, in either case, the description could be applied to him. But if he were so to describe himself he might well convey to the public by these words that he was a registered medical practitioner. Any person falsely representing himself to be a registered or provisionally registered medical practitioner is liable, on proof of the facts, to a fine not exceeding £500.

The penalty for procuring or attempting to procure registration by false declaration or representation is imprisonment for a term not exceeding one year.

Removal from the Register

The name of a registered or provisionally registered medical practitioner may be removed from the Register after conviction of certain offences, after being found guilty of infamous conduct in any professional respect, or as a result of the practitioner failing to reply to a letter of inquiry from the Registrar as to the practitioner's address.

The Registrar is automatically notified, by the Registrar of Deaths, of the death of a registered medical practitioner and on receipt of such notification the name of the practitioner is removed from the Register.

Disciplinary Erasure

Any medical practitioner convicted by any Court in the United Kingdom or Republic of Ireland of any felony, misdemeanour, crime or offence, is liable to have his name removed from the Register. The Courts, in all cases, report the facts to the General Medical Council which then instructs the Registrar.

When a practitioner has been convicted of a felony, misdemeanour, crime or offence, his name may be struck off the Register by direction of the Disciplinary Committee, without the holding of an inquiry. It is, however, customary for the Committee to hold an inquiry so that the practitioner may be heard by the Committee. Particularly in cases of conviction under the Dangerous Drugs Act, or of being in charge of a motor vehicle under the influence of drugs or drink, the Committee has sometimes postponed a decision as to erasure in order to allow the practitioner to undergo medical treatment or so to conduct himself as to be able to present proof of good behaviour at the end of a stated period and thus to avoid erasure.

With regard to infamous conduct in any professional respect, the General Medical Council can act only after holding an inquiry. (See under *Disciplinary Committee*, Chapter 5.)

When the name of a practitioner is removed from the Register on account of infamous conduct in a professional respect (penal erasure) the Registrar reports the fact to any licensing body that has granted him a registrable diploma. The diplomas then may be withdrawn from the practitioner by the licensing body if they so choose. It is open, however, to the Council to restore the practitioner's name to the Register at a subsequent date without awaiting the restoration of the diploma by the licensing body.

Failure to reply to Registrar's Inquiry

As part of his duty of keeping the Register up to date the Registrar is authorized by Section 41 of the 1956 Act to address a letter to persons on the Register to inquire whether they still practise medicine and whether they have changed their address. Failure to reply to this inquiry will result, at the end of six months, in the removal of that practitioner's name from the Register. In view of this it is as well for practitioners to notify the Registrar in advance of the intention to remain abroad for more than a short period. Changes of address should always be notified to the Registrar.

The name of a practitioner so erased may be restored at the discretion of the Council, but such restoration involves trouble and expense. Before restoration is effected it is necessary for the practitioner to produce a statutory declaration and two certificates of identity and good character in a prescribed form, together with a fee of £1 (1957).

Erasure by Request

Registered medical practitioners have not at all times had the right to request erasure of their names from the Medical Register. Applications are at present permitted.

A practitioner wishing his name to be removed from the Register must, under the Standing Orders of the General Medical Council, Chapter 13, support his application by a statutory declaration stating (1) that no registrable degree or diploma held by him has been withdrawn; (2) that he is not aware of any proceedings pending which might lead to penal erasure of his name, or of any cause which might lead to such proceedings.

Temporary Registration

It is possible for a person holding a Commonwealth or foreign qualification recognized by the General Medical Council to be temporarily registered for the purposes of a particular employment in an approved hospital or other institution in the United Kingdom.

Application is made to the Registrar of the General Medical Council and the registration is in force only while the person remains in the particular employment for which the temporary registration applies.

5

DISCIPLINARY PROCEDURE

The doctor, having become provisionally registered, and later registered, and having been accorded the responsible and privileged position in the community that is indicated in the previous chapter, comes also at the same time under the discipline of the General Medical Council. The disciplinary machinery of the Council allows for the lodging of complaints against practitioners, the holding of inquiries following complaints received and notification of convictions in the Courts and the administration of punishment. Before 1953 any inquiry into conduct was held by the General Medical Council sitting as a body, but these functions are now carried out by smaller bodies appointed by the Council from among its members. These bodies are the Penal Cases Committee and the Disciplinary Committee.

The Disciplinary Committee

The inquiries formerly held by the General Medical Council as a whole are now held by a Committee of the Council. This Committee is known as the Disciplinary Committee and consists of the President and eighteen other members of the Council. At least six of the eighteen are elected members of the Council and at least two are laymen. The Committee members are appointed by the Council. Normally not more than nine members (including two elected members and one of the two laymen) are called upon to attend any one inquiry. Decisions are made by majority vote.

The Disciplinary Committee normally meets at the offices of the Council twice a year, in May and November, but may meet more frequently and at other times.

Any question relating to the registration or provisional

registration of an individual, whether it be an appeal against refusal to register, consideration of a conviction, or an inquiry into conduct or an application for restoration to the Register, is first examined by another Committee of the Council known as the Penal Cases Committee. Only the President may serve on both the Penal Cases and the Disciplinary Committees in respect of any one matter. Notice of proceedings must be given to the individual concerned and he is entitled to be heard by the Disciplinary Committee. He may be represented by Counsel or solicitor or the proceedings may be heard in public, but the public may be excluded from all or part of the proceedings. Where it has been alleged that a practitioner has been guilty of infamous conduct in any professional respect and the allegation has not been proved, a finding that he is not guilty must be recorded.

The Penal Cases Committee

The Penal Cases Committee consists of the President, one lay member of the Council, and four registered medical practitioners, two from the Branch Council for England and one each from the Branch Councils for Scotland and Ireland. The Committee is elected by the Council annually. The Penal Cases Committee normally meets in advance of the Disciplinary Committee and considers the cases which may require to come before it.

Procedure for Complaints and Investigation

The case of a practitioner may come to be considered by the Penal Cases Committee under two main headings of complaint, and may be referred to the Committee by the President, to whom the complaint is first reported by the Registrar. Complaints must be made to the Registrar in writing.

The first heading is a complaint sent by any body or person or information sent by a person acting in a public capacity, for example a judge or a court official, to the effect that the practitioner has been convicted by a Court in the United Kingdom or Ireland of a felony, misdemeanour, crime or offence.

The second is a complaint or information, similarly sent to the Council, of conduct which appears to the Registrar to raise the question of infamous conduct in a professional respect. The disciplinary procedure may also be instituted on receipt of information from a licensing body that a practitioner's name has been removed from their list of graduates or diplomates.

Any complaint regarding conduct from an individual not acting in a public capacity must be supported by one or more statutory declarations. Each declaration must state the name and address of the applicant and the source of the information and the grounds for belief in the truth of any fact not within the personal knowledge of the declarant.

The President may at this point decide that the matter need go no further. Otherwise the practitioner about whom the complaint is made is informed and provided with a copy of any statutory declaration. He is told of the date of the next meeting of the Penal Cases Committee, and is invited to submit an explanation in answer to the complaint.

When the complaint and the explanation, if any, have been considered by it, the Penal Cases Committee decides either that no inquiry is to be held or that the matter in whole or in part shall be referred to the Disciplinary Committee for inquiry. If the decision is that no inquiry is to be held the complainant and the practitioner are so informed.

The Penal Cases Committee may make its decision to refer the matter for inquiry a provisional one, pending further investigations or advice from the solicitor to the Council, after which the President may confirm the decision or decide that no inquiry is to take place.

Even if it is decided that an inquiry related to a conviction shall not be held, it may fall to be dealt with later if some subsequent complaint or information regarding a conviction is received.

Once a complaint or information has been referred to the Disciplinary Committee, the solicitor to the Council is required to serve a notice to the practitioner. The notice specifies the matters to be inquired into in the form of a charge or charges and states the day, time and place. At least twenty-eight days' notice must be given, unless the practitioner agrees to its being less. The notice states that the inquiry is to consider the charge and to determine whether or not the practitioner's name is to be erased from the Register. Thus he is left in no doubt as to the gravity of the proceedings. He is invited to answer the charge in writing and also to appear. He may be represented by Counsel or a solicitor, by any officer or member of any organization of which he is a member, or by any member of his family.

Any communication with respect to the inquiry must be addressed to the solicitor to the Council. Any application for postponement, with reasons, must be similarly addressed. In that case it is for the President to decide whether or not postponement will be granted. With the 'notice of inquiry', as it is called, is sent a copy of the Disciplinary Committee (Procedure) Rules. The notice is addressed to the practitioner either at his address on the Medical Register or to his last known address, whichever appears likely to be more effective. A copy of the notice of inquiry (and also of any postponement) is sent to the complainant if there is one.

There is provision in the Rules for the President, if he thinks fit, to rule that an inquiry shall not be held, after the matter has been referred to the Disciplinary Committee. This may, for example, be done on the application of the complainant and, in all cases where there is a complainant, not without his consent. Notice of such a decision by the President is sent both to the practitioner and to the complainant.

The practitioner, as stated above, receives a copy of any statutory declaration in support of the complaint. Any other party to the inquiry may, on payment of the charges in force and on application to the solicitor, receive copies of any statutory declaration, explanation, answer, admission or other statement or communication sent to the Council by a party to the inquiry. Any party may give notice to any other party to produce any document alleged to be in the other party's possession.

The notice of inquiry may be amended at the direction of the President or the Disciplinary Committee, so long as this can be done without injustice. The inquiry may be postponed or adjourned, in consequence of this amendment, if considered expedient and notice in writing is given to the complainant and the practitioner.

If the practitioner does not appear at the hearing, the Committee, if satisfied by the solicitor that a notice of inquiry was duly sent, may proceed with the inquiry.

The procedure to be followed at the inquiry is laid down in the Rules with detailed instructions as to the procedure in cases concerned with conviction and with conduct respectively.

In a case relating to a conviction, proof of conviction is called for followed by evidence of the circumstances leading to the conviction and of the antecedents and character of the practitioner. Subsequently the practitioner may address the Committee and bring to its notice any circumstances or plea which he considers may place his case in a more favourable light. The Committee may decide to postpone judgment or determine the case by deciding whether or not the practitioner's name should be erased from the Register.

In a case concerning conduct evidence is called and the practitioner has an opportunity of showing either that the charge is supported by insufficient evidence or that the facts alleged do not constitute infamous conduct in a professional respect or of refuting the evidence in order to disprove the charge.

If no evidence is adduced to prove the charge, or if the Committee determines that the facts alleged have not been proved to its satisfaction or that such facts as have been proved are not sufficient to support an adverse finding, the Committee records a finding that the practitioner is not guilty of infamous conduct in respect of the matters to which the charge relates. If, however, the finding is otherwise, that the practitioner is guilty of infamous conduct in a professional respect, evidence is called as to the antecedents and character of the practitioner and he may address the Committee 'by way of mitigation', as in a case of conviction. The Committee may then decide to postpone judgment or determine the case by deciding whether or not the practitioner's name should be erased from the Register.

In cases concerning both conviction and a charge of infamous conduct in a professional respect, the charges are considered seriatim in accordance with the procedures which have been outlined above and decisions are come to concurrently on all counts.

Deferment of Judgment

When judgment is postponed, it is deferred until some future meeting of the Committee. Six weeks' notice is given of the date of any future meeting and the practitioner is invited to provide a statement or statutory declaration by himself setting out facts bearing on his case which have arisen since the original hearing or copies of statements or statutory declarations relating to his conduct since the hearing.

These have to be sent to the solicitor to the General Medical Council not less than three weeks before the hearing. Copies are sent to the complainant, where there is one, and he in his turn may submit relevant statements or statutory declarations by himself or any other person. This further meeting is known as the subsequent meeting. If, in the interim, a complaint or information that the practitioner has been convicted is received, this is inquired into in the ordinary way at the subsequent meeting and is then considered together with the previous complaints upon which judgment had been postponed, in the same way as if it also was a similar case on which judgment had been postponed. After hearing or receiving further evidence, as is permissible, the Committee may further postpone judgment. If not, the Committee will come to a decision which, in effect, will decide whether or not the practitioner's name shall be erased from the Register in just the same way as might have been done had a decision been reached at the original hearing (see above).

It is not necessary for the Disciplinary Committee to consist of the same members for the original and the subsequent hearings respectively, but the requirement still holds that a member is debarred from either hearing if he has sat on the Penal Cases Committee when considering the case in question.

It is permitted to hold a joint inquiry into charges against two or more practitioners.

Appeal against Erasure

When penal erasure is decided upon the Registrar serves a notification on the registered person, who has a right of appeal to the Privy Council. The right of appeal applies only in cases of erasure. The appeal must be lodged within twenty-eight days of the service of this notification and in due course will be heard by the Judicial Committee of the Privy Council. The name is struck off the Register at the expiry of the twenty-eight days or, if there is appeal, when it is rejected. There are special rules of procedure laid down in connexion with the lodging of an appeal beginning with the presentation of a 'Petition of Appeal'. These are the Medical Act, 1950 (Judicial Committee Rules) Order, 1951, to which there is a Schedule setting out the scale of fees chargeable for the considerable number of items required in connexion with the appeal.

The complainant has no right of appeal against the decision of the Disciplinary Committee.

Fraudulent and Incorrect Entries

Another type of case which may be considered by the Penal Cases Committee and may be referred by that Committee to the Disciplinary Committee is one in which there is a charge of fraudulent or incorrect entry in the Register. Special rules are formulated for inquiry into such a case. The procedure is on the general lines of inquiry indicated above, the starting-point being a complaint or information received by the Registrar and referred by the President to the Penal Cases Committee.

Application for Restoration to the Register

Following erasure after an inquiry by the Disciplinary Committee, whether for infamous conduct, for fraudulent or erroneous entry or after conviction, application may be made for restoration of a name to the Register. The application is made to the Disciplinary Committee but cannot be made until the expiration of eleven months from the date of erasure or from a previous unsuccessful application.

The requirements and rules in this connexion are the same whether the application is in respect of restoration to the Register or the Provisional Register.

The applicant is afforded an opportunity of being heard by the Committee and the latter may call for any declarations, certificates or oral evidence that it thinks fit as to the identity of the applicant or his conduct since the erasure. The Committee may in its discretion afford an opportunity to the informant or complainant to be heard, whether it be the body granting the qualifying diploma or any body or person on whose complaint the erasure was made.

Appeal against Refusal to register Qualifications

An applicant may appeal to the Council against a refusal of the Registrar or of the Registrar of a Branch Council to enter a qualification in the Register. The appellant gives notice of appeal to the Council, stating the decision against which he is appealing and the grounds of appeal. He receives a copy of a statement of reasons made by the Registrar, together with a notice of the meeting of the Disciplinary Committee at which the appeal will be decided. If the appellant wishes to be heard by the Committee in support of his appeal he is required to give notice to that effect, to the Council, within fourteen days of his receiving notification of the hearing, and the Disciplinary Committee must permit him to appear in support of his case.

6

THE DOCTOR'S CONDUCT AND THE GENERAL MEDICAL COUNCIL

With such a formidable and powerful body as the General Medical Council exercising the main disciplinary control of the profession, it is natural that doctors should look to the General Medical Council for guidance as to conduct. In general only such guidance is obtainable as may emanate from 'case law' in the Council. The kind of ruling to be expected may be gleaned from a study of reports of cases that come before the Disciplinary Committee, and from these reports a realization of what is right and what is wrong will soon emerge. A useful starting-point for a code of behaviour in medicine is the Warning Notice published by the Disciplinary Committee.

The Warning Notice

The Disciplinary Committee issues a Warning Notice* which gives general guidance to the profession. This Warning Notice is not comprehensive but gives general warning as to the type of offence which may lead to erasure from the Register as constituting infamous conduct in a professional respect. The Notice mentions untrue certification or report, covering and association with unqualified or unregistered persons, advertising and canvassing, contravention of the Dangerous Drugs Acts and association with uncertified women practising as midwives.

* See Appendix B.

Certification

Under this heading the substance of the Warning Notice is that any certificate, notification or report concerning a patient must be written and issued with due care as to accuracy. The paths of medical practice are strewn with temptations to depart from this rule. Perhaps the commonest of the temptations is the relative of the patient who calls at the surgery for a National Insurance Certificate for a patient whom the practitioner has not seen that day. The certificate states 'I have examined you on the undermentioned date'. If the practitioner has not examined the patient on this date and yet signs the certificate he is committing an offence which could result in his name being struck off the Medical Register. He is, in fact, committing an act of false certification. No certificate or report should be untrue or misleading.

Covering

Covering is the act of allowing or enabling an unregistered person to attend or treat a patient in any way requiring professional knowledge or skill or to issue or procure the issue of any certificate. Any act on the part of a registered practitioner which enables an unregistered person to act as if he were duly qualified and registered is an offence. Due allowance, however, is made for the instruction of medical students and the legitimate employment of medical auxiliaries, dressers, surgery attendants and the like under the immediate supervision of a registered medical practitioner.

A registered practitioner must not associate with an unregistered person in the treatment of a patient. He must not, for example, administer an anaesthetic for, or assist at any operation by, an unregistered person nor must he consult with him. Were he to issue a certificate of incapacity for work in respect of a person who was receiving treatment from an unregistered person, even though he had examined the patient himself, a registered medical practitioner would lay himself open to a charge of covering, for he would be providing for the patient something that might be required and which could not be given by an unregistered person, that is a certificate by a registered medical practitioner.

Advertising and Canvassing

It is accepted in the profession that any advancement in the profession shall be obtained only in the normal process of building up a good professional reputation. Anything else that a practitioner does, or causes to be done, or even knows is being done, which can be said to enhance his professional standing or reputation or to increase his practice, may be regarded as advertising. Anything which can be construed as a means of attracting patients to him whether indirectly by advertising or directly by canvassing, whether or not they are patients of another practitioner, is likely to incur the displeasure of the Disciplinary Committee and to result in erasure. Various methods of advertising have been known. In this country where there is no direct newspaper advertising by the profession, practitioners may run the risk of a charge of advertising by causing or failing to prevent the frequent appearance of their names in print.

If it comes to the notice of a practitioner that his name has been used publicly without his knowledge or consent by some third party in such a manner as might lay him open to a charge of infringing the Warning Notice on advertising, he should immediately put the facts before his defence organization and carry out the advice given to him. Such action will provide him with an effective answer to any possible charge against him.

Contravention of the Dangerous Drugs Acts

The Warning Notice draws the attention of practitioners to the necessity for strict observation of their obligations under the Dangerous Drugs Act. These are referred to in full in Chapter 21. Particular stress is laid upon the necessity of keeping a register of Dangerous Drugs, their safe custody and the supervision of dispensers.

Uncertified Women practising as Midwives

Before the passing of the Midwives Act, 1936, many patients were attended in their confinements by so-called midwives having no special qualification. Since 1936, however, it is an offence for anyone other than a certified midwife to conduct a confinement or one who is not a certified midwife or registered nurse to nurse or attend a woman in childbirth. A relative or neighbour acting without remuneration in emergency is exempt from these restrictions. A doctor is exposing himself to danger if he attends a confinement in such a way as to 'cover' a person contravening the provisions of the Midwives Act.

Infamous Conduct

The use of the word 'infamous' in the term 'infamous conduct in a professional respect' has been criticized. Dictionaries will generally agree that its meaning in ordinary parlance is conveyed by expressions such as notoriously vile, evil and abominable. It has been argued that such offences as advertising, which may properly be regarded as serious misconduct, can hardly be described as vile and abominable. By use, however, the term 'infamous' has become established and it has been acknowledged that 'if it is shown that a medical man, in the pursuit of his profession, has done something with regard to it which would be reasonably regarded as disgraceful or dishonourable by his professional brethren of good repute and competency, then it is open to the General Medical Council to say that he has been guilty of "infamous conduct in a professional respect".' In quoting this definition drawn up by a fellow Judge, Lord Esher, in the case *Allinson* v. *G.M.C.* (Q.B. 1894 i. 750 pp. 760–1), added that the question was whether what had been done was an infamous thing for a medical man to have done.

There being no definition of the limits of infamous conduct, it is open to the General Medical Council through its Disciplinary Committee to find that the conduct of a member of the profession has in fact been infamous and as such renders him unfit to continue as a member of the profession, even though the offence committed was not directly related to his practice of medicine.

Matrimonial Proceedings and Removal from the Register

There is no written definition of what constitutes professional relationship in the matter of adultery. Therefore, it must be assumed to bear a fairly wide definition. If the practitioner first becomes acquainted with the other party as a consequence of being consulted or called in professionally, as opposed to an ordinary social introduction, such an introduction will probably be regarded as professional relationship even though when the adultery takes place he is no longer the medical attendant. If, at the time of the offence, he is in medical attendance there is no doubt about the question of professional relationship. It is possible for the relationship to be held to include also close relatives (husband or wife) of the patient, the introduction having been effected by reason of the medical attendance on the patient.

The sole concern and duty of the Disciplinary Committee in such a case is to decide whether or not the adultery committed was by a registered practitioner who is or was in professional relationship with the other party. The Committee is not called upon to determine whether or not adultery has been committed. The Medical Act, 1950, states that a finding by a Court of competent jurisdiction in matrimonial affairs that a registered medical practitioner has been guilty of adultery is conclusive evidence against him if he subsequently appears before the Disciplinary Committee. The Committee must be bound by the findings of fact in the Courts and must hear no additional evidence on the point.

A finding by the Disciplinary Committee that the practitioner stood in professional relationship to a party with whom he has committed adultery will almost certainly be regarded by the Committee as infamous conduct in a professional respect and will result in penal erasure. Similar considerations would apply and a similar outcome would be expected in a case of indecent offence.

The Position of the General Medical Council

In disciplinary matters, it is necessary to realize that the General Medical Council is a judge and not a policeman. No name is struck off the Register except after 'due inquiry' by the Disciplinary Committee and no inquiry is held except after receipt of information. Information may reach the Registrar in the form of a charge laid by any individual, or any individual acting in a public capacity, or from information received from the Law Courts (conviction of felony, misdemeanour, crime or offence, or matrimonial cases). These last are automatically notified to the Council by the Courts.

The Council does not itself initiate any action. The Council holds that it is the business of the individual doctor so to conduct himself as not to lay himself open to a charge of infamous conduct. It is of little use for him to try to obtain from the Council an official opinion on whether a projected course will incur its displeasure. Only when a course of action is clearly covered by a previous decision will such an opinion be given. Each case brought before it is determined on its own merits, the yardstick being whether the conduct of the practitioner was infamous in a professional respect.

The Council's custom of not acting except on the receipt of a complaint has been criticized by those who believe that the Council could be far more effective in maintaining professional discipline if it initiated action on its own account.

This, it is said, would adequately compensate for the natural reluctance of most doctors to lodge a complaint against a colleague which amounts to a threat to his professional livelihood. So often some doubtful action, particularly perhaps in the field of advertising, strikes many practitioners as undesirable and unprofessional, yet no single one of them feels himself to be directly affected and none is inclined to act as complainant. At the same time many feel that if the General Medical Council were prepared to initiate proceedings it would prove an effective deterrent to the less disciplined members of the profession. The General Medical Council, however, will not depart from its judicial position other than to issue the Warning Notice. In effect every member of the medical profession is in a position of trust to observe, and if possible to see that his fellows observe, the accepted tenets of the profession and in particular to heed the Warning Notice. This should be done not only as an act of self-preservation, which it is, but also as a practical realization of the important and dignified position that must be held by the profession in the interests of the public. The respect in which the profession as a whole is held must depend, ultimately, upon the conduct of each of its members.

7

MEDICAL ETHICS

Ethical Obligations of Doctors in General

It has been accepted from time immemorial that practitioners of medicine could and should conform in their practices to a general code of behaviour which would ensure that the position of advantage held by the trained physician over the sick should not be abused.

In Babylon, about 2000 B.C., there was, for instance, a code of Hammurabi which laid down a schedule of fees, and punishments for departure from ethical principles which varied from a fine of 10 shekels to the severing of both hands, commensurate with the degree of the offence against ethical principles.

Ethical obligations were crystallized fifteen hundred years later by Hippocrates (born in 460 B.C.), from whose teaching has been handed down the Hippocratic Oath, a translation of which is as follows:

The Hippocratic Oath

I swear by Apollo the physician, and Aesculapius and Health, and All-heal, and all the gods and goddesses, that, according to my ability and judgment, I will keep this Oath and this stipulation—to reckon him who taught me this Art equally dear to me as my parents, to share my substance with him, and relieve his necessities if required; to look upon his offspring in the same footing as my own brothers, and to teach them this art, if they shall wish to learn it, without fee or stipulation; and that by precept, lecture, and every other mode of instruction, I will impart a knowledge of the Art to my own sons, and those of my teachers, and

> to disciples bound by a stipulation and oath according to the law of medicine, but to none others. I will follow that system of regimen which, according to my ability and judgment, I consider for the benefit of my patients, and abstain from whatever is deleterious and mischievous. I will give no deadly medicine to anyone if asked, nor suggest any such counsel: and in like manner I will not give to a woman a pessary to produce abortion. With purity and with holiness I will pass my life and practise my Art. I will not cut persons labouring under the stone, but will leave this to be done by men who are practitioners of this work. Into whatever houses I enter, I will go into them for the benefit of the sick, and will abstain from every voluntary act of mischief and corruption; and, further, from the seduction of females or males, of freemen or slaves. Whatever, in connexion with my professional practice, or not in connexion with it, I see or hear, in the life of men, which ought not to be spoken of abroad, I will not divulge, as reckoning that all such should be kept secret. While I continue to keep this Oath unviolated, may it be granted to me to enjoy life and the practice of the Art, respected by all men, in all times. But should I trespass and violate this Oath, may the reverse be my lot.

In A.D. 1224 the Emperor Frederick II had passed a law requiring a course of training and an examination before a licence to practise was granted. Similar laws were passed in Germany and Italy in the fourteenth century.

In the eighteenth century Percival's Code appeared which stressed the need for humanity to be combined with authority in handling hospital and charity patients. For example, he condemned the discussion of his case before a patient.

Mr Justice Brewer of the Supreme Court of the United States of America, in this century, underlined (*Hawker* v. *New York*, 170 U.S. 192) the need for a high standard of professional behaviour when he stated: 'The physician is one whose relations to life and health are of the most intimate character. It is fitting . . . that he should be one who may safely be trusted to apply remedies.' It is clear that no man can safely be trusted to apply remedies if his first considerations are those of gain and if the interests of his patients are second to his own, and if he takes no heed or little heed of his patients' feelings and desire for secrecy.

The general principles which can be read into the Hippocratic Oath are:

To share a knowledge of medicine with the rest of the profession and to have no secret remedies or processes.
To do no man any harm by the misapplication or criminal application of a knowledge of medicine.
To undertake only such things as are within the competence of the individual practitioner.
To keep secret anything learned as the outcome of professional relationship with a patient which should not be divulged.
To avoid abuse of the doctor/patient relationship.

These general principles have been brought up to date by the World Medical Association and were stated (in 1949) in 'The Declaration of Geneva' and, with some more practical detail, in the International Code of Ethics, both of which are reproduced below.

The Declaration of Geneva

AT THE TIME OF BEING ADMITTED AS A MEMBER OF THE MEDICAL PROFESSION:

I SOLEMNLY PLEDGE myself to consecrate my life to the service of humanity;
I WILL GIVE to my teachers the respect and gratitude which is their due;
I WILL PRACTISE my profession with conscience and dignity;
THE HEALTH OF MY PATIENT will be my first consideration;
I WILL RESPECT the secrets which are confided in me;
I WILL MAINTAIN by all the means in my power, the honour and the noble traditions of the medical profession;
MY COLLEAGUES will be my brothers;
I WILL NOT PERMIT considerations of religion, nationality, race, party politics or social standing to intervene between my duty and my patient;
I WILL MAINTAIN the utmost respect for human life from the

time of conception; even under threat, I will not use my medical knowledge contrary to the laws of humanity.

I MAKE THESE PROMISES solemnly, freely and upon my honour.

The International Code of Ethics

Ethical Obligations of Doctors in General

A doctor must by his conduct in all matters set a high standard.

A doctor in the pursuit of his profession must not allow himself to be influenced primarily by motives of profit.

A doctor shall neither instigate nor condone any advertisement relative to his professional status or work except as allowed by the National code of ethics in his own country.

A doctor shall not accept conditions of service which do not ensure his professional independence.

A doctor shall not participate in any division or sharing of fees of which the patient is not made aware.

A doctor shall not in any circumstances do, authorize to be done or condone anything that would weaken the physical or mental resistance of a human being, except for the prevention and treatment of disease.

A doctor, when called upon to give evidence or to certify, shall only state that which is true or is in accord with his professional opinion.

Ethical Obligations of Doctors towards the Sick

A doctor must always bear in mind the importance of preserving human life from the time of conception until death.

A doctor should not hesitate to propose or to accept consultation with a professional colleague when for any reason it appears desirable in the interests of the patient.

Except when required by the law of the country concerned, a doctor shall not disclose, without the consent of the patient, information which he has obtained in the course of his professional relationship with the patient.

A doctor must give necessary treatment in an emergency unless he is assured that it can and will be given by another.

Intra-Professional Ethical Obligations

A doctor shall maintain friendly relations with his colleagues, paying due regard to their opinions and achievements, and shall in no way undermine the confidence reposed in them by their patients.

A doctor must not seek to attract patients to himself from his colleagues by means other than the normal establishment of a good professional reputation.

A doctor must observe the principles of 'The Declaration of Geneva' approved by the World Medical Association.

This code is in some sense the highest common factor of ethics, designed for application the world over. Customs, particularly in regard to advertising, vary from country to country, but the above tenets should transcend all boundaries and ensure a high standard and the freedom of medicine all over the world.

In Britain the General Medical Council plays a great part in ensuring the maintenance of high ethical standards in that it has, and uses, disciplinary powers in such matters as infamous conduct in a professional respect, advertising and false certification.

It is generally convenient to divide the subject of medical ethics into three main sections—the ethical obligations of doctors in general, the ethical obligations of doctors towards one another and the ethical obligations of doctors towards the sick. The ethics of the medical profession is a subject on which it is both impossible and unwise to be comprehensive in making statements. Whatever ethical rule may be made there can always be circumstances in which, while the letter of the law is obeyed, the spirit, which is the all-important thing, may be violated.

To lay down ethical rules for every possible situation in which a doctor may find himself is acknowledged by most to be impossible, and the best way for a doctor to conform to the requirements of medical ethics is constantly to bear in mind certain principles, of which some may be stated specifically and others may be inferred from particular instances which may be translated into general principles. Thus ethical rules are never to be regarded as a hunting ground for loopholes, and doctors will find that loopholes discovered will not be accepted by their colleagues as justification for behaviour which is contrary to medical ethics.

The aim of a doctor should be always to be able to act in professional matters according to his own professional conscience and not to be subject to orders or directions in professional matters from any non-professional body. He should, consequently, refuse to enter into employment the conditions of which do not allow for the attainment of this aim.

Doctors should not influence one another, say for instance by the mere fact of seniority, in such a way as to interfere with or to overrule the dictates of their professional conscience.

There should be no misuse of the tremendous range of therapeutic weapons. As well as to heal, doctors have an ethical duty to protect their patients from harm. They should at all times so conduct themselves as to justify an implicit trust and respect on the part of their patients. Such trust and respect will be vitiated by any doubtful or improper conduct outside the professional sphere as well as within.

The ethical principles of the profession should be scrupulously observed at all times by all members of the profession whether fully or provisionally registered.

There is never any excuse for departing from the ethical principles, least of all that most tempting reason the fact that a colleague has done so and yet has successfully avoided retribution.

The Warning Notice of the Disciplinary Committee (Appendix B) gives a lead in certain matters. Contravention of the Warning Notice may well lead to a complaint being lodged with the General Medical Council and to the holding of an inquiry (Chapter 5). Nevertheless it is by no means always that a complaint is lodged or that action can be taken by the General Medical Council, and the fact that a practitioner has successfully escaped the notice of the Council is not necessarily a guarantee that his ethical behaviour is unexceptionable. Although there are no penalties so far-reaching as that which may be imposed by the Disciplinary Committee, yet the profession can, and occasionally does, express its disapproval of the behaviour of a practitioner who has transgressed the accepted ethical conduct of the profession. All members of the British Medical Association, for example, are subject to the ethical machinery of the Association, which provides for complaint by one practitioner against another, with consequent full inquiry. A finding against a respondent may result in a warning, an expression of censure or expulsion from the Association. The machinery may also be used for settling disputes of an ethical nature and, by consent, may be used by non-members of the Association prepared to abide by the decisions reached (so long as one of the parties to the dispute, either complainant or respondent, is a member). A practitioner, believing that the conduct of another practitioner has contravened the Warning Notice of the Disciplinary Committee or that he has been guilty of infamous conduct in a professional respect, may lay a complaint with that body (Chapter 5). He may, however, feel that the charge is not one within the purview of the General Medical Council, or he may prefer that the matter shall be thrashed out within the profession under the umbrella of his professional association.

The Ethical Machinery of the B.M.A.

A practitioner feeling aggrieved or wishing to complain about the conduct of another member of the profession and wishing to invoke the machinery of the British Medical Association to put it to rights should state his precise complaint, preferably in writing, before the respondent and then invite his comments in reply to the charge. While in this original communication it is not necessary to produce large volumes of evidence, the complaint should be worded precisely so as to give a clear indication of the specific charges. Subsequently he should submit copies of the complaint to the Honorary Secretary of the local Division of the Association, together with copies of any reply he may have received. The matter is then referred to the headquarters of the Association and, if the Chairman of the Central Ethical Committee rules that there is a prima facie case for investigation, arrangements are made for a hearing in accordance with the rules for ethical procedure of the Association.

The outcome of this may be a dismissal of the case or a finding against the respondent with penalties of the type indicated above. It may, however, be that the conclusion of the case is different from this and is, in fact, a reconciliation between the parties as a result of the explanations which come to light as a result of the inquiry.

It is open to the Association to withdraw the operations of its ethical machinery should the matter be the subject of proceedings elsewhere.

Ethical Code

The general rules on medical ethics are for observance by all medical practitioners. In some special branches of medicine the application of the rules to the particular circumstances may cause difficulty. Guidance to practitioners working in special fields is given in code drawn up by the British Medical Association which, in effect, interpret the general requirements as they apply to these special fields. Examples are the code for Consultation and the Ethical Rules for Industrial Medical Officers. Copies of these are obtainable from the Secretary of the British Medical Association and are reproduced in Appendix C.

8

ETHICAL OBLIGATIONS OF DOCTORS TO ONE ANOTHER

In the interests of themselves and of their patients, doctors should support their colleagues at all times and preserve proper ethical relationships with them. Once jealousy and personal considerations are allowed to creep in between doctors the proper preservation of ethics is endangered. Opinions of colleagues should be respected and, even if disagreed with, any disagreement should not be conveyed to the patient in such a way as to undermine the confidence of the patient in any doctor. Disagreements are bound to occur, as also are critical feelings towards the treatment or advice given to a patient by another doctor. In order that the patient may be afforded the correct treatment or obtain the correct advice, such disagreements should be resolved as speedily as possible. Here is no place for oblique criticism. The solution will often lie in meeting the other doctor in consultation. They can then discuss the case between them and, having conveyed the gist of the matter to the patient, offer advice on the next step, which may well be that of seeking a further opinion.

Only by attaining a professional competence and by the establishment of a good professional reputation should a doctor seek to increase his practice. In so doing he may well attract to himself patients of other practitioners, but he must not take any improper steps to this end.

The ethical obligations of practitioners to one another cannot be separated entirely from other considerations. For instance, advertising and canvassing, whether blatant or hidden, whether personal or by proxy, offend against the Warning Notice of the Disciplinary Committee and also against the ethics of the profession.

Unfair attempts to enhance a practice or a professional reputation at the expense of another practitioner offend against ethical principles even if they do not arouse the interest of the General Medical Council. Other methods, such as derogatory insinuations about other practitioners or claims to technique or knowledge that suggest to the patient a favourable comparison with a colleague, are as despicable as downright advertising. There is no justification for such methods even when a neighbouring colleague appears to be showing such tendencies. Two wrongs do not make a right. A doctor with good intentions need have no worries so long as he does nothing to others which he would not have done to himself.

Setting up in Practice

Even when there is no written agreement to prevent him a practitioner should not set up in practice in an area in which he has been a partner, assistant or locum tenens except with the express consent, in writing, of the practitioner with whom he was associated. An undertaking that he will not accept any patients of his former colleague is hardly valid, for it is almost impossible to give effect to it once he has been introduced into the area. It has been argued that the appointment to a practice vacancy in the area under the National Health Service removes any ethical objection to the setting up in opposition to a former principal; but it cannot be too strongly stated that the arrangements for appointing general practitioners under the National Health Service do not absolve the practitioner from his ethical obligations. In no instance may National Health Service Regulations be regarded as superseding the requirements of medical ethics or as an excuse to act in contravention of the ethical code.

The wise principal will enter into a protective legal agreement on engaging an assistant or on taking a partner but, even if he does not take this precaution, he is entitled to regard the subsequent setting up in separate practice as an unethical act on the part of his erstwhile colleagues unless he himself has given his consent to it. But he must not be unreasonable in his restrictions. The restriction will usually have a time limit of sufficient length (say five years) to nullify any advantage that the other practitioner may have gained from his introduction to the area. The other restriction is that of distance. This will vary, according to the circumstances, from, say, two miles in a large city to a much greater distance in the country. Unreasonable restrictions have been held in law to render an agreement invalid.

The same considerations apply to a practitioner who enters into negotiations, even of a preliminary nature, for partnership but subsequently decides to set up on his own. He is unlikely to have achieved any effective introduction to patients but the knowledge he has gained of the practice may encourage him to set up in opposition and may well enable him to conduct his practice to his own advantage and to the disadvantage of the established principal.

Judgment on the ethical offence of setting up in opposition may be less severe when the principal, by behaving unfairly, causes a breakdown of bona fide negotiations. Even so, the newcomer will be unwise to regard such an eventuality as a heaven-sent excuse to set up in practice without fear of charges of unethical conduct. Before taking any such step he should seek the advice of his professional organization or of other and senior practitioners in the area.

Restrictive Covenants

A restrictive covenant of this kind will be held to protect a successor to a practice in just the same way as it protects the principal at the time the covenant is made.

Should such a covenant be broken and the matter be taken to Court the Court may allow reasonable damages but not necessarily those mentioned in the agreement for these may be unreasonable. They may in fact be out of proportion to the harm done to the plaintiff principal.

The principal may, instead, apply for an injunction to prevent the continuation of the breach of the covenant. Once he has been awarded damages the covenant is annulled. Even so, there may still remain ethical considerations to be taken into account.

If a breach of covenant is threatened the principal should seek legal advice without delay or consult with the secretary of his defence organization.

The Courtesy Call

A practitioner coming new to an area is advised to pay a courtesy call on others already practising in the district. Some consider this custom is unnecessary and to some extent it has fallen into desuetude. Nevertheless, the newcomer will do well to ponder on the advantages of establishing friendly relationships with professional neighbours among whom he is going to practise and, if for this reason only, the courtesy call should not be neglected. The courteous nature of the call may not be fully appreciated at first by some established practitioners but the caller should not feel discouraged by a cool or even a suspicious reception. Professional contacts are bound to occur sooner or later in any case and the fact that the new doctor has, so to speak, offered his bona fides in advance will stand him in good stead and will be of mutual benefit and a help in weathering any little differences that may arise.

Other Doctors' Patients

For one reason or another, including dissatisfaction, either temporary or permanent, with his own doctor, a patient may apply to another practitioner for treatment. It is wrong to advise or treat a patient who is already under treatment by another. Consequently, the doctor applied to must ascertain whether the patient is under treatment and, if he is, he should advise him to return to his own doctor. If, however, the patient refuses he should satisfy himself that the other doctor has been informed of the patient's wish to change. It is even wiser that he should, preferably with the patient's agreement, communicate himself with the other doctor and tell him the facts.

If the patient is under treatment at the time of the change the practitioner should obtain his permission to get into touch about his case with the former practitioner.

In the National Health Service a patient may change his doctor either by obtaining the consent of his present doctor or by giving fourteen days' notice (see p. 232).

Practitioners in all branches of the profession should always exercise the utmost care not to transgress the ethical requirements in general and in particular not to do or say anything which will interfere with the patient's relationship with his own general practitioner or undermine his confidence in him.

A doctor who is treating a patient of a general practitioner should maintain contact with him and return the patient to his care as soon as the circumstances of the case and the requirements of treatment permit. A hospital doctor, for example, whether consultant or house officer, may tend, in his enthusiasm, to continue to treat a patient long after he could well be handed back to his own family doctor.

A practitioner should not accept as his patient any patient or member of that patient's household whom he has attended in the past on behalf of another practitioner, whether in the capacity of assistant, locum tenens, deputy or in consultation, unless, of course, he has the consent of the other practitioner to do so.

It is understandable that, on occasion, a patient already under medical care wishes to be examined by another practitioner without the knowledge of his own doctor and thus to obtain an independent opinion. The practitioner applied to should do all he can to obtain permission to communicate with the patient's own doctor. Opportunity may be taken to point out to the patient the advantages in diagnosis and treatment that accrue from his own doctor's intimate knowledge of the case. If, however, permission is not forthcoming and the circumstances are exceptional an examination may be made and the findings and conclusions conveyed to the patient but nothing but emergency treatment should be given.

Relationships with Consultants

The proper and normal channel through which a patient obtains the opinion of a consultant is by an introduction effected by his general practitioner. In private practice the general practitioner will often arrange the appointment, while in hospital practice an appointment for an out-patient consultation is made by the patient, or the practitioner, with the appointments clerk. The majority of hospitals make appointments for out-patients, who are seen only by appointment, except in emergency. Where no appointments system obtains, the introduction is effected by sending the patient up to the department at the correct time. In every case a letter should be sent with the patient, or in advance, setting out succinctly the particulars of the case and requesting the consultant's advice on diagnosis and treatment.

Consultations in the Home

When a consultant is called out to see a patient, either as a private practitioner or under the domiciliary consultation arrangements under the National Health Service, a mutually convenient time should be arranged so that general practitioner and consultant can meet and discuss the case together. Consultations should be conducted in a manner that preserves the proper relationships. The attending practitioner should render all the assistance he can to the practitioner consulted who in his turn must do or say nothing which would undermine the patient's confidence in his doctor. Neither must he supersede him in the care of the patient either during his illness or in any subsequent illness, except with the attending practitioner's consent. In other words he must remain as one called in for advice and assistance at a specific time and in a specific context and must not take advantage of the position. The British Medical Association has drawn up a careful and precise code for Medical Consultations which is reproduced in Appendix C.

Notification by a Consultant

The usual course for a consultant taking up an appointment or changing his address or changing from whole-time to part-time, thus making him available for private work in the area, and wishing to inform his colleagues, is for him to address a letter to such practitioners in the area as he may properly regard as interested, informing them of the bare facts.

For example, an anaesthetist starting work in an area may wish to draw the attention of his colleagues to the fact that he is available to give anaesthetics. He may notify general practitioners, consultants and dentists. The British Dental Association has stated that it has no objection to the circularization of dentists in this way.

Dichotomy

Dichotomy is the practice of fee-splitting, the classical example of which is the arrangement between a general practitioner and a consultant for the former to receive a part of the consultant's fee. The object of the arrangement is for the consultant to increase his practice by what is in effect a bribe to the general practitioner to supply him with patients for consultation and for the general practitioner to obtain thereby a useful addition to his income. The unethical feature of the arrangement is that it is an undisclosed division of fees, of which the patient is unaware, and that it must lead to a violation of the proper intra-professional relationships acting to the detriment of the patient. In fact what it amounts to is a bribe and it may fall to be dealt with as an offence against the Prevention of Corruption Act, 1906. Conviction may result in a heavy fine or imprisonment and may arise equally from the giving or offering of the bribe, the acceptance of it or the attempt to obtain it. The offence is a misdemeanour and conviction may also result in erasure from the medical register without further inquiry into the facts by the Disciplinary Committee.

If the fee for the consultation or operation is to be collected by the general practitioner any account sent to the patient must show clearly how the account is made up. It may well show in a particular case the surgeon's, assistant's and anaesthetist's fees together with the general practitioner's charges for his own attendance on the patient. So long as it is clearly indicated that all these fees are included in the account it cannot be said that there is undisclosed division of fees, or dichotomy, unless of course adjustments are made after the bill is paid which would turn the transaction into dichotomy.

The usual sharing of fees in a normal medical partnership is perfectly proper and does not come under the heading of dichotomy.

School Medical Officers

There are circumstances in which it may be said that there is some measure of dual responsibility for a patient as for example the statutory supervision of the health of school children by the school medical officer.

A school medical officer may examine a child in the course of his duties, and may find a condition requiring treatment or consultant opinion. He should not refer the patient to a consultant, or arrange treatment, without notifying the general practitioner of his findings and affording him the opportunity to make the arrangements, which he may well prefer to do. Normally this is done by sending a stereotyped notification to the general practitioner which states that if the general practitioner does not reply within a week, the school medical officer will assume consent for him to carry out the necessary arrangements. This system is incorporated in the following agreement between the Society of Medical Officers of Health and the British Medical Association:

(1) Where, in the opinion of a medical officer employed by a Local Authority, a child needs special investigation (other than an ophthalmic examination)* or treatment, he should send the child to a specialist only after prior consultation with the child's own doctor, upon whom rests the responsibility for general medical care.

(2) In consulting the general practitioner, the medical officer should give him the opportunity to make the arrangements for the consultation or to agree—by replying or in the absence of a reply—that the arrangements should be made by the medical officer.

(3) A copy of any special report on the child received by the medical officer should be sent to the child's own doctor.

Further, it has been suggested that copies of reports on patients from consultants to officers in the Public Health Service should be sent to the patient's general practitioner for his information. No opportunity should be lost of close co-operation of this sort between the various sections of the profession. No written rules can cover every possible eventuality but the principles are clear and, in the ultimate interest of the patient, should always be applied.

Industrial Medical Officers

Industrial medical officers have an important and special function in regard to the worker's health in relation to his working environment. It cannot be denied that the ease of access to the works doctor and the appeal to the patient of obtaining medical examination and treatment during his working hours instead of attending his own doctor's surgery in his spare time tend to place the industrial medical officer in an embarrassing position. In order to help the industrial

* The question of the retention of the proviso in brackets is at present (1957) under review.

medical officer in his desire to conform to the ethical requirements of the profession, the British Medical Association has drawn up Ethical Rules for Industrial Medical Officers which show clearly the application of the general ethical rules to the particular circumstances of industrial medicine. These rules are also reproduced in Appendix C and copies are obtainable from the Association. It is clearly stated therein that treatment, other than in emergency, should not be undertaken without the agreement of the patient's own doctor. There is no doubt that this rule is a sound one and applies no principle to industrial medical officers beyond that applied to any other practitioner. It has to be admitted, however, that its observance can place a considerable burden upon the industrial medical officer. In the nature of things the workers in a factory of any considerable size are drawn from heavily populated industrial areas in which there are many general practitioners. Many requests for treatment at the factory will be received but, except in emergency, these should be resisted unless the consent of the patient's own doctor is obtained. Some general practitioners are willing to give an industrial medical officer general consent to treat their patients, relying on them to keep in touch on matters of importance. In this way the burden on the industrial medical officer is minimized, mutual confidence is built up and professional relationships are not impaired.

Examining Medical Officers

There is yet another set of circumstances in which there are ethical rules to be observed, and which have a close bearing upon relationships between practitioners. There frequently arise occasions on which a report from an independent practitioner is required by a third party. Examples are life insurance examinations, pre-employment examinations, medical reports to be used in contesting or defending actions in Courts of Law and examinations by medical referees to ensure that a candidate passes the test for fitness to undertake some venture or other. The examining practitioner, as he is called, in such cases should study and follow carefully the Ethical Code for Examining Medical Officers drawn up by the British Medical Association and reproduced in Appendix C, copies of which are obtainable from the Association.

9

ETHICAL OBLIGATIONS TO THE SICK

The ethical obligations of a practitioner to his patients are largely covered by the Warning Notice of the Disciplinary Committee and by the requirements as to professional secrecy. These obligations will be met almost entirely if the practitioner is careful always to act in the patient's interest to the exclusion of his own. In a busy practice it is all too easy to overlook the fact that it is only rarely that a patient seeks a doctor's advice lightheartedly or frivolously for trivialities. At the back of every apparently trivial approach from a patient may lie fear, ignorance and a serious complaint. It is so easy to forget that the trained medical practitioner and the lay patient are worlds apart in their knowledge of symptoms and medicine generally and to regard apparent trivialities as irresponsible acts on the part of the patient. A practitioner's main ethical obligation to the sick is to regard him as a human being seeking his help and entitled to it. The patient comes to him in need and is entitled to help in the form of diagnosis, treatment and advice. An attitude which accepts this relationship with every patient will ensure the observance of the main ethical and other obligations to the patient.

The keeping of appointments and punctual attendance at the advertised surgery times should always be observed.

Professional Secrecy

The general interest and the common welfare require that the patient shall be able to rely with full confidence upon the secrecy of all communications made to a doctor. Frank speech is frequently an essential to the proper practice of medicine and should be assured of a confidential reception. Subject to the special exceptions mentioned, anything that violates privacy is an offence against the tenets of professional secrecy.

The essence of professional secrecy is that the patient should be able to tell the practitioner everything that is necessary for his medical assessment and treatment. This means that the doctor must hear many things that otherwise would remain in the knowledge of the patient alone. The patient must be entirely confident that nothing he reveals will go further. Once there is a suspicion among patients that their confidences are not safe with a doctor the relationships between them become seriously impaired and quite unsuited to the proper practice of medicine.

There are many pitfalls for the unwary in the matter of disclosure of information about a patient to a third party. Whatever the situation, whatever the request and from wherever it comes a practitioner will experience trouble and difficulty unless he bears constantly in mind the rule that he should not disclose any information which he has learned in the course of his professional relationship with his patient without that patient's consent. It is wise to obtain the consent in writing.

There are situations when the consent is clearly implied by the fact that the patient presents himself for examination. Nevertheless in such instances the practitioner must be satisfied that the patient is aware of the reason for the examination and that the results and consequent opinion of the practitioner will be disclosed to a third party. This particularly applies in examinations for life insurance, for compensation and in connexion with legal actions and in other examinations carried out at the request of a third party such as pre-employment and superannuation examinations. Many of the forms now required for completion for these and allied purposes have printed on them some such sentence as 'I hereby consent to examination and to the disclosing of the results to . . .', to which the patient appends his signature. The consent in these instances is limited and facts should on no account be disclosed to anyone else.

The simplest example of disclosure of information is the medical certificate which usually contains no more professional secret than a diagnosis and an opinion as to fitness for work.

National Insurance Certificates (Forms Med 1, 2A, 2B, etc.) and Private Certificates are normally handed to the patient and, being passed on by him, do not constitute a breach of professional confidence by the practitioner. Even so, a practitioner is wise to protect his patients' interests by not entering on the certificate any clinical details in excess of what is necessary for the purpose of the certificate. If he finds it necessary to inscribe a more elaborate wording he should explain to the patient the possible implications of their disclosure.

It is not difficult for a practitioner to develop and practise a discipline of this sort in regard to certificates and reports such as will effectively protect him from committing a breach of confidence. He needs, however, to beware of what might be described as 'apparent officialdom'. The request for information from an officer of a public body, for example a local authority or a firm, about an employee or a tenant may well have some apparent authority. A young practitioner, who can only be expected to have a sketchy knowledge of the powers and authority of such bodies, may well believe that the source of the request is such as compels him to disclose information. The implication that there is a duty to disclose matters may be further engendered by reference, in the requesting letter, to some Act of Parliament or Regulation. Although it can be rarely, if ever, that such phrases or references are inserted deliberately to trick the unfortunate doctor the catch is there just the same and must be avoided. There is no more obligation to disclose a patient's secrets without consent to a lay official (who has little or no knowledge of medical ethics) than there is to any other third party. Then again a request may emanate from a solicitor. That the solicitor may be acting for the other party and not for the patient must be constantly borne in mind. If a practitioner steadfastly follows the golden rule of always obtaining the patient's consent, however soothing the blandishments, intentional or otherwise, of the requesting party, then he will successfully navigate the treacherous waters of professional secrecy.

But it must not be imagined that written requests constitute the only hazard. Unless a strict discipline is observed the oral inquiry may catch a practitioner off his guard and lead him to a disclosure which he will afterwards regret. The commonest danger in this regard is, perhaps, the inquiry by employer, be it housewife or managing director, about the health of an employee. To the young practitioner it may seem almost boorish to withhold such simple information, but it must not be given without the consent of the patient. And then there is the relative or friend who may turn to the practitioner on leaving his consulting room with an innocent 'By the way doctor what exactly is the matter with . . .?'. The necessary reply conveying that the inquiry should be addressed to the patient can be given tactfully without giving the appearance of pomposity or self-righteousness. Relatives may be particularly difficult over this and special care is needed. The tactful deflection of such inquiries is an art which should be learned first and then exercised. Even a spouse has no right to information.

In the family there are, of course special considerations. Parents may be given information about their children until their majority though it is wise to consider the feelings and desires of older children in this matter. Parents have no right to medical information about older children but a good doctor will know his families well enough to judge when it is proper to depart from the rule. Generally the rule may be considered to be flexible within a family and nothing that is said above should be allowed to interfere with the ordinary passage of information from the doctor to the responsible relative in the house who has care of the patient, provided that it is always borne in mind that there may be matters which should remain a confidence between the patient and the practitioner and which it is unnecessary to reveal.

It is customary, and indeed often clinically wise and in the patient's interest, to withhold certain matters from the patient. Examples are the fact that a patient has some incurable disease or that his condition is such as to hold out little hope of recovery. If such a state of affairs exists it must be regarded as not only proper but essential to convey such information to a close relation. Quite apart from the need to warn the relatives of the probable outcome it may bring to light the need to advise the patient to set his affairs in order, to make a will, or to desist from embarking on some project which requires the patient's continued good health for it to prosper.

Mental Illness

Particular considerations apply to those suffering from mental illness and to their relatives. It is obviously essential in the patient's own interest to ensure a proper supervision of his affairs by or through a relative. In case of certified mental illness a guardian *ad litem* is appointed and the practitioner may confidently and freely discuss the patient's condition with the guardian as is necessary for his welfare.

Where the condition is not certifiable, special care is necessary and professional confidence should only be broken insofar as is necessary. This is clearly a matter for careful judgment by the practitioner in each individual case.

Practitioners are reminded of the danger of addressing a letter to a relative which makes reference to symptoms of mental illness. Mental patients are often on the alert and the surreptitious opening of a letter referring to suicidal tendencies on the part of the patient may well have dire results.

Crime

When there is any question or suspicion of crime the tenets of professional confidence will be stretched to the utmost. In some cases they will have to be set aside. A practitioner is not bound to answer questions put to him by the police nor is he bound to pass on information of his own accord.

When it appears to the practitioner that a patient to whom he has been called is the victim of a crime and is *in extremis* an attempt should be made to obtain a dying declaration (see p. 154). If the patient refuses it may be as well for the practitioner to refuse the care of the patient, but he can only deny treatment when he is satisfied that the patient can be and is transferred to hospital or to some other adequate medical care. A second opinion is a wise precaution. Kitchin* recommends a confidential consultation with the chief police officer of the district in a case in which the practitioner suspects that the patient is being poisoned. Usually a second medical opinion should be obtained before this step is taken. If the practitioner becomes aware that a crime is contemplated by his patient he is entitled to, and indeed should, carry out his duty as a citizen and take what steps he can to prevent the crime. His alternative is, having

* *Law for the Medical Practitioner*. D. H. Kitchin. Eyre and Spottiswoode, 1941, p. 53.

warned the patient, to refuse the patient further medical care and to inform the police lest he be judged an accessory.

Similar considerations apply where the practitioner believes his patient has committed a crime. It is no part of the function of a practitioner to act the part of a detective or to be officious in his attitude. His simple duty as a citizen to prevent crime will almost certainly be clear to him when the occasion arises and he will see at the time how and when this duty must be allowed to transcend his tenets of professional confidence. As far as is feasible he should, before disclosure, point out to the patient the necessity for what he is going to do.

In such a case, however, he would be well advised to consult the secretary of his medical defence organization for there is a distinction between concealing a felony and concealing a misdemeanour. It is his duty to inform the police when he is aware that a felony has been committed, but he has no such duty in respect of a misdemeanour such as attempted suicide (see Chapter 23).

Disclosure to Protect Others

Now and again there will occur the very difficult case in which the practitioner feels it his duty to protect others. The classic example, frequently quoted, is the nursemaid, found to be suffering from venereal disease, who refuses permission to disclose the fact to the mother of the children for whom she cares.

Then again there is the discovery of epilepsy in one whose responsibilities to the public are such that a lapse of consciousness may endanger the lives of many. Such are signalmen, engine drivers and bus drivers. The obtaining of a confirmatory opinion is the first move of the wise practitioner. Thereafter he leaves the patient in no doubt as to his views and advises a change of occupation on grounds of public as well as personal safety. He does all he can to persuade the patient to permit disclosure to his employer and in the face of refusal he may decide to enlist the help of relatives to this end. This, some would say, is as far as a practitioner should go. Others differ and, regarding the patient as adopting an insufficiently responsible attitude, would inform the employer. He should, if such is his final decision, inform the patient of his intention. If at all possible the method of disclosure should be that of conveying the information direct to the employer's industrial medical officer if there is one. In any case the practitioner alone is the final arbiter in the matter and he must act according to his conscience, having carefully weighed up the risks and the consequences of maintaining secrecy.

A practitioner will naturally be anxious lest a disclosure of the fact that a person has venereal disease, or that a transport driver is liable to epileptic seizures, lays him open to damages for defamation. Such a disclosure should only be made where the practitioner believes it to be his duty to others and, if the statement is true and is given without malice, he cannot be made to pay damages for defamation.

Judges have ruled (for example *Tournier and National Provincial and Union Bank* (1924), I.K.B. 461) that an obligation to secrecy applies to doctors. Breach of professional confidence, however, is not, *per se*, a criminal offence. Nor is it necessarily actionable in Civil Courts.

A breach of confidence is likely to be a danger to the practitioner only when it can be shown that it is actuated by malice and is slanderous or libellous. A practitioner is well advised to regard the relationship between him and his patient as implying an undertaking to adhere to secrecy. But it remains a matter of opinion whether a breach of confidence is a tort. Normally he can avoid an issue being made of it in his case by adhering to the general requirement for consent. The truth, of itself, cannot be held to be libellous.

Disclosure of Information in a Court of Law

A practitioner subpoenaed to appear in a Court of Law may find himself called upon to make a disclosure of professional information, for which he has not the consent of his patient. Despite rulings suggesting that it is incumbent upon a practitioner to observe secrecy he has no privilege in this connexion in a Court of Law. One of the duties of a Court is to bring to light all facts relative to the case being heard. Consequently, the practitioner, in common with all other witnesses, is required to disclose anything relevant that is within his knowledge.

On being faced with a question which is an embarrassment to him in this respect the practitioner may appeal to the presiding judge to be excused from answering, on the grounds that to do so would be to violate professional confidence. He may offer to pass written information to the judge who will decide whether or not the information must be given to the Court. If the judge so directs the practitioner must give the necessary evidence, though he may make it quite clear that he does so under protest. Should he persist in his refusal he runs the risk of being committed for contempt of Court, which is a serious position with which to be faced for it almost certainly involves his detention.

That the Courts take a very serious view of the practitioners' duties in this matter is evidenced by the ruling in *Garner* v. *Garner* (1920, 36 T.L.R. 196) that practitioners have no privilege as to communications made to them by their patients, nor as to the nature of the malady from which they are suffering. This is so even if the practitioner is on the staff of a clinic or hospital under the national scheme for treatment of venereal disease which promises secrecy.

Statutory Requirements as to Disclosure

Notwithstanding the golden rule on professional secrecy there are occasions in which disclosure without the consent of the patient must be made because it is a statutory requirement. Examples of such requirements are in the field of infectious disease where notification is required by statute, notification of births and deaths and notification of puerperal pyrexia. Further particulars as to these requirements are to be found under these headings.

The Medical Officer of Health and other medical officers in the Public Health Service in the course of their duty to the local authority employing them may well feel themselves awkwardly placed in the matter of professional secrecy and find it difficult to assess where their loyalties lie. The Council of the British Medical Association has issued the following statement which should prove a useful guide to those in doubt as to their exact position in the matter.

> 'There are occasions when disclosure of confidential medical information is demanded from medical officers in the public health service. The general relationship between doctor and patient will inevitably suffer unless reasonable

precaution is taken to ensure that disclosure is authorized by the individual patient, his parent in the case of a minor, or by some other competent person. It must be remembered that there are instances when the local authority is possessed of statutory authority to receive or to make disclosure of medical information.

'To maintain the confidential relationship of doctor and patient or examinee, it is desirable that information only of a general nature be given to lay persons without revealing intimate or personal details. Not infrequently detailed personal information is sought by such bodies as the children's committee or the welfare committee of the local authority. In those circumstances information should be submitted only through a medical officer nominated for the purpose, who would be responsible for appraising the medical report and deciding the extent to which personal information could be disclosed.

'The medical officer of health as adviser on medical matters to the council of the local authority and its committees should be consulted whenever it was proposed to review medical reports.'

The Dangerous Drugs Act and Disclosure

Another example, though probably rare, is that under the Dangerous Drugs Act the Secretary of State or a person empowered by him, for example the Chief Inspector, has power to demand from a doctor particulars regarding the obtaining or supplying of any drugs or preparations. Consequently a doctor may be statutorily required to disclose particulars relating to a patient.

Reports to Insurance Companies after Death

From time to time a practitioner will be faced with a request from an insurance company for a medical certificate or report on a deceased person who had not in his lifetime undergone an examination for the life insurance. The request may be in connexion with the payment of a claim on a policy for which prior medical examination was not required. The information should be given only after obtaining written authority from the nearest competent relative, to whom the reasons for disclosure and the source of the request should be explained by the practitioner. If, for any reason, the practitioner does not wish to disclose information or refuses to do so, an insurance company may refer the matter to the Industrial Court where it will be dealt with by the Industrial Insurance Commissioner. He may request the practitioner to make an affidavit for his Court, which the practitioner may do without worrying as to legal consequences.

Divorce and Nullity Cases

Medical evidence is clearly necessary in divorce suits under the Matrimonial Causes Act, 1937, where the grounds may be insanity or nullity on the grounds of mental deficiency or disorders, venereal disease or pregnancy. In the latter cases the consent of the patient should, of course, be obtained before disclosure. In the case of mental illness any consent may well be invalid (see p. 176). The Court, however, appoints a guardian *ad litem* in such cases, and it is perfectly in order for information to be given to him. The guardian *ad litem* is usually a responsible relative or the official solicitor.

The practitioner having care of the respondent in a divorce suit should give information or produce records only to the respondent, the guardian *ad litem* or, with consent, to whoever is looking after the patient's interests. He should never communicate information to a third party except with consent or when required to do so by law.

Roman Catholic view on Professional Secrecy

In the view of the Roman Catholic Church, professional secrecy may be broken if to do so is necessary to avert serious injury to Church or State or community, to avert serious harm from an innocent third party or the person confiding the secret or to avert very serious harm from the person in whom the secret has been confided.

Information to the Patient about his Illness

How much and in what terms a practitioner tells his patient has always been regarded as a matter within the discretion of the practitioner. Patients are now more enlightened than they were in former times and are able to show a fuller understanding of their illnesses if explained to them with care. There are patients who prefer ignorance and there are many to whom a little knowledge is but the seed of a growing anxiety, and to whom the giving of information beyond the bare essentials, and in the simplest terms, is, to say the least, clumsy treatment. But, in increasing numbers, there are patients who wish their doctors to tell them all they can about their condition. It cannot be denied that a patient has a right to know the facts and the doctor's opinion about his case. There is not, nor can there be, any rule in this matter. The practitioner must weigh up carefully what is wise, never forgetting the patient's right, and act in the best interests of the patient. If information is requested it should be withheld only for very good reason. Experience will soon make a practitioner master of this problem about which he will then have but occasional anxieties.

One anxiety which will from time to time worry every practitioner is over the decision as to what is to be told to a seriously ill patient. It is probable that many patients who are not told of the incurable nature of their condition are nevertheless aware of it. It is not only from the spoken word that enlightenment is sought or obtained. The sufferer from malignant disease may be aware of it, or half aware of it. One will seem to be happier without firm knowledge while another will insist on knowing and when told the truth will be relieved of his uncertainty and will achieve peace of mind. It is for the practitioner to watch carefully and to decide what is the right course in each individual case. It may be necessary to seek the views of the relatives, one of whom at any rate should be informed of the true state of affairs. Bad news should be given to the patient in guarded, but clear, terms and should not be given without the instillation of some gleam of hope which will sustain the patient in his wish to live. The task is a difficult one and what is virtually a sentence of death should be mitigated by a promise by the practitioner to see that suffering is reduced to a minimum.

The fear of malignant disease, or of impending death in acute illness, is frequently present and more often than not remains unspoken. A practitioner can render service to his patients many times over if he is constantly watching for signs of such fears in patients in whom they are entirely unjustified so that he may immediately dispel them.

An interesting series of viewpoints and much food for thought upon the subject of how much a patient should be told is to be found in a book entitled *Should the Patient know the Truth?*, edited by Samuel Standard, M.D., and Helmuth Nathan, M.D., and published by the Springer Publishing Company, Inc.

Consent to Examination or Treatment

Consent to examination or treatment must always be obtained, though in many instances it may be implied by the patients presenting themselves for examination. In a child under sixteen, consent, preferably in writing, of the parent or guardian must always be obtained. So must it be for a patient over sixteen and under twenty-one, unless living away from parents or from boarding shool, in which case his own consent is sufficient. In any case it is wise also to obtain the consent of a patient between the ages of sixteen and twenty-one.

In the case of a patient unconscious or of unsound mind consent should be obtained from a responsible relative or the guardian *ad litem.* In both these instances where the matter is urgent and neither the legal guardian nor responsible relative is available to give consent it should be obtained from the person who has charge of the patient at the time. In these circumstances the consent of a headmaster or other person standing for the time being *in loco parentis* will suffice, though a close friend or companion has no authority to give consent. In a case where no valid consent can be obtained, treatment should be confined to what is necessary to deal with the emergency. It is advisable to seek a confirmatory opinion as to the proposed course of action from a colleague.

With married persons consent should be obtained from the person undergoing the examination or treatment. Consent of a spouse is not valid except in the special circumstances which are mentioned above of an unconscious patient or a patient of unsound mind. An employer has no right to demand examination of a servant. The consent of the employee should be obtained in the absence of the employer so that it is freely considered and given.

In all cases, the practitioner should be satisfied that the consenting party knows and understands the reason for the examination or treatment and the proposed destination of any report that may arise out of the examination.

Practitioners are advised to take special care with foreigners who have an imperfect knowledge of the language. Special considerations apply to prisoners in custody (see Chapter 24).

In the majority of instances in the course of the practice of medicine it may be safely assumed that, by the very act of attending at the practitioner's surgery or at an out-patient department, consent is implied to examination and treatment. It would, in fact, be cumbersome and even impracticable to seek and obtain the consent of every patient attending for advice. Thus it is for the practitioner to use his judgment and to be on the look out for the occasional instance where it would be wise to obtain specific consent. A man might, for example, be brought somewhat unwillingly to the surgery by an employer or foreman for an opinion and may, for fear perhaps of losing his job, be reluctant to protest at that moment against examination. Or the practitioner may decide to perform a treatment involving some risk to a patient, or some disfigurement. These are fairly clear examples of the need for consent.

It is technically an assault to do anything to a patient either in the way of treatment or with a view to making a diagnosis unless it is done with the consent of the patient, either written or implied. In the vast majority of cases the consent is implied and there is no cause for anxiety. Where there is doubt and where consent is obviously necessary, the patient should be clearly informed of the course proposed and the practitioner should be satisfied that the patient understands the reason for any examination and that, if it be the case, a report on the findings will be submitted to a third party, for example, an employer or an insurance company.

When a patient presents himself for examination as part of the machinery of taking out an insurance policy the implied consent is obvious, but generally speaking it is wiser and more satisfactory for the consent to be given in writing. Not only is it an important protection for the practitioner but also it provides an opportunity to the patient to pause for a moment and to be quite certain of his willingness to submit to whatever procedure is proposed.

It is not always easy for a practitioner to remember that a

patient may submit to a procedure apparently willingly simply because he does not realise what is being done. Subsequently, in a Court of Law, he may be charged with doing something to the patient without his consent.

A patient may present with nasal symptoms and submit to an examination quite willingly. He will accept the introduction of a nasal speculum and an instrument or two as a part of the examination but, should the practitioner then proceed, for example, to remove a nasal polypus without informing the patient that he has moved from the realm of examination to that of operation, he might well be charged with operating on the patient without his consent (i.e. a technical assault) should the case go wrong and should the matter come before the Courts on a charge of negligence.

The majority of hospitals have a stereotyped form of consent which patients are called upon to sign before undergoing an operation. The consent gives permission for the administration of an anaesthetic and for the operation, leaving the extent of the operation to the discretion of the surgeon. The wise practitioner will satisfy himself that the form has been signed in every case and in addition will ensure that the patient understands what procedure is proposed, most particularly in operations in which removal of a limb or an eye or some drastic alteration in function is contemplated.

In short the practitioner must be satisfied always that the patient understands and has given his consent.

Quite apart from the need for the protection afforded by consent the advantages should always be considered of giving a patient as much information as possible about his illness and an explanation of the procedures proposed. Thereby, with the few exceptions to whom the less said the better, one achieves the co-operation of the patient and a freedom from worry on the part of the practitioner.

There are some instances in which a medical examination is a condition of employment. It should never be the duty of the doctor to examine against the employee's wish, even though it may be the duty of the employee to submit. The decision is with the employee. Many employees require pre-employment examinations and examinations for superannuation. An example of a statutory requirement for examination occurs in the

Regulations as to Safety, Health and Welfare under the Factories Acts where every person employed or proposed to be employed in compressed air is required to submit himself for examination by the Appointed Factory Doctor.

Acceptance and Refusal of Patients

There is no legal obligation on a practitioner to accept a patient for medical care but once he has accepted him and is treating him he should not withdraw from the case in such a way as to interfere with the patient's treatment. He should, therefore, notify the patient well in advance of his intention to withdraw from the case and should offer the patient suitable advice as to obtaining treatment from another source. He should offer information to the patient, or in some cases to the relatives, as to the patient's condition and the type of care that is required and should offer to meet the new doctor in consultation, if it is desired.

If a doctor has accepted a patient for treatment he is expected to treat that patient with reasonable care and skill. In accepting him he applies no undertaking to cure a patient, but he does undertake as a practitioner to exhibit and practise a fair, reasonable and competent degree of skill (see Chapter 15).

It has always been the custom for a practitioner to be regarded as being free in a general way to accept or to refuse to treat any particular patient. Thus he may limit his practice by such means as restricting it to those resident in a certain area or by declining to accept patients over and above a certain number. He may decide for personal or other reasons not to accept any individual as a patient. Apart from the occasional individual whom he rejects for personal reasons, a practitioner will welcome such patients as apply to him for medical care as being part of his job and as being an indication of the successful pursuit of his practice, both financially and in prestige. The National Health Service has introduced more definition into this aspect of practice and the great majority of patients are in a definite relationship to a practitioner by virtue of the inclusion of their names in the list of a practitioner. The procedure for changing from one practitioner to another is clearly laid down (see p. 232).

The practitioner, however, still remains free to choose

whether or not he accepts a patient applying for inclusion in his list. The only exception to this is that the Executive Council has power to allot to a practitioner's list the name of any patient who has appealed to the Council as being unable to gain acceptance by any practitioner in the area. Now and again a patient is encountered who, because of unreasonable demands upon his doctor's services, has been the subject of a request for removal from his list and, perhaps because he has already been removed from the lists of other practitioners for similar reasons, has been unable to find another practitioner willing to accept him. Whatever his shortcomings this man may call upon the Executive Council to allot him to a practitioner's list.

The general practitioner in the National Health Service is required under his terms of service to render emergency treatment to any patient, whether on his list or not, who applies for it. If he fails to answer an emergency call the matter may well fall to be investigated by the Medical Services Committee, the Tribunal or, as has happened, the General Medical Council.

Even if the terms of service did not require that a practitioner should attend a patient in an emergency the clear duty of a medical practitioner to render aid to a patient in need must be regarded as transcending any other considerations. In anticipation of emergency calls practitioners normally make covering arrangements for emergencies to be dealt with in their absence for shorter or longer periods. In the National Health Service they are required to do so.

Where the practitioner is himself available, as he normally is, it is his duty as a medical practitioner to respond to an emergency call and to afford the patient such treatment as the emergency requires. If for some reason he is unable or undesirous of responding to the call he should regard it as his duty as a practitioner to ensure that the patient is transferred to the care of a colleague. Until such a transfer is satisfactorily effected and he is satisfied that the patient is in adequate medical care he should regard himself, as he will be regarded by others, as being responsible in the matter.

It is proper that a medical practitioner should view such a matter in the broad light of his prime and humane duty as a medical practitioner and act accordingly and not seek to confine his activities, or lack of them, to a narrow interpretation of what may be required of him by written laws or terms of service. To deny his attendance or services to a patient who applies and who requires treatment is to court trouble and is a violation of an essential ethic of the practice of medicine.

In private practice it is unusual and unnecessary for there to be any written agreement for medical care between the practitioner and the patient. A patient, on applying for medical care may make inquiries of the practitioner as to his fees, but whether he does or does not institute prior inquiries as to fees it may be presumed that the patient enters into a tacit agreement to pay the practitioner's fees.

Medical Treatment to a Relative

The rendering of treatment in minor maladies by a practitioner to his relatives must be very common and there are few who would take exception to it. To take sole responsibility in cases of more serious illness is regarded as being imprudent and inadvisable except, of course, in emergency or other unavoidable circumstances. It is, however, neither illegal nor unethical.

Notification to Patients of Change of Address or Conditions of Practice

A doctor desirous of notifying his patients of a change of address or of other conditions of practice such as an alteration in surgery hours may do so by sending a circular, in an envelope and not on a postcard, to all persons who are his patients. He must exercise the greatest care to limit such notifications to those who are his patients lest he give offence by a circular reaching the patients of another doctor. The fact that patients do change their doctor from time to time makes it possible for such mistakes to occur, but the doctor who can show that he has exercised suitable care in the selection of those to whom the circular has been sent should feel no anxiety should he be called upon to explain the mistake to a fellow practitioner.

10

SUNDRY ETHICAL CONSIDERATIONS

If anyone should try to catalogue all the possible points in medical ethics with a concise ruling attached to each he will soon find his task is a vain one for the list could never be comprehensive. Medical ethics are best observed by adhering to certain principles and often the best way of stating those principles is by quoting examples. It needs only a few examples for the ideas to take root and thereafter, whether consciously or subconsciously, to be allowed to govern conduct. An attempt is made in this chapter to deal with a number of points on the ethics of which doctors need to inquire from time to time. Many of the situations in which a doctor finds himself will be covered either directly or indirectly in these chapters. When, despite reference to the usual principles, it seems difficult to know what is the correct course to take, advice may be obtained on a particular point from the Secretary of the British Medical Association who may, before giving the answer, require to put the point to the Central Ethical Committee of that body.

Advertising and Canvassing

Practitioners are advised to exercise a constant vigilance so that they never lay themselves open to the possibility of a charge of advertising. Advertising and canvassing for patients, either directly or indirectly, by action on the part of the practitioner or by failure to take steps to prevent others from so acting will always be regarded as a serious breach of professional ethics and may place the practitioner in danger of a charge being laid before the General Medical Council.

From time to time attempts to publicize a doctor's name are made by lay bodies, acting purely in the interests of those they represent or seek to serve. Hotel managers, owners of blocks of flats, athletic clubs and business firms may wish to place notices on their premises giving the names and address of a doctor who can be summoned. Such actions should be firmly resisted by the doctor and he should on no account seek to obtain such publicity by the presentation or circulation of his visiting card to any such body.

Any attempt to canvass patients, whether by direct or indirect methods, or through some agency, is highly unethical and, on proof of the facts, is likely to result in erasure from the Medical Register.

Premises

Apart from the fact that a general practitioner in the National Health Service is required to provide proper and adequate premises for the purpose of examining and treating his patients, any practitioner will realize the value to himself of ensuring that the premises in which he practises are suitable to the purpose. If they are not suitable his work may suffer. He may be tempted to skimp his examinations or to court danger by attempting procedures which should not be carried out in inadequate surroundings and without the facilities necessary for success. Sooner or later the practitioner may encounter a charge of negligence which may well have its origin in the inadequacy of his consulting room premises.

Practitioners may be held liable for injuries suffered by persons visiting their premises. Liability is all the more likely to be upheld when it can be shown that the premises are so carelessly appointed or maintained as to constitute a possible danger. An obvious example is the torn linoleum or frayed carpet over which a patient may trip and suffer injury. Inadequate lighting of the approach and consequent concealment in the dark of steps may similarly result in injury to the patient. Even where the utmost care is exercised and the premises are well kept, accidents may happen, as for example when ice has rendered slippery the approach to the surgery premises. The law requires that practitioners should take all reasonable precautions against injury by eliminating possible causes and all practitioners are advised to effect an insurance against claims, which can be done for a very modest premium.

The Brass Plate

A practitioner will appoint his premises according to the needs of his practice. It is customary and perfectly proper for him to draw the attention of the public to the nature of his premises by the exhibition of a plate on the door or gatepost, or on a mount erected within the premises for the purpose. In deciding upon the size and form of his 'brass plate' he should bear in mind that part of the Warning Notice of the Disciplinary Committee relating to advertising, and at the same time also remember the ethical requirements of the profession. There is no rule laying down the size of the brass plate. It is as well to study the brass plates of colleagues in the neighbourhood and to conform to the average. To attempt to go one better by exhibiting a plate which is larger than the others in the neighbourhood is to court trouble in the form of a charge of advertising or, short of that, a breach of professional taste and ethics. The time honoured red lamp has now fallen into desuetude but in some areas where 'shop-front' surgeries are common it is still customary to have the word 'Surgery' painted in large letters on the window.

As to the legend to be inscribed on the doctor's plate, it is best confined to the minimum that is necessary to indicate the presence and availability of a medical practitioner. His name and degrees, without the unnecessary ostentation of all of the many letters he may be entitled to place after his name, are all that is required. There is no objection to the addition, in small lettering, of the surgery hours. Instead of degrees some prefer the legend 'Physician and Surgeon' but any other description such as 'Children's Physician', 'Consulting Physician', or 'Orthopaedic Surgeon' is highly undesirable. One of the reasons for this is that these descriptions are unnecessary as the proper approach by a patient to a consultant is through the general practitioner and not direct. Announcements outside surgery premises such as 'Health Centre' or 'Clinic' are likewise undesirable. The inclusion of a higher degree such as 'F.R.C.S.', however, is perfectly acceptable to the profession.

It is quite proper for those practising in partnership to exhibit their partner's plate with their own.

Location of Premises and Sharing

Professional premises, including branch surgeries, should not be established in buildings used for other purposes such as hotels. Chemists' shops and opticians' premises call for special mention in this connexion. Relaxation of this rule may on occasion be regarded as within ethical requirements where there is no connexion either real or apparent between the sets of premises, which have separate entrances and separate addresses.

Neither should premises be shared with chiropodists (but see p. 88) or other medical auxiliaries. The basic reason behind these requirements is the opportunity afforded by such an arrangement for patients of one party to be directed to seek the services of the other. Even though both parties act in good faith and there is no hint of any arrangement or collusion between them the very proximity of the premises may well prove to be so strong a suggestion to the patient as to constitute direction. Further it is always possible that an innocent decision on the part of a patient to transfer to the list of the practitioner engaged in sharing premises may well be followed by an accusation from the practitioner from whose list the patient has transferred that the patient has been unduly influenced by the situation. From this may develop the charge that the practitioner has preferred to make sharing arrangements in order that advantage may accrue to his practice. Such a charge will be very difficult to defend.

There are known to be a number of practitioners either in consulting or in general practice whose consulting rooms are in the same premises as those of dentists. In some cases, no doubt, the waiting room is shared. Objections have not been raised seriously to such arrangements hitherto and there is no suggestion that any unethical practices arise therefrom. Nevertheless, the practitioner seeking surgery accommodation would be well advised not to make any fresh arrangements of this kind if he can possibly find some alternative accommodation. This advice is tendered not mainly because of the possibility of unethical practices developing as an outcome of the arrangement but rather to avoid any possibility of accusations, however false, being made by other practitioners.

Although, as stated above, it is generally considered undesirable for a medical practitioner to have consulting rooms in premises occupied by an optician or vice versa, exception is made where the attendance of the doctor is as an Ophthalmic Medical Practitioner under National Ophthalmic Treatment Board Association arrangements, which safeguards free choice by the patient of Ophthalmic Medical Practitioner and Optician.

Sharing premises with district nurses is undesirable as being likely to lead to misconstruction on the part of the public and of the profession in the area.

The use of a doctor's premises for a Local Health Authority clinic may be occasionally permissible as, for example, in a rural area where there is only one doctor and all those attending the clinic would be his patients; otherwise, where there is any possibility of professional advantage to the doctor, such an arrangement should only be made with the concurrence of the other doctors in the area or where all doctors in the area have had the opportunity of practising therein.

The sharing of premises with unregistered practitioners is unethical and would not be countenanced by the General Medical Council.

Publications and Lectures Addressed to the Layman

In writing books or articles or contributions to the lay press or in lecturing or broadcasting the practitioner should avoid any action or utterance which could be regarded as promoting his professional advantage. He should avoid mention of patients so that they can be identified.

Discussion of controversial medical matters are more suitable for the medical press. A practitioner should take positive steps to see that his photograph and records of his address and appointments held, laudatory statements or other references to his status or experience are excluded from any publication or announcement of a lecture or broadcast. The need for authenticity and the need for authentic information to the public may one day lead the profession to countenance the publication of names and even possibly some indication of qualifications.

It is probably always wise to avoid reference to appointments and place of practice. Whatever is done, or is permitted to be done in the future, must always be done with exaggerated modesty. Here is no place for false modesty of any kind, nor any cloaking of advertisement by apparent and subtly designed reserve. No matter what rules may be made or what precise words are used in laying down a code of conduct to cover various situations the essential point is that the practitioner shall not advertise.

The skilful and subtle practitioner may well succeed in devising a method of ensuring that on the title page of a book, in the heading of an article or in the announcement of a lecture the wording is such as to promote his professional advantage while at the same time failing to arouse any suspicion as to his intentions. Nevertheless, this conduct is advertising in at least as great a degree as the more blatant forms. The clever avoidance of detection, or of a charge, is no substitute for the observance of the rule.

The frequency with which a practitioner's name may appear before the public without arousing suspicion as to his intentions must, of course, vary with the nature of his work. The research worker differs greatly from, say, the consultant, predominantly in private practice, who is able to meet a demand for some particular line of treatment.

The profession rightly regards with suspicion the frequent appearance of a practitioner's name at the heading of books for the layman or of articles in the lay press, in reported press interviews, in signed letters to the press, in announcements of lectures and broadcasts and in other ways. It is up to a practitioner to ensure that his name does not appear with undue frequency. He must take positive steps to forestall any laudatory statement about himself or the giving of any undue prominence to his name, for the layman responsible for publication of a book or article or announcement for the lay public cannot be assumed to know the requirements of professional ethics, nor, necessarily, to have any particular reason to conform to them.

Interviews to the Press

Particular caution should be observed in granting interviews to the press. The members of the press have their duty to perform and will naturally wish to obtain for publication as much information as they possibly can and with as much evidence of authenticity as is obtainable. It is, therefore, up to the practitioner to make a specific request for the exclusion of certain matter, such as his name, his professional status or other matters where he feels that their inclusion would be contrary to medical ethics or otherwise undesirable. The press may feel entitled to publish anything that is said to a reporter. A practitioner should not hesitate to ask to see a proof of any proposed article or report if he feels unhappy about its possible content in relation to medical ethics.

If he prefers to make no comment or report he should say so and not be persuaded into making half statements.

Disclaimers

Occasionally there appear in the press, more commonly in the local press, statements concerning a practitioner which are inaccurate or misleading and which the practitioner may feel disposed to correct, possibly in his own interest. The most obvious example is a statement that the practitioner is giving up his practice and is leaving the district. Such a statement places the practitioner at a great disadvantage but he can usually counter its effects quite efficaciously by the exhibition of a suitably worded notice in his waiting room and by assurances, in conversation, to those patients who mention it to him.

Many statements in the newspapers are forgotten by the readers in a very short time and to insist upon the issue of a disclaimer serves to call further attention to the original statement and incidentally to the practitioner himself.

The issue of disclaimers in the lay press is generally regarded by the profession as undesirable. When a practitioner is the subject of an inaccurate statement and when some report, even if true, has embarrassed him by giving prominence to his name he should address a letter to the editor, not for publication, pointing out the circumstances and the possible danger or inconvenience to himself and asking him for an assurance that such treatment will not be meted out to him in the future.

Broadcasting

The General Medical Council in 1934 expressed the opinion that broadcasting by registered medical practitioners should be anonymous, that no letters should be forwarded from the public to the broadcaster and that complete anonymity should be observed by the British Broadcasting Corporation in connexion with inquiries arising out of the broadcast.

The British Medical Association in 1953 gave the following definition of anonymity:

> 'Anonymity may be defined for this purpose as withholding the publication or announcement of the practitioner's name or any information, such as particulars of the appointment he holds, which might enable the public to identify him. Identification cannot be completely excluded, but it is incumbent upon medical practitioners who take part in sound or television programmes to ensure that the possibility of identification and publicity is reduced to a minimum. Unless a practitioner insists on anonymity he is not only offending against the ethical principles of the profession but is placing himself in danger of being accused of violating the Warning Notice of the General Medical Council. Should a practitioner, while carefully observing these precautions, be recognized by a section of the public, that fact should not of itself be regarded as evidence of an infringement of the rule of anonymity.'

The policy of the British Medical Association is that there should be strict anonymity for medical practitioners broadcasting on medical subjects and all reasonable precautions to minimize identification by the public should be adopted.

The growth of television in recent years has, of course, made the preservation of anonymity very much more difficult than ever it was with sound broadcasting but, even so, the profession as a whole considers that all possible steps to preserve it should be taken. One of the difficulties in furthering and defending this policy is that to date, despite its opinion expressed in 1934, there has been no action by the General Medical Council against any medical broadcaster who has broadcast with the announcement of his name. But it would be a false argument to say that because nobody has laid a charge before the General Medical Council such action is, therefore, not advertising.

Another difficulty is that it is claimed on behalf of broadcasting authorities and producers of programmes and others that medical information should be given in order to meet public demand and to educate the public, and that the authenticity of the programmes broadcast cannot be adequately established without the announcement of the name of the practitioner giving the programme. This is a view which is held by many and opposed by others but the policy of the profession at present remains firmly on the side of anonymity.

The British Medical Association considers that even a whole-time salaried doctor in a non-clinical appointment who, therefore, by giving his name, could not attract patients and might be thought to have gained no professional advantage by the announcement of his name, should not allow his name to be given. One reason is that those in other fields of practice who could gain a professional advantage and could attract patients might well feel they had a right to emulate a professional colleague and allow their name to be announced.

Another point is that a whole-time doctor, such as described above, could, by his prowess at broadcasting, easily establish a reputation as a successful broadcaster and thereby achieve an advantage in applying for other posts. These considerations in addition to the possibilities of a profitable entry into private consulting practice might apply to holders of whole-time appointments.

There is no objection to broadcasting by doctors on non-medical subjects but even here the doctor would be well advised to consider the dangers to himself were it possible for someone to show that his reputation made in the non-medical field by frequent broadcasting under his own name, duly announced, was to his professional advantage.

An important point stressed over the years by the British Medical Association has been that eminent men in the profession, especially those who have achieved distinction in clinical fields, have a duty to the profession as a whole to set an example to their colleagues by observing strictly the requirements of the profession in this matter.

It is considered to be unethical for a doctor to participate at all in broadcasting programmes, whether sound or television, which are being presented for or on behalf of, firms using sponsored radio as a means of advertising.

Much has and will be said and written on the *pros* and *cons* of this vexed question. The issues have already been considerably confused by well meant attempts to give guidance and to define possible circumstances in which no exception could be taken to the announcement of a medical broadcaster's name.

The essence of this and allied problems is surely that a doctor must not advertise and it is up to each individual doctor so to conduct himself as to run no risk of being charged with violating the ethical tenets of his profession or the Warning Notice of the Disciplinary Committee.

Certificates

The issuing of a certificate is a responsible act never to be undertaken lightly or without care. Usually a certificate states a fact or facts to the best of the practitioner's knowledge and belief and adds his opinion, for example on fitness for employment. A certificate must be dated and signed by the practitioner and should state only such matters as are in his knowledge and belief. It must not be misleading, dishonest or improper.

There are pitfalls in the giving of every certificate. Carelessness, which may well result in the issue of a false or improper certificate, is a fault which will easily lead the practitioner into the position of having to answer a charge of false certification before the Disciplinary Committee of the General Medical Council or before a Tribunal set up under the National Health Service Act. The outcome of an inquiry into such a charge may be removal from the Register, expulsion from the National Health Service or a substantial fine and reprimand.

To those who, in the issue of every certificate, adhere to the basic rules of stating only what is true and what is an honest opinion founded on the facts, the pitfalls need occasion no anxiety.

A certificate may be on a plain piece of paper which gains in authority if the practitioner's address is included. Headed notepaper is an advantage or the use of printed forms which are easily adaptable for the purpose of an individual certificate. More commonly nowadays the patient will present a certificate which he has been asked to have completed and which may be a part of a larger document. Although National Insurance sickness benefit may be obtained by a patient on the presentation of a suitable certificate on plain paper practitioners in the

National Health Service are provided with special forms for the purpose which require the minimum of writing for completion (see page 236).

Certificates are requested from practitioners for many purposes and opinions of practitioners are constantly sought on a wide variety of issues covering such things as medical priorities for housing and other benefits and freedom from communicable disease as well as, sometimes, recommendations on non-professional matters. The practitioner should not hesitate to decline to complete a certificate if his knowledge is insufficient to form an opinion. In such a case he should obtain a second opinion, if necessary from a consultant who may be the one eventually to complete the certificate. Obviously it is possible for a practitioner to include a diagnosis on a certificate which is later proved to be erroneous. He need not fear that such certification will be regarded as false if he has acted in good faith.

The National Insurance certificates require the insertion of a diagnosis which should be as accurate as possible. Occasions often arise in which it is in the patient's interest, to save him from anxiety, to word the diagnosis in such a way as not to alarm him. This difficulty is normally overcome by the use of technical terms but occasionally may be followed by an inquiry from the Regional Medical Officer for elucidation, which should be readily given and will be treated in confidence (see also p. 249). The certificate form in the National Health Service is handed to the patient and the disclosure to any third person, usually the Insurance Officer, is by the patient and is not a breach of professional confidence. The patient may obtain a copy of the certificate from the National Insurance Officer but only for approved Friendly Societies and recognized Trade Unions in order that the patient may obtain additional benefits.

For other purposes, most commonly for his employer, a patient may obtain a 'private' certificate from his doctor. The patient should be warned should there be any possible harm to him, or should his employment be endangered, by the employer's seeing the diagnosis on the certificate.

In conformity with the general rule as to secrecy the consent of the patient should always be obtained before a certificate is passed to a third party.

Absolute legal immunity from the consequences of issuing a

certificate cannot be assumed by the practitioner though he is unlikely to suffer if he can show that he has acted in good faith and without malice or ulterior motive. If any difficulties arise or seem imminent the facts should be placed before the practitioner's defence organization. Apart from the National Insurance certificates a specific diagnosis on a certificate is best avoided if at all possible.

A certificate should never be given in respect of a patient who has not been seen and hearsay evidence should never be recorded on a certificate without qualification. Requests for such certificates reach every practitioner from time to time by messenger and difficulties are caused thereby. The circumstances are often such as to tempt a practitioner to relax his certification, but he should never allow himself to be so tempted. He may, if he feels justified, give partial satisfaction to the patient by a definite and true qualification of the certificate in such form as 'Though I cannot state it as a fact from personal knowledge, I am informed that . . . and have no reason to doubt the truth of this statement'. Such difficulties commonly arise when a man has remained off work for two or three days for some minor complaint which did not require the attendance of his doctor. On return to work he is called upon by his employer to produce medical evidence to support his explanation of absence. Only at this point, when completely recovered and fit again for work, does he apply to his doctor, whose action in refusing a certificate of unfitness on days on which he has not seen him may well be regarded by the patient as unreasonable.

Patenting and Commercial Enterprises

For many years it has been regarded as ethically undesirable for a medical practitioner to take out a patent for any article or device intended for medical purposes with a view of deriving from the patent the financial results of a monopoly either directly or by the use of his name in the advertising of the article. The British Medical Association in 1932 stated that it would welcome a system of dedication of patents in the medical field to the use of the public and that until some such dedicatory system was established patenting by medical practitioners was undesirable.

Since the establishment of a body known as the National Research Development Corporation, the Association has declared that there is no longer any objection to the patenting of inventions for which members of the medical profession are responsible, provided that such patents are assigned to the National Research Development Corporation with a view to their administration in the best interests of the community.

It is clearly desirable that any invention in the medical field should be made available to the whole profession for the benefit of patients and that there should be no monopoly of any kind. To achieve this end the practitioner having an invention he wishes to patent should place the matter before the National Development Corporation with whom he should discuss the procedure best calculated to benefit the community at large.

It is not always possible, owing to uncertainty of demand, to persuade a commercial firm to buy from the practitioner his interest in an instrument or appliance he has designed, but if possible this should be done as being preferable to the practitioner's retaining his interest and drawing royalties. There is no objection to the practitioner's name being attached to the instrument, but only if he has sold out his interest.

For a practitioner to be associated with the sale of pharmaceutical specialities, or to have a financial interest in any preparation he may have to recommend or prescribe, are regarded as undesirable. Practitioners are warned not to give testimonials for commercial products unless a legal guarantee is given that the opinions will not be published.

Nursing Homes

Nursing homes fall easily into two categories. The first is the more usual type in which the proprietors provide accommodation and nursing but leave the medical treatment of the patient to the practitioner in charge of the case. In the second type medical treatment is arranged for and provided by the nursing home, the patients being admitted to the care of a practitioner or practitioners who are appointed as medical officers to the nursing home. Advertisements for those in the latter category should appear only in the medical press. If these are advertised in the lay press the medical officers place themselves in danger of a charge of contravening the Warning Notice of the Disciplinary Committee in respect of canvassing. The advertisement in the medical press may properly include the names of the medical staff, including their degrees, but on no account should any statement be included which is laudatory to the members of the staff or the treatment given.

Practitioners on occasion have a financial interest in a nursing home. If a practitioner recommends a patient to enter such a nursing home he should inform the patient of his position in relation to it.

Insurance Agency

A practitioner who acts as an agent for an insurance company must inform any prospective clients of the fact.

Relations with Dentists

The paths of the doctor and the dentist frequently cross. Difficulties which may arise can normally be avoided by each having respect to the other's sphere of action and applying to their relationship principles akin to those obtaining between doctors. In some, but not all, respects a dentist stands in similar relation to a general practitioner as does a consultant.

A doctor should not criticize or comment upon the treatment given by a dentist to his patient or make any remark which may undermine the confidence of the patient in his dentist and he is justified in expecting a reciprocal attitude on the part of the dentist. In advising a patient to consult his dentist, as he will often have occasion to do, he should not express his views as to the line of treatment the dentist should adopt. When the patient, having no dentist, asks the doctor to suggest one he may properly do so, but he should in no instance say anything to a patient which might lead the patient to change his dentist when he already has one.

When a patient is already having dental treatment, out of which arises the condition for which he is consulting his doctor, the doctor should seek the patient's permission to communicate with the dentist. If this permission is not forthcoming he may, however, give whatever emergency treatment is necessary. If any further consultation or reference is required, such as for an X-ray or pathological investigation or reference to another dentist, this should be done in consultation with the dentist.

A dentist may be expected to communicate with the doctor when he proposes to operate, under an anaesthetic, upon a patient who is receiving medical attention. The dentist may choose his anaesthetist who may not necessarily be the patient's doctor. If he chooses an anaesthetist other than the patient's doctor he should raise no objection to the latter's presence at the operation should he or the patient so desire.

Occasionally disputes of an ethical nature arise between doctor and dentist. A doctor having an ethical complaint about the conduct of a dentist may, if he wishes, invoke the joint ethical machinery of the British Medical Association and the British Dental Association in order that his complaint may be investigated.

It is not desirable for a doctor and a dentist to join in partnership. The British Dental Association has expressed the view that such a partnership is ethically objectionable as it affects the free choice of doctor, or of dentist, however indirectly.

Relations with the Clergy

There is no ethical objection to co-operation between doctors and clergy in promoting the well-being of a patient. There are occasions in which the doctor has reason to believe that the patient's recovery may be hastened or his peace of mind be restored by the ministrations of the clergy and he need have no qualms about engaging in such co-operation with the clergy as is necessary for this purpose.

Relations with Chemists and Opticians

A doctor must ensure that he does not use his relationships with chemists or opticians, or with any other medical auxiliaries, to his professional advantage. Obvious examples to be avoided are the circulation of professional cards to or the institution of any salary or commission arrangements with any chemist or optician. There must be no arrangement which would influence the doctor to direct his patients to any particular chemist or optician. He must not, for example, have any financial interest in a local chemist's or optician's business. Subject to the considerations mentioned above, under Patenting and Commercial Enterprises, there is no objection to his holding shares in a large business which may have branches in the area of his practice so long as he is careful not to allow this fact to influence him in directing patients to a branch of the business.

The question of sharing premises with a chemist or optician is dealt with on p. 75.

Relations with Medical Auxiliaries

The N.H.S. (Medical Auxiliaries) Regulations, 1954 (S.I. 55 of 1954) introduced compulsory registration of medical auxiliaries of various categories.

The regulations provide for admission to the register of those holding a certificate issued by the appropriate body (see below) that they have attended a course of training and passed an examination approved by the Minister. Provision is made for those who have trained and passed an examination overseas which is recognized by the Minister and the appropriate body. Those in the employ of one of a large number of authorities on March 31st, 1954, were also admitted to the register as also were those who, although not having the necessary qualifications, but by virtue of their training and experience, had their names on a list kept by the appropriate Minister.

The British Medical Association recommends that practitioners should not employ auxiliaries in these various spheres of treatment unless they are members of a Society approved by the Board of Medical Auxiliaries or by the Chartered Society of Physiotherapy.

The appropriate bodies which lay down the requirements and are empowered to issue the certificates are:

Chiropodists
The Joint Council of Chiropodists.
The Society of Chiropodists.

Dieticians
The British Dietetic Association.

Medical Laboratory Technicians
The Institute of Medical Laboratory Technology.

Occupational Therapists
The Association of Occupational Therapy.

Physiotherapists

The Chartered Society of Physiotherapy.
The Faculty of Physiotherapists.
The Physiotherapists' Association.

Radiographers

The Society of Radiographers.

Speech Therapists

The College of Speech Therapists.

A National Register of Medical Auxiliaries is maintained by the Board of Registration of Medical Auxiliaries, Tavistock House North, London, W.C.1.

Chiropodists

The profession affords recognition to chiropodists who confine their practice within definite limits except when acting under the direction and supervision of a registered medical practitioner.

A practitioner employing or recommending a patient for treatment by a chiropodist on the National Register may, with confidence, assume that the limiting conditions as to practice prescribed by the Board of Registration of Medical Auxiliaries will be observed. Such persons are, for example, not permitted to treat any patient who is at the time under the care of a medical practitioner without his knowledge and consent.

The sharing of premises with chiropodists is generally regarded as undesirable. It is possible that there may be special circumstances where this is not so as, for example, where a practitioner employs a chiropodist for part of his time as a dispenser or book-keeper. Where such a situation obtains there are obvious difficulties, not to say ethical dangers, which may be overcome, at any rate partially, by the chiropodist treating only patients of his part-time employer or possibly by ensuring from all practitioners in the neighbourhood that they will raise no objection to the proposed arrangements. Nevertheless it is hardly possible to eliminate all the dangers.

11

ASSISTANTS, LOCUMS AND PARTNERSHIPS

Under Medical Ethics there have been described the relationships that should be preserved by one doctor in his dealings with any other doctor under whatever circumstances their paths cross. We come now to descriptions of the closer relationships between doctors working together as principal and assistant, principal and locum or in partnership. All the ethical considerations still apply but in addition it has to be remembered that here is a business relationship as well and there are a number of special considerations to be observed.

Assistants in General Practice

The employment of an assistant demands a clear understanding of the relationship of the assistant to the principal. He is his agent and his employee and the principal is liable for acts of negligence on the part of the assistant. The assistant is also responsible in law for his own acts. This is yet another, and one of the strongest, arguments for the principal's belonging to a defence organization. He should also insist on his assistant's being subject to similar protection. An assistantship agreement is most strongly advised in the interests of both parties. Model forms and advice may be obtained from the Medical Practices Advisory Bureau, which advises that the following conditions should be included:

(1) The assistant to give diligent and faithful service.

(2) The assistant to give his whole time and attention to the practice under the direction of the principal. He is entitled to reasonable and regular off-duty times and holidays.

(3) The assistant to receive mutually agreed rates of payment for his services.

(4) The assistant to keep just accounts and to pay over to the principal all monies received on behalf of the practice.

(5) Arrangements in case of illness of the assistant with provision for a fixed period of payment.

(6) Period for the duration and termination of the agreement.

(7) A restrictive clause as to practice by the assistant during and after the termination of the employment (see also Chapter 8).

(8) Membership on the part of both parties to a defence organization during the agreement and for six years after.

(9) Provision for the settlement of disputes by arbitration.

Where a subsequent partnership is promised or intended, this should be written into the agreement, including detailed intentions as to the projected partnership.

In the Trainee Assistant Scheme under the National Health Service specially approved practitioners are permitted to accept assistants for training for a period of one year. In all other respects the relationship between principal and assistant is the same as in an ordinary assistantship and a similar agreement should be drawn up.

The agreement may contain provisions as to summary dismissal for such causes as absence, incompetence or misconduct on the part of the assistant, but a principal would be well advised to consult his defence organization before embarking upon such a step.

Occasions will arise where, on the death of a principal, the assistant will carry on the practice, being employed for the time being by the widow or the executors of the principal. An assistant so employed would not be charged with 'covering' (see Chapter 6) so long as he is subjected to no interference or direction of any kind in professional matters.

Locum Tenens

A locum tenens is engaged for a specific purpose and it should be agreed between him and the principal employing him, in advance, what are to be his duties, his remuneration and the period of his employment. In general practice the first can hardly be in other than general terms and may be taken to cover any work that may arise and require to be done in the practice by the principal were he to be working in the practice during the period. A locum tenens taken on as an extra pair of hands when none of the principals was absent would in effect be regarded as a temporary assistant and would be expected to undertake such duties as were assigned to him by the principals. In a case of illness it may be that the period of the locum tenency would not be defined. Then it should be clearly understood that the term is not definite but that due notice of termination, say a week or a month, should be expected from either party.

The locum tenens must not keep for himself any fees or remuneration without the knowledge and consent of the principal, his salary as a locum tenens covering all the professional services he renders during the period of his locum tenency. He is, however, entitled to retain payment for any services rendered after the termination of the period. These requirements are laid down in the Prevention of Corruption Act, 1906, for the purposes of which the locum tenens is an agent and must not profit from the work he does for the principal other than the remuneration that he is paid by the principal for the work. Penalties including damages, fine and imprisonment can follow a successful prosecution for violation of the Act.

It is perhaps rarely that a written agreement is made for the ordinary locum tenency, which, most commonly, is an arrangement to cover the practice during comparatively short holiday absence. It is however understood that, as with a partner or assistant, a locum tenens must not do or say anything which is harmful to the principal or to his practice. To practise subsequently in opposition to the principal, without his written consent, is normally regarded as unethical for it is bound to carry with it the probability of unfair advantage from the confidential introduction to patients in the area and of using it to the detriment of the principal's practice (see Chapter 8). The absence of written agreement or bond does not vindicate in any way such conduct on the part of an erstwhile locum tenens. In general the ethical rule is the same for partner, assistant and locum tenens though in the latter case, after a short period locum tenency, the rule may be capable of some relaxation after passage of time. A practitioner in this position seeing an opening in the area and having the opportunity to establish himself in practice should not do so without obtaining the written agreement of the former principal. If this seems to be unreasonably withheld, which holds out fair promise of an impending charge by the principal of unethical conduct, advice should be sought from senior practitioners in the neighbourhood or, perhaps with a view to greater security, the ethical machinery of the British Medical Association. If the advice is against setting up in practice in opposition to the former principal it should be taken and the practitioner should seek an opening elsewhere. The temptation may be great but the acceptance of advice will save the practitioner from a great deal of trouble and, possibly, disgrace among his colleagues. If the advice of the British Medical Association is in his favour he may safely go ahead with his project but will be well advised to do all he can to avoid taking advantage of his previous introduction to the principal's practice.

As with an assistant, the principal is responsible in general for the acts of a locum tenens and, therefore, he would be unwise not to ensure that his locum tenens is a member in benefit of a medical defence organization. The subject of liability for the negligence of others is dealt with in Chapter 15.

Partnerships

It cannot be stressed too often that a partnership should always be covered by a partnership agreement. Such are the pitfalls of medical partnerships, some common to all partnerships and others particular to the medical profession, that legal advice should always be sought prior to entering into partnership and a solicitor versed in medical partnership agreements should be employed to draw up an agreement, or to scrutinize the agreement drawn up by the other party. The advice of anyone with any knowledge of medical practice is to place no reliance upon a 'gentleman's agreement' or an 'understood partnership' even though it be between relations or close friends. Whatever the form of partnership an agreement must be regarded as essential. No partnership should ever be entered into with anyone who is not a registered medical practitioner.

The *Medical Practitioners' Handbook* (published by the British Medical Association) gives an excellent and concise account of the main points to be borne in mind, the responsibilities of partnership and the bearing upon the matter of the Partnerships Act, 1890, which applies to partnerships even when no agreement exists.

A useful memorandum on medical partnerships under the National Health Service (Scotland) is obtainable from the Scottish office of the British Medical Association (7 Drumsheugh Gardens, Edinburgh), which has set up a Partnership Advisory Committee to whom reference may profitably be made in cases of difficulty.

The real purpose and necessity for agreements is that there shall be a record of what was agreed and what was intended. After the passage of years memories play tricks and therefore the provisions of the partnership, variations of shares, provisions for termination and other points should be clearly set down, showing also the agreed interpretation. This makes it a job for a lawyer. An agreement forestalls trouble and often expense and incidentally can provide protection from opposition subsequently.

The essence of partnership is that it is an equitable relationship, each partner behaving fairly and in good faith towards the other and in the mutual interest of the partnership. An unfair clause in an agreement will not necessarily be accepted as valid by the Courts. Co-operation between practitioners may or may not be regarded as a partnership under the Partnership Act. The Court would decide in an individual case, depending on the circumstances and the agreement. Such matters are important should a dispute arise. The best safeguard is to have an agreement. It is wise, considering the inevitable harm to a practice brought about by a legal action, to provide for arbitration in the case of a dispute arising.

The Act defines the general requirements of a partnership, mentioning the principles to be adopted if radical changes are proposed, if a partner is to be expelled and the admission of a new partner or a successor.

A partnership is regarded as a unity with common or shared liability and responsibility on each partner whether it refers to pledging credit or conduct of the practice as carried out by one partner. A doctor may find that he is joined in an action against his partner arising out of his practice. This is particularly important should there be charges of negligence. Consequently the insistence in a partnership that all its members should belong to a medical defence organization is more than an act of wisdom, it is practically an essential. A practitioner who voices a criticism of the conduct of his partner is not only committing an act of disloyalty but, if it is expressed to an outside party, is committing the partnership, and therefore himself, to an admission of fault.

Dissolution of Partnership

A partnership normally continues in being until a situation arises which is provided for in the deed, such as death of one partner, his inability to continue, his misconduct or the expiration of the period of time agreed for the continuance of the partnership. In the last instance a continuation of the partners in the practice maintains the partnership, it now being a partnership at will.

A requirement for due notice of dissolution is often written into the deed, but if it is not the dissolution takes effect from the date of the notice so long as this does not operate unreasonably or arbitrarily to the detriment of the other partners.

Dissolution may be claimed as a result of permanent incapacity or unsoundness of mind on the part of one partner, his erasure from the Medical Register, a serious and wilful failure to carry out his obligations according to the partnership deed or any act or omission likely to bring discredit upon or to interfere with the partnership. Faced with some such serious defection as those mentioned above on the part of a partner, the other practitioner or practitioners should immediately seek legal advice, for an application to the Courts may be necessary in order to obtain an order dissolving the partnership. The partnership remains in being, with all that that implies, until the dispute is settled.

Lesser differences of opinion between partners must arise from time to time but should not normally be regarded as reasons for dissolution. An arbitrator to settle differences is usually provided for in a partnership agreement and may be the best course, though practitioners should bear in mind the help that may be obtained in these circumstances by reference of the matter to the ethical machinery of the British Medical Association.

A partnership is dissolved by bankruptcy of one of the partners or may be dissolved if he charges his share for his personal debts. If a partnership is dissolved the survivors may collect the partnership debts.

Erasure from the Medical Register of a partner would seem to be good grounds for dissolution of a partnership because if he continued in practice the remaining partners would lay themselves open to erasure for associating with a practitioner no longer on the Register. When dissolution is sought by partners on account of misbehaviour of one partner it is unlikely that an application to the Courts would succeed where it seemed that there had been some comparatively minor aberration of which the partners were taking unreasonable advantage or using it as an excuse to suit their premeditated ends. An application is likely to succeed only where it can be shown that there has been grave damage to mutual confidence or to the good name of the partnership.

12

COURTS OF LAW

A medical practitioner may have occasion to appear for various purposes in a Court of Law. He may appear as a witness, either ordinary or expert, he may be suing for fees or appear as defendant in an action of negligence. In appearances in an action initiated by himself, or as a defendant, he will be under the guidance of his solicitor or the solicitor for his medical defence organization. Information as to his appearance as an expert or ordinary witness is given below. If he is in any doubt as to his appearance or its implications he should not hesitate to consult his solicitor or his medical defence organization as appropriate. In any case a superficial knowledge of the Courts of Law that exist in Britain is useful and the important facts are given below.

Courts of Law in England and Wales

The Coroner's Court

The main function of the Coroner is to inquire into all cases of violent, sudden, suspicious or unexplained deaths which occur within his jurisdiction and to bring in a verdict as to the cause of death. Medical practitioners are frequent and highly important witnesses in the Coroners' Courts. Witnesses are on oath and, although the proceedings are always attended with less formality than in other Courts of Law, evidence should be given with the same scrupulous care as is required in other Courts. In Scotland there are no Coroners' Courts but the functions of the Coroner are carried out by the Procurator Fiscal.

A doctor, in common with other witnesses, will normally be questioned firstly by the Coroner. At the discretion of the

Coroner he may be examined by other persons regarded as properly interested. The Coroner may disallow questions if he deems them to be irrelevant or improper. A witness is not compelled to answer a question which may possibly incriminate him and the Coroner will normally inform the witness that he need not answer if such a situation arises.

The doctor's evidence may be read over to him and he may be required to sign it as his deposition. He should listen carefully in order to ensure that what is in the deposition is what he said in evidence. If he wishes to modify what is in the deposition, either to correct an error in transcription or to effect a modification of what he said, he should seek permission of the Court. Similar considerations apply to appearances as witness in other Courts as well. The deposition may be referred to in a higher Court at which the case is subsequently heard.

The doctor must not leave a Court until given permission to do so. Permission may be requested by or on behalf of the doctor and will normally be granted. Sometimes a Coroner will ask the doctor if he wishes to leave without waiting for him to ask permission.

Magistrates Court of Petty Sessions

This is a Court presided over by two or more Justices of the Peace or by a Stipendiary Magistrate. It is a Court of Summary Jurisdiction in which punishments for minor offences are administered. The Magistrates Court, or Police Court as it is commonly called, also undertakes the preliminary examination of prisoners charged with more serious offences, known as indictable offences. Determination is here made as to whether there is justification to send the case for trial in a higher Court. Evidence of witnesses is taken down in writing and signed by the witness, who is entitled to make any necessary corrections. In the higher Court the witness may be cross-examined on his statement.

The County Court

The County Courts are presided over by County Court Judges and exist for the hearing of civil disputes which, in general, do not involve sums of over £200. The Judge is addressed as 'Your Honour'.

Quarter Sessions

The Courts of Quarter Sessions must consist of at least two Justices of the Peace and are usually presided over by a Recorder, who is a barrister of not less than five years standing and is addressed as 'Your Worship'. It tries all but the more serious indictable offences (e.g. treason, manslaughter, murder) and a miscellany of certain cases under special statutes. It also acts as a Court of Appeal in certain matters such as convictions of the Magistrates Courts. The Court normally sits once a quarter in each county and in some boroughs.

The Assizes

These Courts try civil and criminal cases out of London. They are presided over by High Court Judges who are appointed to one of the seven circuits in England and Wales. Their jurisdiction includes those cases which are excluded from the jurisdiction of the County Courts and Quarter Sessions. They are addressed as 'My Lord', the appellation given in all higher Courts (see below).

The Central Criminal Court

This Court is the Court of Assize for London, and some of its immediate neighbourhood. The Court sits each month at the Old Bailey where several Courts, presided over by either a High Court Judge, a Judge of the City of London Court, the Recorder of London or the Common Serjeant, may sit concurrently.

The Court of Criminal Appeal

Three Judges preside over the Court of Criminal Appeal, which consists of the Lord Chief Justice and the Judges of the Queen's Bench Division. Appeals on questions of law and, where leave is given, on questions of fact, or against sentence, are heard against convictions and sentences passed by Quarter Sessions or Assizes.

The High Court of Justice

This Court has three Divisions:

(1) *The Queen's Bench Division* for common law cases such as libel, slander and breach of contract; for actions outside the

competence of the County Courts by reason of important points of law or large claims.

(2) *The Chancery Division* for cases in such as those concerned with marriage, trusts and partnerships.

(3) *The Probate, Divorce and Admiralty Division* for maritime problems, probate of wills and divorce.

There is no Jury in the Chancery Division, but in the other two there may be a Jury in certain cases.

The Court of Appeal

This Court hears appeals in civil cases from the County Courts, the Assizes and the High Court. It is drawn from the Master of the Rolls and some of the Lords Justices of Appeal.

The House of Lords

This is the highest Court of Appeal. It consists mainly of the Lord Chancellor and the Lords of Appeal in ordinary and hears every class of appeal.

The Judicial Committee of the Privy Council

This body hears appeals from some Dominion and all Colonial Courts. Its findings do not rank as judgments for they require to be confirmed by Her Majesty in Council. Of particular interest to the medical profession is the function of this body to hear appeals from decisions of the Disciplinary Committee of the General Medical Council.

The Scottish Courts

The Procurator Fiscal

The duties corresponding to the Coroner's Court of England and Wales are undertaken by the Procurator Fiscal, a whole-time officer who is a solicitor appointed by the Lord Advocate and has duties beyond those of a Coroner. He conducts investigations into deaths such as would be investigated by a Coroner, but his inquiries are private and his reports are made to Crown Counsel (see p. 114).

The Procurator Fiscal acts as Public Prosecutor and carries out investigations, and hears witnesses privately before deciding whether or not to proceed with a hearing. Again he reports to Crown Counsel and if there is to be a prosecution the case is tried by the Sheriff or the High Court of Justiciary. In the Sheriff Court the Procurator Fiscal usually acts as prosecutor.

As Crown Inquiry agent the Procurator Fiscal acts in various other matters touching the interests of the Crown, investigation of fires and explosions and also of complaints from a variety of sources.

Justices of the Peace Court

This Court is presided over by at least two Justices of the Peace. It is concerned with minor offences and licensing matters but can also deal with recovery of debts not exceeding £5 and with breaches of the peace and minor offences. Justices are addressed in Court as 'Your Honour'.

The Burgh Court or Police Court

This Court has similar civil and criminal responsibilities to the Justices of the Peace Court and is presided over by a Magistrate or Baillie who is addressed as 'Your Honour'.

The Sheriff Court

The Sheriff Court is presided over by the Sheriff Principal or the Sheriff Substitute, both of whom are lawyers of standing appointed by the Crown. The majority of civil actions, except those such as divorce and legitimacy, are heard in the Sheriff Court. Although the judgment of a Sheriff Substitute can be appealed against to the Sheriff Principal only in certain circumstances is there appeal from the Sheriff Court to the Court of Session in civil cases. The Sheriff deals also with actions such as the recovery of debts up to £20 in the Small Debt Court.

In the Sheriff Court are tried criminal cases, either summarily without a Jury or, in indictable cases, with a Jury. Punishment that may be awarded is limited to six months' imprisonment in cases of summary jurisdiction and two years in indictable cases. Cases of greater gravity, likely to warrant more extensive punishment, and cases of treason, murder, attempted murder and rape are heard in the High Court of Justiciary either in the first instance or when remitted there by the Sheriff. The Sheriff Principal or Sheriff Substitute is addressed as 'Your Lordship'.

The High Court of Justiciary

All crimes, except minor offences, are tried and appeals from inferior Criminal Courts in cases of summary jurisdiction are heard in the High Court of Justiciary which is presided over by the Lord President, the Lord Justice Clerk and Judges of the Court of Session. The Court sits in Edinburgh and also may go on circuit. It is the supreme Criminal Court in Scotland.

The Court of Appeal

Appeals from the Court of Justiciary on questions of law and sometimes of fact may be brought before the Court of Appeal, as also may an appeal against a sentence where this is not fixed by law. There is no right of appeal from the decisions of this Court to the House of Lords. The Court consists of three Judges of the High Court of Justiciary.

The Court of Session

The Court of Session deals with civil cases and is the supreme Civil Court. There may be up to fifteen Judges, including the Lord President and the Lord Justice Clerk. The Outer House is a Court of first instance dealing with actions relating to status, such as divorce, which are, as noted above, excluded from the functions of the Sheriff Court. The Inner House deals mainly with appeals from the Outer House and from inferior civil Courts (e.g. the Sheriff Court). There is appeal from this Court to the House of Lords.

Verdicts in Courts of Law

The only verdicts permissible in criminal trials are 'Not Guilty' and 'Guilty', with the addition, in Scotland only, of a third alternative 'Not Proven'. The verdict in all trials by Jury in England and Wales must be unanimous. If the Jury are not unanimous they are required to reconsider their verdict. If then they do not agree they are discharged and a new trial is held before a fresh Jury. In Scotland majority verdicts are accepted.

13

PROCEDURE IN THE COURTS

It is but rarely that a doctor is required to appear in a Court of Law. Perhaps only once or twice in his practising career will he be called upon, or he may be one of those who are called more often. The latter must be regarded as less fortunate because appearance as a medical witness is always something of an ordeal even to the experienced. The medical witness is a person who can be of important assistance to the Court but in order to be so must be fully aware of what is required of him. His conduct and bearing in the Court and the manner and content of his evidence will be most carefully noted and will be all the more correct for a prior knowledge of procedure. In this chapter is to be found the essential information regarding the appearance in Court of the medical witness. A doctor having any doubts regarding his appearance in Court is advised to consult the secretary of his medical defence organization or his professional association.

Subpoenas and Citations

A subpoena (or, in Scotland, a citation) is a writ which must be obeyed on pain of being committed for contempt of Court. A writ for calling a witness to bear evidence is known as a *subpoena ad testificandum.* A writ may also be issued for a person to bring documentary evidence, for example clinical notes, to court and this is known as a *subpoena duces tecum.*

Evidence may in certain civil cases be given by affidavit or before a special commission.

If illness prevents a practitioner's attendance, he should inform the Court at once, with a supporting medical certificate. Mere inconvenience to the practitioner will never be accepted as an adequate reason for non-attendance. The summons which interferes, for example, with the practitioner's departure on holiday may well be a source of very great inconvenience. He may inquire into the possibility of a postponement of the hearing, but if this is not granted he must forego his arrangements and attend.

The fact that a practitioner thinks he has no evidence to give does not constitute grounds for refusing to obey a subpoena or citation.

When a witness appears in Court and is called he is first examined by Counsel for the party calling him, then cross-examined by opposing Counsel and he may also be re-examined by the first Counsel. In addition questions may be put to him by the Judge and by the Jury.

A witness is compelled to answer every question put to him unless protected by privilege or public policy or if he claims that the answer will tend to incriminate him. A witness may not say anything he likes. He may only state what is within his knowledge. He must not give an opinion unless he is asked to do so or is an expert witness. What is within his knowledge is clearly distinguished from hearsay, which is not normally permitted in evidence. There are exceptions to the rule eliminating hearsay, such as certain statements made by persons who cannot themselves be called as witnesses because they are dead, unfit to attend or overseas and statements in certain public documents. The Evidence Act, 1938, made it possible in civil cases, subject to the permission of the Judge, for a witness to be allowed to produce case records and similar documents for the Court to see and also hospital notes and registers recording information given by others.

There is no privilege for professional confidence. A practitioner can even be compelled to disclose facts of which he is aware by virtue of attending a patient at a venereal disease clinic, which is subject to the secrecy provisions of the Venereal Diseases Regulations, 1916. (*Garner* v. *Garner* (1920), 36 T.L.R. 196.)

In giving evidence a witness should address himself to the Judge or the Jury. The Judge has to take down evidence in longhand so that the evidence should be given clearly, distinctly and not fast.

An expert witness should reserve his opinion to matters on

which he is an expert and should not give opinions on matters on which others in the Court can pronounce.

The Evidence

In giving his evidence the practitioner should bear in mind that his duty is to the Court, not to the party that has called him, and his function is to assist the Court to come to the right conclusion. His evidence must be entirely without bias and will be of most value to the Court if he speaks slowly and clearly, keeps as far as possible to simple terms, avoiding all but essential use of technical terms, and ensures that facts and opinions are clearly distinguishable to his hearers.

Facts are of the utmost importance and it is therefore advised that the practitioner, in anticipation of his appearance as a witness, should carefully record his findings at the time of the event, or shortly afterwards. He is entitled to bring his original notes (not copies) to the Court and there to refer to them in order to refresh his memory. If he does not fully understand a question, or has insufficient knowledge upon which to base a true answer, he should not reply. The subject of professional secrecy in the Courts is dealt with under that heading (p. 55).

Evidence should be given calmly and the practitioner should be on his guard against allowing himself to be rattled by the persistence or apparent insinuations of the questioner.

Depending partly on his status as a witness, a witness may be permitted to remain in Court during the hearing of the evidence of other witnesses before giving his own. Customs and rules vary. In general, by rule and custom, Scottish Courts are more strict in this matter. In any case most practitioners have too many other calls upon their time to wish to remain in Court after the giving of their evidence. It is quite proper, after examination and cross-examination, to seek permission from the Judge to leave the Court. Such permission will normally be granted if it appears unlikely that he will need to be recalled.

Evidence in Courts is given on oath or after solemn affirmation. The oath is given by repeating the following set form of words, while holding up in the hand a New Testament, 'I swear by Almighty God that the evidence which I shall give shall be the truth, the whole truth and nothing but the truth'.

In Scotland the words are slightly varied. Those of the Jewish faith hold an Old Testament. A witness declaring that he has no religious belief or that he has an objection to taking an oath may make the following solemn affirmation, 'I, ——, do solemnly and sincerely and truly declare and affirm that the evidence which I shall give shall be the truth, the whole truth and nothing but the truth'.

The Medical Witness

A practitioner called upon to give evidence in a Court of Law, whether criminal or civil, may do so in one of two distinct capacities. Either he is a witness to fact or he is called as an expert witness.

The Witness to Fact

In the former case he is called as one having knowledge of the facts of a case, for example the nature and extent of an injury or disease. Whereas he may be called upon only to disclose the facts that arise from his knowledge of the case he may well be asked to give his opinion upon these facts, for example as to the degree of disablement occasioned by an injury. The giving of such an opinion does not convert him into an expert witness. A practitioner called to give evidence of this kind will be well advised to prepare himself in advance of the hearing in case he should be called upon to expand his evidence in this way.

The Expert Witness

An expert witness is one who, by virtue of his standing in the profession and his knowledge of the particular medical condition in question, is called in order to guide the Court in its assessment of the case. He is one who has no connexion with the case but is qualified to give technical advice to the Court. If he has sufficient knowledge of the subject and information on the case he may, if asked, comment on any medical aspect of the case.

An expert witness is often asked to make a report first on the matter at issue. If the solicitor considers the opinion will be helpful to his case he will arrange with the witness to attend, either with or without a subpoena.

A witness should exercise the utmost care in the compilation of reports and should beware of changing his opinion on a matter between writing the report, for example to the solicitor, and giving evidence in Court. In the compilation of a report it is as well to bear in mind the risk of libel which might arise from defamatory statements made in a report.

Fees for Medical Witnesses

The distinction between the two classes of medical witnesses has its economic side for higher fees are paid to expert witnesses. The fees vary also with the status of the Court. Guidance as to the amount of fees (known as allowances) payable in Civil Courts and in Criminal Courts can be obtained from the *Medical Practitioners' Handbook.*

Civil Cases

In civil cases, it is advisable for his fees for the following to be agreed in advance between the practitioner and the party (or his solicitor) calling him:

(*a*) a medical report;
(*b*) for qualifying to give evidence (which means studying the case, in preparation);
(*c*) for each day that he is required to attend the Court;
(*d*) for holding himself in readiness to attend Court.

Travelling expenses, if received, are returnable if the person is not, after all, required to attend Court.

If it proves impossible to reach agreement before the hearing the practitioner is entitled, before giving evidence, to inform the Judge of this fact. He is entitled to allowances which are reasonable in the circumstances and it may be necessary to bring an action for recovery of allowances from the party calling him (or the solicitor if he has made himself personally liable). The amount payable is what is considered reasonable, as decided by the Judge if it proves necessary to bring an action. The fact that his fee is not agreed or paid does not absolve the witness from his duty of giving evidence.

Criminal Cases

The same considerations as in civil cases apply where the allowances of the party calling the practitioner are not to be met from public funds. Where the allowances are to be met from public funds the Witnesses' Allowances Regulations* apply. These provide for a maximum professional witnesses' allowance (which is normally not more than the second-class railway fare) and a night allowance where such absence from home is necessary, or the expense reasonably incurred for board and lodging whichever is the less. This maximum applies whether evidence is given in one or more cases. An absence from his practice of not more than four hours normally reduces the maximum by half, except that where he attends to give evidence in more than one case the daily maximum may be held to apply.

The above are in respect of a practitioner attending to give professional evidence. An expert witness, however, may be allowed such allowance as the Court may assign as reasonable for attending to give evidence and for the preparatory work involved.

If any difficulty is experienced the police officer in attendance at the Court will always assist and direct the witness to the proper official of the Court to deal with his inquiry concerning the amount and payment of fees.

Scotland

Fees for attending Civil Courts (Court of Session and Sheriff Court) are fixed by Act of Sederunt. Additional charges intended to compensate for time, travelling and for trouble and expense of preliminary investigations are allowed. These charges are in the discretion of the Court auditor, but may be appealed against to the Court itself. These provisions in Scotland are designed to regulate recoverable expenses and are a matter for arrangement in each case. The scale of allowances for evidence and reports required by the Procurator Fiscal is shown in the *Medical Practitioners' Handbook.* For Criminal Courts the same scale applies.

Agreeing the Medical Evidence

Often much time and expense may be saved by arranging for the medical witnesses who are to be called by both sides to meet and to agree the evidence. This is not intended as a device to

* See Appendix D.

persuade witnesses to alter their views and should never be used as such. Where such agreement is possible it is useful to the Court. The view has been expressed, however, by the Court of Appeal (*Proctor* v. *Peebles* (1941), 2 All E.R. 80) that in some cases, especially where prognosis is important, it is probably of more value to the Court to hear the witnesses.

A Judge may refer a case for opinion to a special expert referee. If the referee examines the patient in the presence of the doctors acting for both parties to the action the evidence may be agreed by these doctors and they may not need to be called. The doctors may see the referee's report to the Court but, of course, they need not agree it.

A Judge may limit the number of expert medical witnesses to be called.

14

THE CORONER

Even if a doctor goes through his professional career without ever being called upon to give evidence in a civil or criminal Court, there must be few in England and Wales who do not at some time or other find themselves in the Coroner's Court, usually to give evidence of findings and opinions as to the cause of death. It is useful, therefore, for the doctor to have some knowledge of the method by which the Coroner receives notifications of deaths, what action he takes and, when an inquest is necessary, how it is conducted. In this chapter are mentioned also the parallel inquiries made in Scotland by the Procurator Fiscal. Further particulars of the Courts and functions of these two officers are to be found in Chapter 12.

A Coroner must be a barrister, solicitor or registered medical practitioner of not less than five years standing in his profession (Coroners (Amendment) Act, 1926). This also applies to Deputy Coroners and Assistant Coroners. A Coroner cannot also fill the office of the sheriff, mayor, alderman or councillor in the same area. There are about 270 Coroners in England and Wales of which only a few are full-time Coroners. The majority are not medically qualified.

The Coroners' Acts provide for the holding of an inquest where there is reasonable cause to suspect a violent or unnatural death, or in cases of sudden death from cause unknown. When a post-mortem examination which is ordered by a Coroner shows that the death occurred from natural causes the Coroner need not hold an inquest unless there is some good reason to hold one, such as may seem to arise from a complaint from a relative of the deceased.

The Coroners' Rules, 1953, state clearly that the proceedings and evidence at an inquest are solely to be directed to ascertaining the following matters:

(*a*) who the deceased was;
(*b*) how, when and where the deceased came by his death;
(*c*) the persons, if any, to be charged with murder, manslaughter or infanticide, or of being accessories before the fact should the jury find that the deceased came by his death by murder, manslaughter or infanticide;
(*d*) the particulars for the time being required by the Registration Acts to be registered concerning the death.

Notifications to the Coroner

Medical Practitioners

In mental hospitals, all deaths have to be reported by a keeper.

Apart from this there is no statutory duty particularly laid upon a medical practitioner to report a death to the Coroner. The Births and Deaths Registration Act, 1953, states however that a medical practitioner in attendance shall issue a death certificate. For further discussion upon the practitioner's position see also Chapter 17. The Registrar will report to the Coroner if, after scrutiny of the death certificate, he deems it is required of him to do so.

A doctor is advised, though not required, to notify the Coroner of deaths in the following circumstances:

Accidents and violence.
Sudden unexpected deaths.
After abortions following possible interference.
Alcoholism or drugs.
Operations, anaesthetics.
Poisoning.
Food poisoning.
Deaths due to employment.
Deaths due to pneumoconiosis.

The Police

The police must inform the Coroner if they receive information of a sudden death.

The Registrar

The Registrar must inform the Coroner:

(1) where a death occurs when no doctor has been in attendance or no death certificate is forthcoming;

(2) where he has reason to believe that the death is associated with unnatural causes, for example, violence, accident, neglect, or there are suspicious circumstances or the cause is unknown;

(3) deaths of lunatics;

(4) where death has occurred after operation necessitated by injury, or under any operation or before recovery from an anaesthetic;

(5) if it appears from the medical certificate that the deceased was not seen by a medical practitioner after, or within fourteen days immediately preceding, death;

(6) any alleged still-birth, where he has reason to believe the child was born alive;

(7) deaths of foster children;

(8) deaths possibly due to industrial diseases notifiable under the Factories Act, 1937.

The Position of the Doctor

There is no legal obligation on a practitioner to report the death. He may, if he is able to certify the cause of death, mark the Space B on the back of the form when he completes a death certificate. If he does this the Registrar, on seeing the cause of death, will report the matter to the Coroner or his officer. It saves time, trouble, and, incidentally, possible distress to the relatives if the practitioner reports the death directly to the Coroner and acts in accordance with his advice regarding the issue of a death certificate.

If the practitioner has not been in attendance during the last illness he cannot normally give a certificate. On the other hand he may from previous knowledge of the patient be aware of a likely cause of death. If the circumstances of the death accord with his expectations he may issue a death certificate if he feels competent to do so, but is advised to report the matter to the Coroner. The Coroner may express himself satisfied, may seek further information from the practitioner or may order a post-mortem examination or an inquest or both.

The practitioner should provide the Coroner or the Coroner's officer with such further information as he requests but may, if he so wishes, withhold any information until he appears as a witness if and when an inquest is held. If a written report is requested by the Coroner the practitioner is entitled to a fee (see Appendix F) as also he is for a post-mortem examination, if ordered by the Coroner, or for attendance at the inquest.

Coroner's Action on Receiving Notification

On a death being reported to him a coroner may do one of three things. He may permit the patient's doctor to issue a death certificate, in which case he issues a covering form which is known as Pink Form A to the Registrar. Alternatively, he may order a post-mortem examination and, if satisfied as to the cause of death, issue Pink Form B without an inquest. Pink Form A and Pink Form B are parts of Form 100 and serve as a notification by the Coroner to the Registrar that an inquest is not necessary and that the death may be registered.

If he is unable to do either of the above two things, he may hold an inquest, which he must do in cases of unnatural death or suspicion of unnatural death and where death occurs in a prison. He may order a post-mortem examination in any case.

Post-mortem Examinations

The Coroner may direct or request a post-mortem examination. The Coroners' Rules, 1953, state the considerations to be borne in mind by the Coroner in selecting the practitioner to make the post-mortem examination. In the majority of instances the choice falls on a pathologist. The form of direction is worded as follows:

> 'I, in pursuance of section twenty-one of the Coroners' (Amendment) Act, 1926, hereby direct you to make a post-mortem examination of the body of C—— D—— and to report the result thereof to me in writing.'

The examination must be made in premises which are adequately equipped for the purpose, which means that there shall be running water, proper heating and lighting facilities and containers for storing and preservation of material.

No post-mortem examination may be made in a dwelling-house or licensed premises.

The practitioner making the examination shall make provision as far as possible for preservation of specimens which have a bearing on the case. He must report his findings on a form such as is set out in the First Schedule to the Coroners' Rules or in a similar form. No copy of the report may be supplied to anyone else without the authority of the Coroner. Similar considerations apply to the making of special examinations.

The Coroner must inform certain persons and bodies of the proposed post-mortem examination. Among these are the deceased's regular medical attendant, who is entitled to attend the examination though he must in no way interfere with its performance. Certain other persons or bodies may also, if they wish, be represented at the examination by a registered medical practitioner. The Coroner has discretion to notify any person of the examination and to allow him to attend.

The question occasionally arises of a medical practitioner requesting a post-mortem examination when there appears to be to the Coroner no reason for ordering one. The medical practitioner has no right in any case to insist upon a post-mortem examination, but if he gives good reason he will normally receive co-operation from a Coroner on this matter, though different Coroners have different attitudes.

The Coroner may send his officer to interview a doctor in order to obtain information relating to a death. The doctor need not answer the officer if he does not want to and he may state his preference for giving the information at the inquest. The Coroner does not serve a subpoena on a doctor but merely asks him to attend. A doctor should always attend on receiving such an invitation.

In a case in which no doctor has been in attendance in the last illness the Coroner may seek the opinion of any doctor in the area as to the cause of death.

The Inquest

The Coroner should normally view the body, except in exceptional cases as provided by statute. He should take evidence of identity, evidence of the circumstances leading to death, evidence of the fact of death and evidence relating to its cause.

If the post-mortem examination shows that the cause of death is natural, he may dispense with the Jury. So may he in certain other cases. The Coroner's inquest is to find out the identity of the deceased and how and when he died. No-one is on trial and although the Coroner may commit for trial for murder, manslaughter or infanticide, there is no question in the Coroner's Court of trying civil liability.

Fees

The Coroners Act, 1954, amended the provisions for regulations to be made by the Home Secretary for the fees and allowances payable to medical practitioners summoned by the Coroner to attend as witnesses and making post-mortem examinations at the Coroner's request.

The Regulations made under this Act are the Coroners (Fees and Allowances) Rules. Fees are laid down for a post-mortem examination, for making a post-mortem examination and attending as witness at an inquest, for each subsequent day of attendance at the inquest and for each day of attendance at an inquest otherwise than in connexion with a post-mortem examination. A reduced fee is payable for other inquests held on the same day.*

An expert witness may be paid such expert witness allowance as the coroner may consider reasonable. Travelling and night allowances may also be paid, where appropriate, as prescribed in the Rules.

The Procurator Fiscal

In Scotland there are no Coroners. Corresponding duties are carried out by the Procurator Fiscal (see Chapter 12). In cases of sudden or suspicious death he holds a private inquiry in the first instance. If a post-mortem examination is decided upon, and depending upon its result, he may certify the cause of death to the Registrar. The holding of a public inquiry is necessary in the case of a fatal accident occurring in an industrial employment and in any case of sudden or suspicious death whenever it appears to the Lord Advocate to be expedient in the

* For fees see Appendix F.

public interest. Such inquiries are held before a Sheriff and a Jury of seven. This Court, in addition to finding the time, place and cause of death, may add a finding of fault against a person or against the factors causing or contributing to an industrial accident. If there is any possibility of responsibility for the death being attributed to him in whole or in part the Procurator Fiscal will notify the practitioner of the inquiry. The practitioner should seek legal representation at the inquiry and should ask permission also of the Procurator Fiscal to be represented at a post-mortem examination if held, bearing in mind that, although notified of the inquiry, he will not be notified of the intention to hold a post-mortem examination.

The Procurator Fiscal may request a practitioner to make an external post-mortem examination. If he wishes a full post-mortem examination he will first require to obtain an authorizing warrant from the Sheriff. Then the practitioners named in the warrant, normally more than one, may proceed but must do so according to a prescribed plan. Two witnesses must identify the body for them, and their names and addresses must be recorded. Thereafter, only the examiners named in the warrant remain unless, as may happen, the Procurator Fiscal grants permission to a registered medical practitioner to attend to watch the interests of any accused person. The role of such a visitor is confined to that of a spectator (as in England and Wales).

15

NEGLIGENCE

Definition of Negligence

Negligence in a legal sense is the breach of a duty owed by one person to some other person to exercise care or skill or both. Applied to the practice of medicine this means that a doctor when treating a patient must bring to his task a reasonable degree of skill and knowledge, and he must exercise a reasonable degree of care. A doctor is not liable under the law of negligence merely because someone else with greater skill and knowledge would have prescribed different treatment or would have operated in some other way. He is only liable if he himself has failed to exercise that standard of skill and care which could reasonably be expected of a normal prudent practitioner of the same experience and status working under similar conditions. A doctor should not, however, except in emergency undertake treatment requiring particular skill unless he is fitted for it, and it is his duty to know whether he is so fitted or not. A specialist clearly professes a higher degree of skill and knowledge than a practitioner who does not claim any special training or ability, and accordingly a higher standard of skill and knowledge is expected of a person holding himself out as a specialist whether in fact he possesses it or not. Where there are special circumstances which increase the risk attendant on some act or operation not usually dangerous, or where the act or operation is from its nature likely to cause injury unless special precautions are taken, the degree of care required is proportionately higher. But a doctor is not liable if, owing to a peculiarity or variation in the patient's constitution, which the doctor was not negligent in failing to discover, the treatment which he prescribes proves to be injurious. Failure to exercise the required standard of skill and care will in law amount to negligence, and renders the doctor liable for any damage or loss suffered by the patient which is directly attributable to such failure. To be actionable however, the negligence complained of must have caused damage. It is not sufficient for the plaintiff merely to show that the defendant was negligent; he must also prove that the loss in respect of which he seeks to recover damages flows directly from that negligence.

The doctor's liability for negligence arises out of tort, that is to say the breach of a duty primarily fixed by law requiring him to exercise skill and care. When, as will often be the case, a contractual relationship exists between the doctor and his patient, there arises an implied agreement on the part of the doctor that he will exercise a reasonable degree of care and skill in his treatment. If in such a case, the doctor fails in his duty to exercise that care and skill, the patient can maintain an action against him for damages for negligence, i.e. breach of duty, or for breach of contract, or both.

Reasonable Skill and Care

In all cases where the relationship of doctor and patient subsists, the doctor owes a legal duty to the patient to exercise a reasonable degree of skill and care throughout his treatment. There is no fixed standard as to what constitutes the care and skill required for this must vary according to the circumstances of each individual case, the qualifications and experience of the doctor concerned and the standard of medical practice and knowledge prevailing at the time. As medical knowledge progresses so the standard by which 'reasonable care and skill' is judged becomes proportionately higher. Procedures unknown or known by few today, often become the normal practice or the normal precaution—that is the reasonable care and skill—of tomorrow. Conversely, acts or omissions which today may constitute negligence, would not have been regarded as such if they had happened a few years ago. For example, it is becoming increasingly difficult to contend that a patient whose history suggests the possibility of a fracture, but who has not been X-rayed, has received 'reasonable care and skill' yet there must be many doctors still practising who remember when an X-ray was a luxury far beyond the reach of the majority of doctors and patients. In those days an X-ray, when facilities were available, was regarded as something out of the ordinary whereas nowadays in claims for negligence against doctors one frequently finds the allegation that the defendant was negligent because he did not refer the patient for radiological examination. This should not be taken to imply that failure to have a patient X-rayed, even if it proves subsequently that an X-ray was essential to confirm or correct diagnosis, will necessarily be held to be negligence on the part of the doctor. The whole circumstances of the case including the history as given to the doctor and the result of his own clinical examination must be looked at before it can be said that in failing to refer the patient for X-ray examination the doctor did not exercise reasonable skill and care.

It is the normally accepted practice and standard of knowledge prevailing at the time of the act or omission complained of that must be applied when deciding whether the doctor has exercised reasonable care and skill. This is well illustrated by two cases, both involving anaesthetists, recently tried in the High Court.

In the case of *Crawford* v. *Board of Governors of Charing Cross Hospital*, 1953 (*The Times*, December 8th), the plaintiff suffered a brachial palsy, following an operation during which he received a blood transfusion whilst his arm was abducted. In the course of his evidence the anaesthetist admitted that at the time of the operation he had not read an article published a few months previously in *The Lancet*, drawing attention to this danger. The trial Judge held that the anaesthetist was liable and evidently took the view that a failure to keep abreast of the literature in professional journals amounted to negligence. In the Court of Appeal, however, it was held that there was no evidence of negligence by the anaesthetist and the verdict of the lower Court was set aside. Lord Justice Denning, in his judgment, referring to *The Lancet* article said: 'It would be putting too high a burden on medical men to say that they must read every article in the medical press'.

In the case of *Woolley and Roe* v. *Ministry of Health and Others* (1954), 1 W.L.R. 65, the facts were as follows:

> On October 13th, 1947, each of the plaintiffs underwent a surgical operation at the Chesterfield and North Derbyshire Royal Hospital. Before the operation in each case a spinal

anaesthetic consisting of Nupercaine, injected by means of a lumbar puncture, was administered to the patient by the second defendant, a specialist anaesthetist. The Nupercaine was contained in glass ampoules which were, prior to use, immersed in a phenol solution. After the operations the plaintiffs developed spastic paraplegia which resulted in permanent paralysis from the waist downwards. In an action for damages for personal injuries against the Ministry of Health and the anaesthetist, the Court found that the injuries to the plaintiffs were caused by the Nupercaine becoming contaminated by the phenol which had percolated into the Nupercaine through molecular flaws or invisible cracks in the ampoules, and that at the date of the operations the risk of percolation through such flaws in the glass was not appreciated by competent anaesthetists generally.

HELD: Having regard to the standard of knowledge to be imputed to competent anaesthetists in 1947, the anaesthetist could not be found to be guilty of negligence in having failed to appreciate the risk of the phenol percolating through molecular flaws in the glass ampoules and contaminating the Nupercaine.

The plaintiffs' subsequent appeal to the Court of Appeal was dismissed.

Since the introduction of the National Health Service in 1948 and the passing of the Legal Aid and Advice Act, 1949, there has been a considerable increase in the number of actions against doctors and hospitals for negligence. This appears to have caused some people—doctors as well as patients—to believe that there has been some recent change in the law of negligence insofar as it affects the legal duty and liability of a doctor. Some doctors have expressed the view that Courts of Law are always ready to impose liability on doctors and hospitals whenever treatment in a particular case has had some unfortunate and unexpected result causing injury to the patient. There is in fact no foundation for either of these beliefs. As already stated the legal duty owed by a doctor to his patients is merely to exercise a *reasonable* degree of care and skill, and this has been so since that duty was first laid down in the case of *Lanphier* v. *Phipos* in 1838. Those who hold the view that in a Court of Law the dice is loaded heavily against the doctor and that those who sit in judgment, not being medically qualified, do not appreciate the difficulties with which doctors must contend, may perhaps derive comfort from the following words of Lord Justice Denning, when giving judgment in the Court of Appeal in the case of *Woolley and Roe* v. *Ministry of Health and Others* (*supra*):

> 'We should', he said, 'be doing a disservice to the community if we imposed liability on hospitals and doctors for everything that happens to go wrong. Doctors would be led to think more of their own safety than of the good of their patients. Initiative would be stifled and confidence shaken. A proper sense of proportion requires us to have regard to the conditions in which hospitals and doctors work. We must insist on due care for the patient, but we must not condemn as negligence that which is only misadventure.'

Doctor/Patient Relationship

The duty which the law imposes on a doctor to exercise skill and care only arises when there exists the relationship of doctor and patient. If, for example, a doctor passes the scene of a street accident in which some person is seriously injured and in need of immediate medical attention, he is not guilty of negligence if he does not stop to render assistance because the relationship of doctor and patient does not arise, and in consequence the doctor owes the injured person no *legal* duty. However, if the doctor does go to the aid of the injured person a professional relationship at once comes into existence and the doctor has a duty to exercise reasonable skill and care in treating him. It matters not that the doctor has no expectation of reward, since liability for negligence is not dependent on payment for services rendered. The mere fact that a patient submits to his surgical or medical treatment imposes upon the doctor a duty to exercise reasonable skill and care in giving such treatment regardless of whether his services are being rendered for reward or gratuitously.

A doctor is only liable for negligence when he has undertaken the care or treatment of a patient—not, for example where he has merely examined a person at the request of someone else.

If, for instance, a person taking out a life assurance policy or seeking employment is required to undergo a medical examination by a doctor nominated by the insurance company or prospective employer, that person by submitting himself for such examination does not become the patient of the doctor carrying it out. The doctor in such circumstances is not treating the person, but is merely examining him for the purpose of reporting on his condition to the insurance company or employer to guide them in independent action. Consequently, if the doctor is negligent in his examination, with the result that he reports the applicant as healthy when in fact he is suffering from some serious disease, that person, although he may suffer damage because his true condition was not detected, nevertheless has no legal remedy against the doctor. The insurance company or employer, if they suffered damage as a result of the doctor's negligent report, would however have a claim against the doctor for breach of contract. The position would be different if during the course of the examination the doctor, through negligence, inflicted some physical injury on the person being examined; for example, if when syringing his ear, the doctor through lack of care or skill, damaged the man's ear-drum. The doctor owes a duty to the person examined not to injure him physically, but subject to this he owes him no legal duty since the relationship of doctor and patient does not exist.

In the case of *Thompson* v. *Schmidt* (1891) the defendant, a medical practitioner, gave to the plaintiff's wife a letter saying that her husband was of unsound mind and dangerous, although the defendant had not seen the plaintiff for eighteen months before giving the letter, which he gave on the wife's request and on information supplied by her. The plaintiff was not of unsound mind or dangerous, but the Court of Appeal held that the defendant was not liable for negligence on the ground *inter alia* that he owed no duty to the plaintiff whom he did not advise and who was not his patient.

Res Ipsa Loquitur

The burden of proof in an action for damages for negligence rests primarily on the plaintiff. If he fails to satisfy the Court by evidence that the defendant was negligent and that the injury or loss for which he claims damages was a direct result of that negligence, the plaintiff's claim will fail.

An exception to the general rule that the onus of proof of the alleged negligence falls upon the plaintiff occurs however when the facts established are such that the proper and natural inference to be drawn therefrom is that the injury or loss complained of was caused by the defendant's negligence and no reasonable alternative explanation can be given. To these cases the legal maxim *res ipsa loquitur* applies. In cases where this doctrine is applicable, a presumption of fault is raised against the defendant who, to succeed in his defence, must show that the act complained of could reasonably happen without negligence on his part. In other words, the onus of proof shifts from the plaintiff to prove positively that the defendant was negligent, to the defendant to demonstrate that some other equally likely cause outside his control was responsible for the damage suffered by the plaintiff. The application of the doctrine *res ipsa loquitur* is well illustrated by the case of *Cassidy* v. *Ministry of Health* (1951), 1 All E.R. 574, the facts in which were as follows:

> The plaintiff, who was suffering from a contraction of the third and fourth fingers of his left hand, was operated on at the defendant's hospital by Dr. F., a whole-time assistant medical officer of the hospital. After the operation, the plaintiff's hand and forearm were bandaged to a splint and they remained so for some fourteen days. During this time the plaintiff complained of pain, but apart from ordering sedatives, no action was taken by Dr. F. or by the house surgeon who attended the plaintiff in his absence. When the bandages were removed, it was found that all four fingers of the plaintiff's hand were stiff and that the hand was practically useless. The plaintiff sued the defendants for negligence by their medical and nursing staff in the post-operational treatment which he received.
>
> It was held that the evidence showed a *prima facie* case of negligence on the part of the persons in whose care the plaintiff was which had not been rebutted by the defendants. Consequently the defendants were liable to the plaintiff whether the negligence was that of Dr. F. or of the house surgeon or of a member or members of the nursing staff.

Recent trends however seem to indicate that the Courts are reluctant to apply the doctrine of *res ipsa loquitur* in cases of alleged negligence in medical treatment (see *Woolley and Roe* v. *Ministry of Health, supra*) and are more inclined to insist on proof of negligence. Too rigid a reliance on the application of the doctrine to cases in which medical treatment has had some deleterious and unexpected sequel could quite easily result in grave injustice.

Functions of Judge and Jury

In a Court of Law, the question whether a doctor has in the circumstances of a particular case exercised a reasonable standard of care and skill is decided by the Judge or the Jury (if there be one) on the evidence adduced. The answer will normally require a knowledge of medicine which neither a Judge nor a Jury can be expected to possess and in such cases the Judge or Jury must be guided in their decision to a large extent by the evidence of 'expert' witnesses—independent medical practitioners of standing and experience—who are called to state their opinions on the medical facts. It will be seen therefore that expert witnesses play an important part in defining what does or does not amount to negligence in a particular case. When, as will of course often happen, there is a conflict of 'expert' opinion the Judge (or Jury) has to decide whose evidence is the weightier and more acceptable.

Actions based on alleged negligence are usually tried by a Judge alone, but it is open to either party to apply for the case to be tried by a Jury. The decision whether the application shall be granted is a matter of discretion for the Court exercisable by the Master with a right of appeal to the Judge in Chambers.

If a trial takes place with a Jury, the Judge may withdraw the case from the Jury and enter a verdict for the defendant where a *prima facie* case is not made out, for example, where there is no evidence, or no sufficient evidence, given on behalf of the plaintiff of negligence on the part of the defendant. The Judge may also withdraw the case from the Jury where, although negligence on the part of the defendant is established, it would be unreasonable for any Jury to find that it was the natural or effective cause of the damage suffered by the plaintiff.

Contributory Negligence

In an action for damages arising from negligence it is a defence if the defendant proves that the plaintiff, by some negligence on his own part, directly contributed to the damage he suffered in the sense that it was his own negligence which was the effective cause thereof. When this is proved the plaintiff's negligence is said to be contributory. In order that a plea of contributory negligence may be successful it must be shown either that there was negligence on the part of the plaintiff which contributed to or caused the injury, or that notwithstanding the defendant's negligence, the plaintiff could, by exercising ordinary care, have avoided the injury. The following hypothetical case is an example of one in which contributory negligence might be successfully pleaded. X having fractured his leg is admitted to hospital where the fracture is reduced and the leg immobilized in a plaster cast. He is thereupon discharged with instructions to report back to the hospital in seven days' time, but he is warned that if he suffers undue pain or discomfort or observes any discoloration of his toes he is to return to the hospital at once. Notwithstanding experiencing pain and discoloration of his toes in the meantime, X does not report back to the hospital until a week later when it is found that his leg is gangrenous and has to be amputated. X brings an action against the hospital and/or doctor concerned alleging negligence in treatment. At the trial it would be open to the defendants in addition to denying negligence, to plead in the alternative that the plaintiff had been guilty of contributory negligence which was the effective cause of his misfortune.

Where any person suffers damage as the result partly of his own fault and partly of the fault of any other person or persons, a claim in respect of that damage is not defeated by reason only of the fault of the person suffering the damage, but the damages recoverable in respect thereof may be reduced to such extent as the Court thinks just and equitable having regard to the claimant's share in the responsibility for the damage.

Inevitable Accident

Where an accident takes place which could not be avoided by any ordinary care, caution and skill on the part of the person sued, the accident is said to be inevitable. Inevitable accident is distinguished from an act of God in that the latter term, although capable of being included within the definition of inevitable accident, is not applied to occurrences which to some extent have their origin in the agency of man and are not wholly dependent on the agency of natural forces. It is a defence to an action for negligence that the accident was inevitable and that there was no want of care on the defendant's part.

The plea of inevitable accident is illustrated by the facts in the case of *Gerber* v. *Pines* (1934), 79 S.J. 13 which were as follows. Mr and Mrs Gerber claimed damages against Dr Pines alleging that in the course of a hypodermic injection on Mrs Gerber the defendant left part of the broken needle in her body. The defendant denied liability. He said that the breaking of the needle was due to a sudden muscular spasm, and that no skill on his part could have prevented the piece of needle being drawn into the patient's body. The Judge who tried the action found that there was no negligence on the part of the defendant so far as the fracture of the needle was concerned. On a secondary issue, however, he found that the doctor had been negligent in not informing the patient or her husband at the time that the needle had fractured and that a piece of the needle was still in the patient's body. In respect of this he awarded the plaintiffs £5 5*s*. damages but without costs.

Consent: Volenti Non Fit Injuria

In actions based on the breach of a duty to take care it is a good defence to show that the plaintiff consented to the breach of duty and voluntarily accepted the risk involved. To such cases the maxim '*volenti non fit injuria*' applies. In order to establish this defence it must be proved that the plaintiff was aware of the danger, and that he fully appreciated and voluntarily accepted the risk to which he was being subjected. The defence '*volenti non fit injuria*' most frequently arises in cases affecting master and servant, and the occasions when it is appropriate as a defence to an action for negligence against a doctor may be rare. However, circumstances do arise when such a defence is open to a doctor; an example being the case where a person with full knowledge of what he is doing and of the risks involved, volunteers to undergo experimental treatment for research purposes and suffers injury in consequence.

Statutory Defence—Action commenced out of Time

No action for negligence where the damages claimed consist of or include damages in respect of personal injuries may be brought after the expiration of three years from the date on which the cause of action accrued. (Section 2, Limitation Act, 1939, as amended by Section 2 of the Law Reform (Limitation of Actions, etc.) Act, 1954). For this purpose 'personal injuries' include 'any disease and any impairment of a person's physical or mental condition'. An action is brought on the date when the summons is taken out or writ is issued by the plaintiff. The cause of action accrues at the time of the negligence, because it is then that the damage is caused although its consequences may not become apparent until later. If, however, the cause of action is concealed by the fraud of the defendant or his agent, the period of limitation does not begin to run until the plaintiff has discovered the fraud, or could with reasonable diligence have discovered it.

If on the date when the right of action accrued, the person to whom it accrued was under some legal disability, e.g. was an infant or person of unsound mind, an action may be brought at any time within three years of his ceasing to be under such disability, provided that the plaintiff proves that the person under disability was not, at the time the action accrued to him, in the custody of a parent.

On the death of a person, a cause of action subsisting against him, or vested in him, survives against, or, as the case may be, for the benefit of his estate. An action *against* the estate of a deceased person must however be commenced not later than six months after the date of grant of probate of his will or of letters of administration to his estate.

Negligence Causing Death—Fatal Accidents Acts

Prior to the coming into force of the Law Reform (Miscellaneous Provisions) Act, 1934, any right of action vested in a person at the time of his death as a result of the negligence which caused his death died with him. The maxim *actio personalis moritur cum persona* applied. By virtue however of the above Act, a cause of action for negligence vested in a deceased person at the time of his death now survives for the benefit of his estate. The damages recoverable for the benefit of his estate do not include exemplary damages but, in addition to any actual pecuniary loss, a claim may be made in respect of pain and suffering actually undergone by the deceased before death and for loss of expectation of life, and for funeral expenses.

The rights conferred by the above-mentioned Act for the benefit of estates of deceased persons are in addition to any rights conferred on the dependents of deceased persons by the Fatal Accidents Acts, 1846 to 1908. Under these Acts an action may be brought for the benefit of the wife, husband, parent or child of the deceased in all cases where the injured person, if he had lived, could have maintained an action against the person responsible for the injury. For this purpose 'parent' includes grandparents, step-parents, parents by adoption and putative parents; 'child' includes grandchildren, step-children, illegitimate and adopted children. It also includes a child *en ventre sa mère* but a claim cannot be made on behalf of the child until it is born.

Damages in claims under the Fatal Accidents Acts are assessed according to the pecuniary benefit, actual or expected, which the plaintiffs might reasonably have enjoyed had the deceased not been killed, and the damages are apportioned by the Court according to their respective losses amongst the parties for whose benefit the action is brought.

Damages

To entitle a person to maintain an action for negligence he must have suffered some actual loss or injury which must be directly due to the negligence complained of. To compensate him for such loss, damages are awarded and these should as nearly as possible place him in the same position as that in which he would have been but for the injury sustained. Damages may be awarded in respect of matters upon which an exact money value cannot be placed, e.g. pain and suffering, permanent disability or loss of expectation of life. Such damages are known as 'general damages'. Damage which is capable of exact calculation in terms of money, e.g. actual out-of-pocket expenses, loss of wages, medical, nursing and hospital expenses, is called 'special damage' and must be strictly proved.

General damages awarded for pain and suffering, injury to health, personal inconvenience and loss of expectation of life cannot be a perfect compensation, but the sum awarded must be arrived at by a reasonable consideration of the circumstances of the plaintiff and by making allowances for the ordinary chances of life. When the negligent act is committed in circumstances which tend to aggravate the damages, such circumstances may be pleaded and may increase the damages awarded. On the other hand a defendant may, to diminish the damages, show that the plaintiff has not done his best to minimize his loss or that the loss has been increased by the conduct of the plaintiff, or that part of the loss would have been sustained in any event even if there had been no negligence on his part.

In actions brought for the benefit of a deceased's estate for damages for loss of expectation of life, the amount of damages should be what is fair and moderate in view of the uncertainties and contingencies of human life. It was laid down in the case of *Benham* v. *Gambling* (1941), A.C. 157 that the thing to be valued is not loss of years, but loss of prospective happiness independently of whether the deceased had the capacity or ability to appreciate that his further life would bring happiness. No regard may be had to financial losses or gains during the period of which the victim has been deprived or to differences in social position or prospects of worldly possessions. In the case of a child, damages should be reduced on account of the risks and uncertainties of childhood. Damages may be claimed on behalf of the deceased's estate for loss of expectation of life notwithstanding that death was instantaneous.

Damage which is not a direct, necessary and natural result of the negligent act complained of is said to be 'too remote' and is not recoverable.

Liability for the Negligence of Others

At law a master is liable for the negligent acts of his servant committed in the course of his employment. If, therefore, when carrying out the duties he has been employed to perform the servant, through want of due skill, care or diligence causes injury to some third person, the master is liable as if he had himself caused the injury. This principle of vicarious liability arises from the legal maxim *qui facit per alium facit per se*. It is no defence for the master to show that he had expressly forbidden the servant to commit the act which caused the injury, or that the servant has exceeded his instructions. The master has put the servant into a position to do a certain class of acts on his behalf and he must therefore accept responsibility for the manner in which the servant performs those acts.

Assistants

The relationship of master and servant exists between a general medical practitioner and his qualified assistant. It follows therefore that if, during his treatment of a patient, the assistant is negligent, the principal can be held liable for the damage sustained by the patient. The assistant is also liable for his own negligent acts, and the patient may claim against the principal or the assistant, or against both. The practitioner is on the same principle responsible for the negligent acts during the course of their duties of all other servants employed by him, e.g. dispensers, nurse-receptionists, etc. If, for example, his dispenser negligently makes up a prescription which causes injury to a patient, the doctor is liable.

The relationship of master and servant does not however apply to a case where a doctor employed by a hospital is acting as assistant to another doctor on the hospital staff. Here both doctors are servants of the hospital, and the senior doctor could only be held responsible for the negligent act of the doctor acting as his assistant if he himself had also been guilty of negligence, as for example, where he delegates to the 'assistant' a duty which he knew, or ought to have known, the assistant was not qualified to perform, or where the negligent act complained of was the result of negligent advice or directions given by him to the doctor assisting him.

Partners

It is provided by statute that where by any wrongful act or omission of any partner acting in the ordinary course of business of the firm, or with the authority of his co-partners, loss or injury is caused to any person not being a member of the firm, the firm is liable therefore to the same extent as the partner so acting or omitting to act (Partnership Act, 1890, Section 10.) Every partner is jointly and severally liable with his co-partner for everything for which the firm becomes so liable while he is a partner therein (*ibid.*, Section 12). Partnership deeds often provide that if a partner through negligence or other wrongful act renders the firm or his co-partners liable to pay damages, the partner guilty of negligence shall indemnify the other partners therefrom. Such a clause in a partnership deed or agreement only affects the financial liability of the partners *inter se* and does not enable the innocent partners or partner to escape liability to a third party. Suppose, for example, that A, B and C, three general medical practitioners, are practising in partnership, and that B is negligent when treating a patient. The patient can either sue B or the firm and if he sues the firm, A, B and C are jointly and severally liable for the payment of any damages awarded. If, however, their partnership deed or agreement contains an indemnity clause to the effect mentioned above, A and C will be entitled to recover from B any sum which they have been required to pay, or any loss they have sustained, as a result of the judgment awarded against the firm.

Nurses

A doctor would be liable for the negligence of a nurse actually employed by him in the conduct of his practice. However, the relationship between a doctor and a nurse in a hospital is not, as a general rule, such that the doctor is liable for the negligence of the nurse in carrying out, or failing to carry out, his instructions. The relationship of master and servant does not exist between them. However, there may be a case where it is shewn that the negligent act of the nurse was the result of wrongful instruction given to her by the doctor or that the doctor was negligent in instructing a nurse to give treatment which he knew, or ought reasonably to have known, she was not qualified or experienced enough to give. In such a case the doctor might be held liable, either solely or jointly with the nurse, for the damage resulting from her negligent act. The doctor's liability however would not arise from the relationship of master and servant, but from the fact that he had himself failed to exercise reasonable care.

Locum Tenens

The question whether a doctor is legally liable for the negligent acts of a person acting as his locum tenens depends on whether the locum tenens was at the time acting as the servant or agent of that doctor. If he is then the doctrine '*respondeat superior*' would appear to apply and the doctor will be liable. If, however, a locum tenens is appointed for a doctor employed by a hospital authority during his absence from duty, the locum tenens is the servant or agent of the hospital authority and consequently the doctor holding the appointment will not be liable for the negligence of a locum tenens acting for him in his absence.

Students

A doctor employed in a teaching hospital will not be liable for the negligent act or omission of any medical student in his charge unless it can be shewn that the doctor himself was personally negligent, for example, that the wrongful act of the student was performed under his immediate direction or supervision and that with ordinary care he could have prevented the negligent act from being committed, or that he instructed the student to give treatment which he knew, or ought reasonably to have known, the student was not qualified or experienced enough to give.

Employer's Right to Indemnity or Contribution from Servant

A master who has been held liable for damages occasioned by the negligence of his servant may seek indemnity or contribution from such servant, but it is entirely a matter for the discretion of the Court under the Law Reform (Married Woman and Tortfeasors) Act, 1935, whether it should order any, and, if so, what contribution or indemnity by the servant. This principle is illustrated by the case of *Jones* v. *Manchester Corporation and Others* (1952), 2 All E.R. 125, in which the facts were as follows:

The second defendant, a physician who had been qualified for some five months, was employed by the third defendants, a hospital board, her duties including the administration of anaesthetics at the hospital. A patient was brought into the hospital suffering from burns to the face. Under the instructions of a surgeon, who was about to treat the burns, the second defendant administered to the patient nitrous oxide gas and oxygen by a mask held over the patient's face. It appeared that the presence of the mask prevented proper treatment of the burns, and so the doctors decided to cease administering the gas and to give an injection of pentothal. The second defendant gave the injection but, owing to the fact that the patient was already partly anaesthetised and to the amount and method of administration of the drug, the patient died. In an action by the widow of the deceased patient for damages for negligence against the second and third defendants.

HELD: an employer is not entitled to an indemnity from an employee if he has himself contributed to the damage done by the employee or bears some responsibility for it or if the negligence of some other and senior employee has contributed to the damage; in the present case the hospital board had been negligent in leaving the administration of a *dangerous* anaesthetic to an inexperienced doctor without adequate supervision, and their employee, the senior surgeon, had also been negligent; the second defendant had been guilty of a substantial degree of negligence and so was not entitled to a contribution amounting to a complete indemnity from the Board; and under the Law Reform (Married Women and Tortfeasors) Act, 1935, Section 6 (2), the contributions of the second defendant and the Board should be in the proportion of one-fifth and four-fifths respectively.

Liability of Hospitals for Negligence of Medical Staff

The law relating to the liability of a hospital authority for the negligence of doctors employed by them has undergone important changes in recent years both in England and in Scotland.

In England prior to the case of *Cassidy* v. *Ministry of Health* (1951), 1 All.E.R. 574, the Courts had always taken the view that a hospital authority, provided it had taken reasonable care to appoint duly qualified and competent doctors to its staff, was not liable for the negligent acts or omissions of such doctors in the performance of their professional duties. The principle that a hospital authority, provided it exercised reasonable care in appointing him, was not responsible for the negligence of a doctor on its staff, was until 1942 held also to apply to nurses, radiographers and other medically unqualified staff employed in the hospital on duties requiring professional skill. If, however, the negligence complained of arose out of the performance or non-performance of administrative duty—as opposed to a duty requiring professional skill—the hospital authority was always considered to be liable under the doctrine *respondeat superior*, that is the vicarious liability of a principal for the negligence of his servant or agent.

The gradual development of the English law with regard to a hospital authority's legal responsibility may be gathered from the short facts and results of the following decided cases.

In the case of *Hillyer* v. *The Governors of St. Bartholomew's Hospital* (1909), 2 K.B. 820, the facts were:

> The plaintiff entered St Bartholomew's Hospital on March 28th, 1907, for the purpose of being medically examined under an anaesthetic by Mr Lockwood, a consulting surgeon attached to the hospital. He alleged that for the purpose of the examination he was placed on an operating table in such a position that his arms were allowed to hang over its sides; that his left arm was burned by coming into contact with a hot water tin projecting from beneath the table and that the inner upper part of his right arm was bruised by the operator or some other person pressing against it during the operation. The plaintiff claimed that as a result of these injuries he suffered traumatic neuritis and paralysis of both arms, and he had since been unable to exercise his profession as a medical man. The defendants denied the alleged negligence and pleaded that if they owed any duty to the plaintiff it was to exercise reasonable care in the selection of the hospital staff, in which duty they had not failed.

HELD: The plaintiff had produced no evidence that the defendants had been guilty of a breach of their duties towards the plaintiff—the duty of using reasonable care in selecting as members of the staff persons who were competent, either as surgeons or as nurses, properly to perform their respective parts in the surgical examination, and the duty to provide proper apparatus and appliances.

The correctness of the decision in the last-mentioned case was expressly left open in the House of Lords in the case of *Lindsey County Council* v. *Mary Marshall* (1937), A.C. 97—a case which concerned a maternity patient who developed puerperal fever—and the Court of Appeal in the case of *Gold* v. *Essex County Council* (1942), 2 K.B. 293, declined to hold itself bound by the earlier decision in *Hillyer's* case. The facts in the latter case were as follows:

In June and July, 1940, the plaintiff, Ruth Ann Gold, aged five years, was taken by her mother to Oldchurch County Hospital, for treatment for warts on her face. She was seen by a doctor, who ordered treatment by 1,000 units of Grenz rays and sent the plaintiff to the radiology department. The treatment was given to the plaintiff by a qualified and competent radiographer, named Mead, who was employed by the defendants under a contract of service. While the plaintiff was undergoing the treatment her face was covered with a lead-lined rubber cloth which protected all but the affected part of her face. As the warts did not yield to this treatment, the doctor ordered the number of units of Grenz rays to be doubled and the mother again took the plaintiff for treatment. On this occasion, Mead was admittedly negligent in that he covered the plaintiff's face only with a piece of lint. As a result the plaintiff's face was permanently disfigured. In an action for damages, the plaintiff alleged that Mead had been negligent in his treatment of her and that the defendants, whose servant or agent he was, were responsible for his negligence.

HELD: A local authority carrying on a public hospital owes to a patient the duty to nurse and treat him properly, and is liable for the negligence of its servants even though the negligence arises while a servant is engaged on work which involves the exercise of professional skill on his part.

In *Collins* v. *Hertfordshire County Council and Another* (1947), 1 K.B. 598, the defendant authority was held liable for the negligence of a student in her last year and not then a registered medical practitioner, who was employed in the capacity of a resident junior house surgeon.

In the case of *Cassidy* v. *Ministry of Health* (1951) (the short facts of which are given on page 122) the defendants were held liable for the negligence of a qualified medical practitioner employed as a whole-time assistant medical officer at a hospital.

The decision in *Cassidy's* case and the dicta in judgments given in that case and other cases decided since support the proposition that a hospital authority is at law now vicariously liable for the negligence of all members of its medical staff, whether employed full or part time. Although it has not yet been actually held in a decided case that the hospital authority is liable for the negligence of a consultant employed on its staff, there can be little doubt in view of judicial opinion expressed in *Cassidy's* case and in subsequent cases that it would be so held if the question were ever put to test in a Court of Law.

In Scotland, prior to the decision of the Court of Session in the case of *Hayward* v. *Board of Management for the Royal Infirmary of Edinburgh* (1954), hospital authorities had never been held liable for the negligence of members of their medical staff since Scots Law did not recognize the principle of *respondeat superior* as applying to the relationship between hospitals and doctors employed by them. The Court's decision in *Hayward's* case that a hospital is now legally liable for the negligence of a member of its medical staff was based not on a judicial extension of the principle of *respondeat superior*, or on decisions of the Courts of England (by which the Scottish Courts are not bound) but by the Court of Session's interpretation of Section 3 of the National Health Service (Scotland) Act, 1947. This imposes on the Secretary of State the duty of providing throughout Scotland (*a*) hospital accommodation, (*b*) medical nursing and other services required at or for the purposes of hospital, and (*c*) the services of specialists. In giving judgment, Lord President Cooper said '. . . the older Scottish decisions are no longer applicable to a fundamentally different situation. Under the new Act and regulations the obligation on the State is in my view to treat the patient and not merely to make arrangements for his treatment by, and at the sole responsibility of, independent contractors'.

The present position is therefore that both in England and in Scotland, hospital authorities are now legally liable for the negligence of members of their medical staff, although this result has been achieved at different times and for different reasons.

Scotland

In the main, the principles set out above equally apply to the practice of medicine in Scotland. There are, however, certain distinctions between the legal systems in England and Scotland and the following notes are directed to drawing attention to the more important of these.

Doctor/Patient Relationship

In Scotland, the right to reparation (or compensation) flows *ex delicto* (i.e. breach of duty) and not *ex contractu* (i.e. breach of contract). A husband who employs (i.e. contracts with) a doctor to treat his wife cannot himself sustain an action against the doctor based on breach of his contract, arising out of failure in proper treatment; but the wife can, in respect of the doctor's failure to exhibit the proper standard of skill and care. (*Edgar* v. *Lamont*, 1914 S.C. 277.)

Reasonable Skill and Care

The standard set out above applies equally in Scotland. In a recent case, concerning the breakage of a needle during the course of an intra-muscular injection of penicillin, the First Division of the Court of Session laid down the following guides as governing this question of competence. There must be 'so marked a departure from the normal standard of conduct of a professional man as to infer a lack of that ordinary care which a man of ordinary skill would display. . . . Even a substantial deviation from normal practice may be warranted by the particular circumstances. To establish liability by a doctor when deviation from normal practice is alleged, three facts require to be established. First of all, it must be proved that there is a usual and normal practice. Secondly, it must be proved that the defender has not adopted that practice, and thirdly (and this is of crucial importance) it must be established that the course the doctor adopted is one which no professional man of ordinary skill would have taken if he had been acting with ordinary care. There is clearly a heavy *onus* on the Pursuer to establish these three facts—and without all three, his case will fail. If this is the test, then it matters not how far or how little he deviates from the ordinary practice. For the extent of the deviation is not the test. The deviation must be of a kind which satisfied the third of the requirements just stated.' (*Hunter* v. *Hanley*, 1955 S.C. 200.)

It should be noted also that in an earlier unreported case in 1941, the First Division of the Court gave a clear expression of opinion that failure by a general practitioner to seek the assistance of an X-ray to confirm or disprove his clinical diagnosis in a case of a suspected fracture would *in itself* amount to negligence, unless the failure so to do were displaced by sufficient reason. (*MacDonald* v. *Milne and Another*, March 28th, 1941. Unreported.) When analysed, this expression of opinion does not differ in essentials from the standards above set out.

Res Ipsa Loquitur

The Scottish Courts have never shown the same reliance in the application of this maxim as in England. More credence is placed on the proof of actual negligence than on a deduction that the act alleged must speak for itself.

Function of Judge and Jury

The normal rule in Scottish practice is that all cases involving compensation are tried before a Jury (Court of Session Act, 1850) unless for special cause shown or by consent of parties. In medical cases, trial by Jury rather than by Judge alone is the normal procedure as the question at issue is largely one of fact, on the medical aspects of which the Jury can be guided by expert opinion.

Statutory Defence

In the case of a person receiving fatal injuries, an action may be brought by any person to whom the right to pursue the action has accrued within three years after the date of such death, but *only provided* that the deceased person would himself have been entitled to pursue such an action. (Law Reform Limitation of Actions) Act, 1954.

Fatal Accidents Acts

These Acts do not apply to Scotland. The content of damages in Scotland is divided into (*a*) Solatium, i.e. recompense for bodily suffering and physical pain and (*b*) Patrimonial loss, i.e. recompense for all material loss sustained, e.g. reduction in earning capacity, restriction of expectancy of life or loss of financial support as well as any damage to property. Unless a claim has been intimated or an action commenced by an injured party before his death, the right to compensation dies with him and cannot be sustained at the instance of his executors. In this sense, the maxim *Actio personalis moritur cum persona*, still applies in Scotland. A widow, children, or even remoter ascendants or descendants, if dependent on the earnings of the deceased, can however pursue a claim for patrimonial loss sustained by them as the result of the death of the bread-winner and the consequent loss of financial support, which however would not include any award for loss of expectation of life of the deceased person. No cognisance is taken in Scotland of the distinction between Special and General Damages, as an award is always expressed as a total sum to include all elements of damage satisfactorily established. The elements governing the assessment of an award are however similar in both systems, though the tendency is to give a higher figure in England than in Scotland.

Contribution from Servants

As in England, a master is wholly liable for the act or neglect of his servant, arising from the performance of his duties. The master however is entitled, in law, to recover from the servant any damages paid by him on the principle that the wrongdoer is always liable for his own wrong, though in practice such repetition is not enforced as the servant is usually unable to meet the claim. The position is of course different with professional men where they themselves are the 'servants'; and consequently such a possible liability only underlines the need for professional insurance cover.

As in England, the Courts in Scotland, by virtue of the Law Reform (Miscellaneous Provisions) Act, 1940, as amended by the Law Reform (Contributory Negligence) Act, 1945, may apportion damages among joint wrongdoers in such ratio as the Court may deem just.

Liability of Hospitals for Medical Staff

Prior to the National Health Service (Scotland) Act, 1947, hospital doctors were considered as employed under a 'contract for services' and not a 'contract of service'. The legal implication was that the governors of a hospital provided facilities (accommodation, beds, operating theatres, etc.) to which sick persons could resort where they would find medical men who were competent and willing to treat their disorders. The hospital function therefore was solely that of bringing together, by the provision of facilities, the sick and those who were prepared to treat them. Since the *Hayward* case above referred to, the position has radically changed, in virtue of the interpretation by the Courts of the meaning of the Act, and is now in Scotland to all intents and purposes the same as in England as is above stated.

16

BIRTH

The only formality normally required of a doctor attending a woman in her confinement is the notification of the birth of a child. Notification of a stillbirth is referred to in the next chapter. In an emergency it occasionally falls to the doctor to baptize an infant who is *in extremis* and it is useful for him to know what are the simple requirements. The baptism of adults is similar and is also dealt with in this chapter for convenience.

Notification of Births

Section 203 of the Public Health Act, 1936, calls for notification of births to the Local Authority. This requirement is additional to, and not substitute for, the requirements of any Act relating to the Registration of Births, which means the Births and Deaths Registration Acts, 1836–1936, consolidated by the Act of 1953, which do not require a practitioner to issue a certificate of a live birth for the Registrar.

The notification is required within thirty-six hours of the birth and refers to any child which has issued forth from its mother after expiration of the twenty-eighth week of pregnancy. The notification is the duty of the father (if residing on the premises at the time) and of any person in attendance at the birth or within six hours after. The notification is made to the Medical Officer of Health either by posting a prepaid card or by delivering a written notice at his office or residence. The Local Welfare Authority, on application, supplies stamped addressed postcards for the purpose to any medical practitioner or midwife. Failure to effect the notification involves liability to a fine of 20*s*. unless the practitioner can satisfy a Court that he had reasonable grounds for believing the notice had been given by someone else.

The Medical Officer of Health of a County District sends a duplicate of the notification to the Medical Officer of Health of the County, except where the Council of the County District is also the local supervising authority under the Midwives Acts, 1902–36. The Registrars of Births and Deaths have access to notifications received by Medical Officers of Health, or to any books in which the notices received by the Medical Officers of Health are recorded.

Confinement Certificates

In certain cases mothers may claim maternity benefit. A claim for maternity benefit after confinement, or post-natal benefit, must be supported by a certificate of confinement. For this purpose a confinement is defined as 'a labour, premature or not, resulting in the birth of a living child or labour after at least twenty-eight weeks' pregnancy resulting in the birth of a child, living or dead.'

So long as the practitioner has examined the mother after the confinement he may sign such a certificate. There is no need for him to have been present at the birth.

Baptism

While normally the office of baptism is carried out by a Minister of Religion yet there are occasions on which it becomes necessary for a lay person to undertake the duty so that the infant, being in imminent danger of death, does not die without having been admitted to the Church.

When the urgent necessity for baptism arises and no Minister of Religion can be summoned in time it may fall to the practitioner present to perform the office. The desired names should be ascertained from the parents or other relatives if possible. If it is not possible the practitioner may choose a name. He then makes the sign of the Cross on the infant's forehead with a finger dipped in water, saying: 'I baptize thee . . . in the name of the Father, the Son and the Holy Ghost.' The baptism should be reported to a Minister of Religion.

Baptism into the Roman Catholic Church

The Roman Catholic Church does not accept making the sign of the Cross as a substitute for pouring water on the child.

It has dealt with the requirements for emergency baptism in great detail. Distinction is made, for example, between absolute baptism and conditional baptism. The conditional baptism may be applied to a presenting part which may prove later not to be regarded as a human being, or to a monster. It may also be used when there is doubt as to whether or not a foetus or monster is born alive, no matter at what stage of pregnancy the birth takes place. In such cases conditional baptism should include some such phrase as 'If thou art a human being, I baptize thee . . .'. The other occasion for conditional baptism is when there is some doubt as to whether baptism has been fully carried out before, for no human being may be baptized a second time. The office should in these instances begin: 'If thou hast not already been baptized, I baptize thee . . .'.

The following Canons of the Roman Catholic Church on the subject appear to cover all the possibilities and to make abundantly clear the requirements of the Church.

Canon 746. §1. No child shall be baptized in the womb if there is a probable hope that it may be born alive and then baptized.

§2. If the head of the child is born and there is danger of death, it shall be baptized on the head; nor shall it be again baptized conditionally if it is born alive.

§3. If another member is born first and there is the same danger, the child shall be baptized on that member; but if the child is then born alive, it shall be baptized again conditionally.

§4. If a mother dies during pregnancy, the foetus shall be extracted by those whose duty it is and, if it is certainly alive, it shall be baptized absolutely; if there is doubt as to whether it is alive, it shall be baptized conditionally.

§5. A foetus baptized in the womb shall be again baptized conditionally after birth.

Canon 747. Abortive foetuses, no matter at what stage of pregnancy they are born, shall be baptized absolutely if they are certainly alive and conditionally if life is doubtful.

Canon 748. All monstrous and remarkable foetuses shall be baptized at least conditionally; if there is a doubt as to whether there is more than one human being in the birth, one shall be baptized absolutely and the others conditionally.

The Roman Catholic Church requires baptism to be performed by a Priest or Deacon, or failing such preferably by a man, not the parent if this is avoidable. If baptism is necessary before birth takes place the practitioner should undertake it even if a priest is present and even if the priest is also a medical practitioner.

The words to be used are: 'Name. I baptize thee in the name of the *Father* and of the *Son* and of the *Holy Ghost*.' The word 'Amen' should not be added. Pure natural water is to be used but a very small quantity of an antiseptic solution is permitted if necessary to preserve asepsis. The water should be poured on each time as the words italicized are spoken. The water must touch the skin and flow over it, and a single pouring is accepted as valid. The words must be audibly enunciated but not necessarily so that all can hear.

Monsters include anencephalics which are to be baptized on the rudimentary head.

Uterine Baptism (*Roman Catholics*)

Uterine baptism is only to be done when there is little or no hope of a live birth and cannot be done until the membranes have ruptured. The membranes must not be ruptured for this purpose if the foetus is not visible. Otherwise they may be ruptured for this purpose so long as the procedure does not involve serious risk to the mother. Baptism cannot be conferred on the umbilical cord.

In cases of abortion, where it is doubtful if the foetus is alive, baptism should be conditional as also it should be in respect of the doubtful half of a monster or of conjoined twins which could possibly be regarded as two beings.

Baptism of Adults into the Roman Catholic Faith

It will rarely be necessary for a practitioner to baptize an adult. If it is impossible to obtain the services of a priest in time and it is clear that the wish of the patient is 'based on a realization of the rudimentary meaning of baptism into the Catholic Faith', then it may be done. Baptism on an unconscious patient should not be performed unless he or she has expressed a wish for it before losing consciousness.

17

DEATH

The responsibilities of the doctor at the time of a death are of the highest importance. A clear knowledge of the requirements of death certification is essential to practice. From time to time a doctor may be asked to advise on various problems associated with death, some of which are not of a medical nature. A working knowledge of the essentials of various of these problems will enable him to advise and assist his patients to the best advantage.

Certification of Deaths

The Births and Deaths Registration Act, 1953, which consolidates the laws on death certification, states that in the case of death of any person who has been attended in his last illness by a registered medical practitioner such practitioner shall sign and transmit to the Registrar of Deaths a certificate on a form prescribed stating, to the best of his knowledge and belief, the cause of death. This appears to be regarded as an absolute duty so that, strictly, he should issue a certificate in cases of violent death. It seems probable, however, that reporting to the Coroner will always suffice instead.

Normally, in a case which must obviously be referred to the Coroner, the medical practitioner will communicate with the Coroner himself and thereafter act according to his instructions. The difficulty occurs where the medical practitioner whose duty it is under the Act to certify the cause of death to the best of his knowledge and belief, is, in fact, quite unable to state what is the cause of death. It is argued by some that the proper course under these circumstances is to complete the certificate, but to insert some such word as 'Unknown' in the line indicating the cause of death. Others, however, state that if the practitioner has no knowledge of the cause of death he cannot complete a certificate and, therefore, should not.

The conflicting opinions on this point are to some extent theoretical. The matter can be resolved by consultation with the Coroner who will, no doubt, assist the practitioner in advising him what he should do in any particular instance. Alternatively he may complete the certificate to the best of his ability and also complete space A on the reverse (see p. 148) and report the matter to the Coroner.

Although a practitioner as such is not obliged to inform the Coroner it is advisable for him to do so in any death caused by violence, or in suspicious circumstances. If the practitioner is in any doubt he is advised to consult the Coroner.

It is not essential that the practitioner should see the body of the deceased before or after issuing the death certificate, but it is usually practicable to do so and is also advisable as, occasionally, serious errors have occurred including, as a result, the concealment of a crime or fraud. Relatives probably regard it as a courtesy to be expected of the practitioner.

A duplicate death certificate must never be given. Relatives desiring a duplicate may obtain one from the Registrar.

The practitioner should not give a certificate if he has not been in attendance at the last illness. In general 'attendance' should be regarded as meaning on more than one occasion, although this is not a statutory requirement. The practitioner should aim at giving an accurate certificate, adhering to the rules according to the Registrar-General's classification if possible, though he is allowed to depart from this if, in doing so, he provides a more accurate certificate.

If neglect is a contributory factor to the death it must be mentioned.

A doctor may on occasion be faced with the question of whether to report neglect in a case in which he believes that the dependence upon the attentions of a Christian Scientist to the exclusion of medical attention was a contributory cause of death. An individual has a right to refuse to obtain medical treatment on his own account, but where the parent or guardian of a child has refused to obtain medical attention for a child and death has ensued the question of neglect merits serious consideration. It would be for the Courts to decide in an individual case whether or not the child had been wilfully neglected 'in a manner likely to cause such child unnecessary suffering or injury to its health', which is a misdemeanour. An interesting account of the legal position of Christian Science, with quoted instances, is to be found in *Taylor's Principles and Practice of Medical Jurisprudence.**

Some Special Requirements

There are statutory requirements regarding deaths occurring under special circumstances which must from time to time be borne in mind.

The death of a patient of unsound mind in a mental institution or in single care requires a written notice to the Coroner, accompanied by a statement of the facts, within forty-eight hours. This notification must be given by the medical officer of the institution, residential licensee or other person in charge. If such a patient dies in a registered hospital or nursing home or in a house where patients are received as single patients, the notification must be given by the practitioner attending the patient in his last illness.

In the case of an habitual drunkard detained under the Habitual Drunkards Act, 1879, the principal medical attendant is required to draw up a statement for the Coroner giving the name of any person present at the death. A copy of this statement, certified in writing by the licensee of the retreat, is sent to the Coroner. If the patient at the time of death is absent from the retreat under licence a statement is drawn up by the medical practitioner in attendance and a copy is forwarded to the Coroner by the person having charge of the patient.

For special requirements in cases of death from pneumoconiosis, see p. 163.

Whereas in England and Wales the doctor is required to furnish a death certificate forthwith, in Scotland he may do so within seven days of the death. Thereafter he is required to do so within three days of receiving a request from the Registrar.

In Scotland the certificate is handed to the informant to take to the Registrar. While this may be done in England and

* *Taylor's Principles and Practice of Medical Jurisprudence,* Sydney Smith and Keith Simpson. Churchill: 11th Edn., Vol. I, 1957, p. 77.

Wales at the discretion of the doctor, it is more usual for the certificate to be posted to the Registrar.

Notice to Informant (*England and Wales*)

A notice of having signed a death certificate (see under The Medical Certificate of the Cause of Death) must be given to the informant who shall be one of the following persons:

(1) the nearest relative present at the death or in attendance at the deceased's last illness;

(2) in default, any other relatives residing in the district;

(3) if not available a person present at the death and occupier of the house;

(4) an inmate of the house or person causing the body to be buried.

One of these persons must register the death with the Registrar within five days.

The Medical Certificate of the Cause of Death

These certificate forms, commonly known as death certificates, are obtained, free, in books of twenty, from the Registrar of Births and Deaths for the sub-district in which the practitioner resides. The forms are not to be used for registering stillbirths (*q.v.*).

The death certificate consists of three parts easily separable one from the other. The right hand portion is a notice to be handed to the 'informant' who is usually the nearest relative (see above). When completed by the practitioner it merely states that a death certificate has been signed. The instructions to the informant are set out on the form.

The centre portion is the death certificate on which the cause of death is entered and which can be completed only by the registered medical practitioner who has been in attendance during the deceased's last illness. The practitioner also states whether he has seen the body after death and the date on which he last saw the deceased alive. If this latter is more than two weeks before death the Registrar will report the fact to the Coroner, who may then see fit to consult with the certifying practitioner. On the reverse are spaces for completion, where applicable, when the practitioner has reported the case to the

Coroner (space A), or wishes to intimate that he may be in a position later to give additional information for the purpose of more precise statistical classification (space B). Only those qualifications which are actually registered against his name in the Medical Register must be entered in the appropriate space on the form and not any degrees or diplomas which he may happen to possess but has not registered.

The third portion is a counterfoil for the practitioner's own retention. In the practitioner's own interests its completion should never be omitted.

On completion the death certificate, or centre portion, must be enclosed in one of the franked addressed envelopes which are supplied by the Registrar of Births and Deaths and transmitted to him.

Deaths may only be certified on the official form. Practitioners are advised to study carefully the cover and opening pages of the book of certificate forms for therein are to be found not only a description of the statutory requirements, but also many helpful notes and suggestions regarding the completion of the forms and the method of certifying a death.

The certificate used in Scotland is different in some particulars. There is no 'Notice to Informant', nor is there additional information or space A or B. There are other minor differences as well.

So long as a practitioner completes the certificate with care, in good faith and to the best of his knowledge and belief he need have no fear as to his position should subsequent investigations prove him to be wrong. The issue of a fraudulent certificate, however, is a criminal offence which would be expected to lead to conviction by the Courts and erasure from the Medical Register.

It is lawful for a registered medical practitioner to issue a death certificate in respect of a relative if he has been in attendance in the last illness. It is advisable, however, for him to call in a colleague during the last illness and to leave to him the completion of the death certificate.

Stillbirths

The Births and Deaths Registration Act, 1953, gives the following definition: ' "Still-born" and "still-birth" shall apply to any child which has issued forth from its mother after the twenty-eighth week of pregnancy and which did not at any time after being expelled from its mother breathe or show any other signs of life.'

Although no certificate of the cause of stillbirth is required by the Act (Births and Deaths Registration Act, 1953, Section 11 (1)), the Act requires all stillbirths to be registered. A certificate that the child was not born alive is to be given by the practitioner (or certified midwife) who has been in attendance at the birth or has examined the body of the child. The stillbirth is not to be certified on the ordinary death certificate form, but on a special form for the purpose which is obtained from the Registrar of Births and Deaths. The certificate is to be handed to the parent or other informant, who produces it to the Registrar.

There are two parts of the certificate, the first for completion when the certifier was in attendance, and the second if the certifier was not in attendance but has examined the body.

In Scotland the procedure is similar with the main exception that the certifier is required to state the probable cause of death.

If the child has breathed or has shown any sign of life after birth it should not be regarded as stillborn.

Notification to Medical Officer of Health

Notification of a stillbirth to the Medical Officer of Health is required as is the notification of a live birth (see Chapter 16).

A Local Health Authority would appear to be justified in requiring notification of the birth (after twenty-eight weeks) of a macerated foetus even though it died before the twenty-eighth week of pregnancy. By custom carneous mole and a foetus papyraceus born with a surviving sibling are rarely regarded as stillbirths although perhaps, on a strict interpretation of the law, they should be notified and registered as such.

A medical practitioner would regard clinically a foetus that died before the period of viability is reached (twenty-eighth week) as a missed abortion, irrespective of the fact that it might not be born until after the twenty-eighth week, and would be inclined not to regard it as a stillbirth. This point has never been tested in a Court of Law, but on a strict interpretation of the law it would probably be wise to regard such a foetus as a stillbirth if extruded after the twenty-eighth week. Another point which seems doubtful is whether the twenty-eight weeks refers to the period of amenorrhoea, which would normally represent twenty-six weeks of pregnancy, or, as commonly regarded clinically by practitioners and midwives, to a date twelve weeks before the estimated date of confinement (forty weeks). There appears to be no special provision in the law for a foetus remaining *in utero* for a significant length of time after its death. Presumably a case of this sort would, if the occasion arose, be interpreted by the Courts on a common sense basis with due regard to the circumstances of the individual case.

That particular care is necessary in distinguishing between a stillborn and a live child is evidenced by the increasing awareness on the part of the lay public of the entitlement to income-tax rebate if the baby lives and dies in the neo-natal period.

Wills

Witnessing a Will

Medical practitioners are at times asked to assist in the drawing up of a will.

The commonest and simplest assistance for which he is asked is the witnessing of a will. For this it is neither necessary nor customary for the witness to know the contents of the will. His function is merely to witness the fact that the testator has signed the document. If he is to be a beneficiary under the will he should not witness it for he thereby forfeits his benefit. It is wise for a practitioner to inquire the nature of any document, the signature to which he is witnessing, for, if it is a will, the witnessing of the signature by a medical practitioner is generally taken to imply that, at the time, the practitioner regards the testator as of sound mind, conscious of what he is doing and mentally capable of making disposition of his property. If the practitioner does not so regard the testator he should decline to witness the will. So also should he decline to assist in the preparation of a will.

Drawing up a Will

The confidence of a patient in his doctor is sometimes such as to lead him to prefer his advice and assistance in drawing up a will to that of his lawyer, or, alternatively, in an emergency when death seems imminent the doctor may be the only person available to provide the necessary assistance. If practicable the patient should be reminded that the drawing up of a will is best done by a lawyer and he should be urged in the interests of testator, executors and beneficiaries alike, to summon a lawyer for the purpose.

If the patient is adamant on the point, or the summoning of a lawyer is impracticable, the doctor may have to advise. He should, therefore, remember certain salient points concerning wills. The will should state, at the beginning, that, 'This is the last Will and Testament of . . .'. This should be followed with a statement revoking all former wills. The disposal of property should be stated clearly, item by item, in the simplest possible language. The word 'money' is best avoided, though, of course, sums may be stated. Finally, there should be a disposition of the residue of the property followed by the wording 'In witness hereof I, the said . . . , have hereunto set my hand this . . . day of . . . 19 . . .'. The signature (or mark) should be witnessed by two persons, not beneficiaries of the will, who should state that they have witnessed the signature of the will by . . .

Other points to be remembered are that 'children' includes illegitimate children. Adopted children are also included if the will is made after the date of the adoption order. The inclusion of an adopted child in the provisions of a will cannot be effected by a codicil. The word 'children' in the will of the natural parent does not include a child who has been legally adopted by someone else.

Full names and addresses, if possible, of all persons mentioned should be written into the document, as also should accurate titles of charitable and other bodies to which bequests are made. Bequests should be made 'Free of duty'. A codicil must mention the will to which it is a codicil. The signature to the will, or to a codicil, must be at the end. Initials, a mark, a guided signature or that of a deputy are all valid so long as it is quite clear that the testator was intending it to be a signature and realized its purport.

In Scotland any words giving clear expression of intention will be acceptable provided the declaration is subscribed. It is better that the will should be witnessed but it is a legal will in

Scotland if not witnessed provided it is written in the testator's own hand and subscribed by him and the words 'written by my own hand' appear between the declaration and the signature.

Testamentary Capacity

There have been cases in the past in which wills have been contested on the grounds that the testator was not of sound mind at the time of making the will. The signature and witness of a medical practitioner present at the signing of the will and certifying the soundness of mind of the patient is strong evidence in favour of the validity of a contested will. Consequently in cases of doubt on this point solicitors may ask for the presence of a doctor to witness or countersign the will. The doctor, if satisfied, may append a statement that in his opinion the testator, named, is of sound mind and fully understands the will drawn up by his solicitor to which he has put his signature (or mark). A doctor should on no account sign such a statement or witness a will if such is not his opinion.

Not only this, but he should also discourage the making of a will if he feels that the would be testator is at that moment not capable of remembering what property he has and of disposing of it reasonably. In making up his mind on this point he should be particularly careful where a patient has shown signs of delirium or confusion. It may happen that, in the interval between detailed instructions being given by the testator to his solicitor regarding the drawing up of his will and the presentation of the will for signature, the condition of the patient has so changed that at the time of signature it is not possible for the doctor to state that the patient's condition fulfils the requirements for the signing of a will. If the doctor is satisfied that the testator can call to mind that he gave his solicitor instructions to prepare a will, making certain dispositions of property, and is satisfied that his solicitor has given effect to the intention then the will, if properly drawn up by a qualified lawyer, may be declared valid even though the patient is too ill to read the will over himself.

The doctor is guaranteeing the testamentary ability of the patient and he has to ensure that the dispositions made are not unduly influenced or incapacitated by senility, mental affection or other illness. The patient must be capable of knowing how much property he has and how he wants to dispose of it. This does not necessarily require, for example, absolute normality of the mind. The making of a will may be during a lucid interval, which has been described as an interval 'in which the mind, having thrown off the disease, has recovered its normal habit' (*A.G.* v. *Parnther* (1792), 3 Bro.C.C. 441) and also, 'The morbid affection no longer obscures or vitiates the judgment' (*Hoyland, exparte* (1805), 11 ves. 11). It is necessary to be sure that there exist at the time no hallucinations or delusions which would affect the will, poison the patient's decisions or pervert his sense of what is right.

A sound and sensible will would appear in itself to be strong evidence of satisfactory testamentary capacity.

The practitioner may be considerably helped in his estimation of testamentary capacity by asking the testator questions about his property and his reasons for particular bequests and seeing whether the answers are reasonable. A general test of the state of mind can be made in the form of simple questions about the date, his surroundings, simple current events and the like, and further support may be forthcoming by questioning relatives as to recent behaviour. Notes should be kept as they may be needed in Court if the will is contested.

In the case of a patient unable to speak, and whose will is therefore drawn up by the method of questions and indicated assent, the testamentary capacity may require specially sound proof if the will is contested before the Courts.

Legacies and Gifts

Practitioners will do well to bear in mind the possible difficulties that may arise from the receipt of legacies and gifts from patients.

Legacies, for example, may be contested by others interested in the estate of the deceased on the grounds that the special relationship between doctor and patient enabled the doctor to exert influence in his favour with the patient. When the doctor is aware of a patient's intention to leave him a legacy, or to make him a gift which might possibly be contested, he should advise the patient to seek advice from a third party, for example his solicitor, before coming to a final decision in the matter.

A general practitioner in the National Health Service is not permitted to accept any fee or other remuneration from patients for whose treatment he is responsible under the Terms of Service. The acceptance of a gift, even though not actually monetary, is almost certain to be regarded as an infringement of this requirement. There is no objection to the acceptance of a legacy from a patient for whose treatment he has been responsible.

Dying Declaration

A dying declaration is a statement relating to some important matter made by an individual who is aware of the imminence of death. When asked to take down a dying declaration a practitioner should be satisfied that certain requirements are met.

If time allows when the patient expresses a desire to make a statement a magistrate or, in Scotland, a Sheriff should be found and asked to undertake the task and the responsibility. In any case it is advisable that there shall be a witness or witnesses to the proceedings, if available. The patient must be of sound mind and be in a state of mind sufficiently clear to appreciate what he is doing and saying. He must be fully convinced that he is dying and must say so in the declaration. Any qualification of the expectation of death will render the declaration invalid. Thus the declaration should begin with some such words as: 'Knowing that I am about to die and without hope of recovery I . . . hereby make this solemn declaration. . . .' Thereafter the declaration must be taken down precisely as it is spoken by the patient and without alteration, even of grammar. There must be no prompting and no interference with the utterance of the declaration, except it be a request for repetition of a word or phrase imperfectly heard. In fact, nothing must be done which would make the matter other than a pure, unaltered statement by the declarant.

The declaration being completed it must be read over to the patient who, if able, must sign it or set his mark. Thereafter it is signed by the witnesses and by the practitioner taking it down, who should add his qualification and address and the date, time and place at which the declaration is made. The document should then be handed to a police officer.

It is but rarely that a practitioner will be called upon to undertake the responsibility of a dying declaration, but when it is imperative, owing to the impossibility of summoning a magistrate before death supervenes, it may well be that a statement of the most solemn importance will be made calling for the scrupulous attention to the requirements mentioned above. Such a statement may be of far-reaching importance in criminal matters, for example, in manslaughter, criminal abortion or poisoning.

A dying declaration may be used only in charges of murder or manslaughter in which the death of the declarant is the subject of inquiry, and only as evidence as to the actual circumstances of the death.

There will be occasions when a doctor has a duty to inform the patient that he is certain to die and to invite him to make a dying declaration. He should himself inform the patient of the certainty of death and should satisfy himself that the situation accords with the various conditions mentioned above.

Deposition

When the patient is unaware that he is about to die he may make a deposition, which in law is distinguished from a dying declaration. For this purpose a magistrate must be summoned in order to see that the legal requirements are complied with.

There is a difference in Scotland in that a declaration or deposition by one party can also be used in an inquiry relating to the death of, or injury to, some other person so long as the author of the declaration or deposition would have been a competent witness if still alive. He must be a material witness, his life must be in danger and he must be in a sufficiently clear mental state to give reliable evidence.

Bequest of Eyes for Corneal Grafting

The possibilities of bequeathing eyes for corneal grafting was recognized in the Corneal Graft Act, 1952. A person wishing to bequeath eyes must express the wish to do so either orally or in writing before two witnesses. The consent of near relatives is obtained, after the death, before the bequest is carried out. If this is not forthcoming the bequest is thereby nullified. Immediately upon death the nearest ophthalmic centre or special centre where corneal grafting is carried out should be notified, either by the relatives or by the family doctor. To be successful the graft should be obtained within ten hours after death.

The Roman Catholic View

On May 14th, 1956, the Pope informed an international gathering of ophthalmologists that there was no moral or religious objection to the post-mortem removal of the cornea for grafting purposes.

Bequest of a Body for Anatomical Purposes

A patient seeking advice about how to leave his body for dissection should be informed that, legally, on his death the right of disposal of his body rests with his next of kin or the executor of his will. He should, therefore, acquaint the executors of his will, or any near relatives who may at the time of his death be his next of kin, with his intention and satisfy himself that they will have no objection. His intention should be clearly set down in writing and be signed by him and placed so that the statement is easily available on his death, preferably with his will or other papers.

The body may be sent to a medical school for dissection only in the absence of any objection by a near relative. So that it will be seen that a right of an individual to leave his body for dissection is not absolute. A form, A.A.1 (obtainable with full instructions from H.M. Inspector of Anatomy, Ministry of Health, Savile Row, London, W.1) requires to be sent by the executor or next of kin requesting the removal of the body for anatomical examination not less than forty-eight hours after the time of death. This form has to be accompanied by a certificate* stating the cause of death, to be completed by a medical practitioner in accordance with Section 9 of the Anatomy Act of 1832. H.M. Inspector of Anatomy will then arrange to send a hearse and coffin for the body. The Registrar's certificate for disposal should be given to the undertaker who removes the body.

Thereafter the Professor of Anatomy concerned is responsible

* Form A.A.4, on the back of which is quoted the relevant section of the Act. This form will be provided with Form A.A.1.

for the body until it is ready for burial, which must be within two years of the death. The burial is conducted by a clergyman of the deceased's faith and full particulars are forwarded in due time to the person who completed form A.A.1 mentioned above. Expenses connected with the removal and burial of the body are normally borne by the medical school sufficient to provide a simple funeral. Any additional expenditure for cremation or amplification of the funeral arrangements that are desired will be expected to be met by the executor or next of kin.

At the Time of Death

It is difficult at times for a doctor, having care of a dying patient, to know what he should do and what he should not do for the patient, with special reference to the use of drugs and procedures which he knows may bring comfort to the patient and yet hasten death. No rules can be laid down and each case must be judged on its merits. Doctors may be guided by an aphorism uttered by the late Lord Horder who said: 'It is the duty of a doctor to prolong life. It is not his duty to prolong the act of dying.'

The Roman Catholic Church requires that in the hour of death nothing shall be given to hasten death. Pain-relieving drugs are not to be given in doses large enough to take away the patient's use of his faculties, if his affairs are not in order, spiritually and temporally. It is wise that a relative should be warned that the patient is dying, or the patient should be warned that his life is in danger. This knowledge will enable the priest to be summoned, which the Church desires to be done, if possible, when the patient is still fully conscious.

Opening of an Artery or Vein after Death

Occasionally a patient with a fear of being buried alive will ask a practitioner, either by personal request or by an instruction in a will, to sever a main artery. Requests of this kind are not common and there is no objection to the instruction being carried out. Due care, of course, is necessary so that there is no such interference with the body if there is any suggestion of death from unnatural causes or if, for any reason, the death has to be reported to the Coroner.

The Roman Catholic Church does not allow the opening of an artery or vein if the purpose is to kill the patient if not already dead. Such a purpose may, of course, be in the mind of a patient requesting the carrying out of such a procedure who has a fear of being buried alive. It is, however, permitted by the Roman Catholic Church as a test, the effects of which can be counteracted, of whether the patient is dead.

Cremation

The Cremation Act, 1952, lays down the requirements of the law for this method of disposal of the dead. The cremation form to be completed does not abolish the need for the issue of a death certificate in the usual form and the registration of the death.

Cremation is not permitted if the deceased has left an instruction to the contrary, if the deceased is unidentified, if the cause of the death is not definitely ascertained or if other inquiry into the death is necessary.

Application for cremation is made on a special form which the relatives or executors normally obtain from the undertaker. Medical practitioners are concerned with the completion of Forms B and C on this form. Form B is completed by the practitioner in attendance in the last illness. In Scotland, where no medical practitioner has attended during the last illness, Form B may be completed by the ordinary medical attendant of the deceased so long as he is registered and able to certify definitely the cause of death.

Form C is a confirmatory certificate to be completed by a practitioner of not less than five years' standing, who must see and question the practitioner who completed Form B. He must not be a relative or partner of the practitioner who has completed Form B. The certificates are scrutinized by a medical referee specially appointed for the purpose. If the referee is satisfied that the cause of death is ascertained and no further inquiry or examination is required he issues an 'authority to cremate' (Form F). The referee may order a post-mortem examination before issuing the 'authority to cremate' if the death might be due to poison, violence, illegal operation, or neglect.

Practitioners are normally paid a fee for completion of

either Form B or C*, but if the practitioner completing Form B does so in the capacity of an officer employed under Part II (Hospital Services) of the National Health Service it is regarded as part of his duties under the Hospital Service and he may not claim or receive a fee.

In a case dealt with by a Coroner by ordering a post-mortem and not holding an inquest, or by holding an inquest, the Coroner completes a Form 'E' which takes the place of Forms B and C. Thereafter the application is passed to the medical referee for completion of Form F as in a normal case.

The medical referee may order or undertake a post-mortem examination before authorizing cremation.

Cremation of the Stillborn

A stillborn child may be cremated if the stillbirth is certified by the practitioner in attendance or if a post-mortem examination has been made and there are no suspicious circumstances, subject to the satisfaction of the medical referee.

Post-mortem Examinations

A doctor may if he so wishes perform a post-mortem examination of his patient but before doing so he must obtain the consent of the personal representatives of the deceased. If the death has been reported to the Coroner the doctor should not conduct any examination of the body except with the consent of or at the request of the Coroner. If he has any reason to suspect that the post-mortem examination may show that the case might be within the jurisdiction of the Coroner, he should undertake no examination, but should report the matter to the Coroner.

Post-mortem Delivery

Where a woman dies during pregnancy, the foetus will usually predecease her. Where the death is sudden the foetus may live for a short time. Death may precipitate labour and the head may be found on the perineum in which case a forceps delivery carried out at once may save the life of the child. Otherwise when the mother's heart and breathing have ceased and the foetus is still living, immediate Caesarean

* See Appendix F.

18

INFECTIOUS AND INDUSTRIAL DISEASES

Notifications of certain infectious and industrial diseases are required by the authorities in the public interest. The information so obtained enables the accurate compilation of statistics which give a valuable picture of the incidence of a particular disease at various seasons and in various localities. Apart from its interest to research workers, the information obtained from notifications is often of the utmost importance in checking the source and preventing the local spread of an infectious disease, or in bringing to light some defective working condition in a hazardous employment. Doctors are statutorily required to notify the diseases named in the regulations, which are listed in Appendix H.

Notification of Infectious Disease

The law relating to notification of infectious disease is to be found in the Public Health Act, 1936, the Public Health (London) Act, 1936 and the Public Health (Scotland) Act, 1945 and in the regulations made under these Acts.

Any medical practitioner attending on a patient is required to notify the Medical Officer of Health of the district, as soon as he is aware that the patient is suffering from a notifiable disease, of the patient's name, address and notifiable disease. The penalty for failure to do so is a fine not exceeding 40*s*.

Notification of infectious diseases is made, on a form provided, to the Medical Officer of Health. A practitioner is not absolved from this liability because he believes he can prove that the notification has been made by someone else. A telephone call to the medical officer of an isolation hospital to arrange admission, for example, does not constitute notification.

For each notification a practitioner is entitled to a fee (see Appendix F).

Except under special circumstances of emergency a Local Authority, before exercising its right to require notification of a disease in its own area other than diseases already notifiable by general regulations, must obtain the approval of the Minister of Health. Thereafter one week's notice is required before such local order is in force. An advertisement is inserted in a local newspaper and a notice is sent individually to each medical practitioner known to be practising in the district. Cancellation of such an order is carried out in like manner.

Prevention of Spread of Infection

There are provisions in the Acts for controlling the spread of infection by preventing the attendance of those liable to spread infection in public places or places of work, the transfer and sale of bedding and clothing, including to laundries and cleaners, and the attendance of children at schools.

Application for facilities for disinfection should be made to the Local Authority. Library books should not be returned to the Library, but application should be made to the Local Authority for instructions.

Persons suffering from notifiable diseases are not permitted to enter a public vehicle such as a bus or a train. In the case of a taxi or other hired vehicle prior notification must be made to the owner or driver, who may recover the cost of disinfecting the vehicle.

The Local Authority, on a certificate of the Medical Officer of Health, has powers to insist upon and, in some circumstances, to carry out the disinfection of premises and articles contained therein. The Authority may also require the removal of persons, not themselves sick, from premises for the purpose of carrying out disinfection and may provide for them temporary shelter.

The Local Authority has powers to remove persons to a suitable hospital or institution and detain a person suffering from a notifiable disease, where a Justice of the Peace is satisfied that such action is necessary on the grounds of avoiding serious risk to others.

Notification of Industrial Diseases

A list is given in Appendix H of industrial diseases which require to be notified by a practitioner in attendance on the patient. The notification is made on a form supplied by the Ministry of Labour and National Service which may be obtained from the local office of the Ministry. The notification is made to the Chief Inspector of Factories, Ministry of Labour and National Service, 8 St James's Square, London, S.W.1.

These notifications are required under the Factories Acts, 1937 and 1948, and the Lead Paint (Protection against Poisoning) Act, 1926.

The notifications relate to the contraction of any of the diseases mentioned in a factory or in certain other premises such as electrical stations and building sites, and in relation to certain occupations in ships and docks. Notification of lead poisoning extends to other places where persons are employed in painting buildings, or in which women or young persons are employed in the use of lead compounds for certain processes. A fee is payable for notification (see Appendix F).

Pneumoconiosis

Although pneumoconiosis is not a notifiable industrial disease, deaths from this cause should be notified to the Coroner (in England and Wales) or the local office of the Ministry of Pensions and National Insurance (in Scotland) for a post-mortem examination may be required to determine the diagnosis in order that the dependents may benefit.

Compressed Air Illness

Section 66 of the Factories Act requires every case of compressed air illness to be reported to Her Majesty's Inspector of Factories for the district if it occurs on premises subject to the Factories Acts. The notification is made on Form 44.

19

MENTAL DISORDER AND DEFICIENCY

The Board of Control

While the National Health Service Act vested in the Minister of Health the functions of licensing, registration and certification of homes, hospitals and other places for the reception of mental cases and mental defectives, the Board of Control, acting under the Minister of Health, supervises them and their patients by visitations and examination of documents to determine whether the statutory requirements, including those relating to certification and detention, are properly observed. Its functions extend to patients and mental defectives cared for by private individuals under the Lunacy, Mental Treatment and Mental Deficiency Acts, but not to persons of unsound mind who are so found by inquisition (see p. 171). In Scotland similar functions are undertaken by the General Board of Control acting in an approximately similar relationship to the Secretary of State for Scotland.

Acute Mental Cases

One of the major anxieties with which a practitioner is faced from time to time is the acute mental case. Quite apart from the clinical problems of diagnosis which are nearly always the cause of sufficient anxiety by themselves, the disposal of the patient is a problem in itself.

The Duly Authorized Officer

The Duly Authorized Officer, an officer of the Local Health Authority, is able to place a person in a suitable hospital without the need to call a doctor. The authority is vested in him in respect of persons who are not under proper care or have no relatives or friends to act as petitioners under the Lunacy and Mental Treatment Acts or otherwise to arrange for their reception into proper care. The Duly Authorized Officer has also responsibilities for the care and aftercare of sufferers from mental illness and of mental defectives.

This action by the Duly Authorized Officer is known as a Three Day Order (Lunacy Act, 1890, Section 20). If the patient recovers within the three days he will be discharged. If he does not, the medical officer of the hospital may authorize detention for fourteen days under Section 21A of the Lunacy Act, 1890 and the Ninth Schedule of the National Health Service Act (1946), or a Summary Reception Order may be obtained.

The Duly Authorized Officer will always be glad to have the support of a medical practitioner in his action. Although not obliged to by law the practitioner can help by giving a note stating his opinion that the patient is in need of care and observation to determine his soundness of mind. This is particularly helpful when the patient is to be the subject of a Three Day Order.

A private patient is best dealt with by means of an urgency order.

Probably the best way for a doctor to handle cases of acute psychosis is to enlist the assistance of the Duly Authorized Officer. He will be able to assist in the placing of the patient and will arrange for the ambulance which is specially provided for the purpose by the Local Health Authority.

Practitioners will find it helpful to have a note of the telephone number of the Duly Authorized Officer so that he can conveniently and immediately obtain his advice and assistance when necessary.

In Scotland an acute case can be dealt with by a Certificate of Emergency, which requires one medical certificate and a petition. This allows retention in hospital for three days.

Delirium Tremens

Particular care is needed in cases of delirium tremens as the possibilities of action for wrongful certification on recovery are great. If possible certification should be avoided and in any case a general practitioner is advised not to proceed with certification, or an urgency order, on his own responsibility. It is best to arrange with the relatives for the patient to be placed under care and supervision in his own home or elsewhere, according to the circumstances, and for treatment of the medical condition to be instituted.

Control by Force and by Sedatives

In dealing with an excited patient in emergency the doctor may feel the necessity to control the patient by the use of force or by the administration of a sedative. Such action should be avoided if at all possible or kept to a minimum, particularly when force is to be used. It is wise to obtain the written consent of the relative having charge of the patient before embarking on such measures.

Certification

The Lunacy Act, 1890, governs the certification of persons of unsound mind and the Mental Treatment Act, 1930, introduced 'voluntary patients' and 'temporary patients' as additional categories for the classification and disposal of patients suffering from mental illness.

Full Certification

The purpose of certification is the protection of the patient and the public and the placing of the patient under necessary treatment. This is effected by a petition submitted by a relative or other persons specified in the Act to a specially appointed judicial authority. Two medical certificates are required to accompany the petition, one of which should be by the usual medical attendant. The certificates are given on a prescribed form and the medical practitioners certifying must conform to the following conditions:

They must not examine the patient together.

They must not be related to each other (or incidentally to the patient) or be in relationship as partner or assistant.

They must be practising.

They must not be interested in payments made on the patient's account.

The utmost care must be exercised in making statements

firstly for the obvious reason that certification is a step having the gravest consequences to the liberty of the patient, and, secondly, that it ranks equally with evidence given on oath in a Court. There must be no mis-statements.

A wise step is for the medical practitioner to hear the story of the case from others (whose names should be given) before seeing the patient. This will make it easier for him to make the necessary distinction, which is required in the certificate, between his own observations and those of others. Distinction should also be made between his own observations made at the time of certification and those he may have made from previous acquaintance with the patient. Full notes should be made and preserved lest they be required even years afterwards, the possibility of a subsequent action for wrongful certification being always present. Appearance, memory, homicidal or suicidal tendencies, inability to answer questions and general bearing may all call for mention, the patient's actual words being quoted where they constitute important evidence.

The practitioner's approach to the examination must, of course, be entirely without bias. His attitude should be almost one of regarding the patient as sane and noting evidence to the contrary. He should be satisfied, as far as he can be, that the action of the relatives in petitioning is in good faith.

If, subsequently, a patient wishes to bring an action for wrongful certification he requires to obtain leave of the High Court, which will not be granted unless there appears to be ground for a charge that the practitioner did not act in good faith and with reasonable care. Thus, if a practitioner exercises care and acts in good faith he need have no qualms as to a future action which he may be called upon to defend.

On receipt of the petition and the two medical certificates the reception order is signed by the specially appointed judicial authority, the patient is admitted and the order remains in force for a year.

Once detained under a reception order the patient remains 'certified' by means of certificates and reports sent to the Board of Control by the medical officer of the institution at the end of the first, second, fourth, seventh and twelfth years after certification.

There remains among the public a deep-rooted antipathy

to certification, which is commonly regarded as a stigma not only on the patient but also on the family. Consequently a doctor will often meet with reluctance on the part of relatives to petition for any form of certification. The doctor can often do a great deal to reassure relatives by explaining the unsubstantial nature of the stigma and the prospects of modern treatment where likely to be relevant and by disabusing the minds of the relatives of the commonly held belief that certification is more or less irrevocable.

The discharge of a patient from certificate may be readily procured by the petitioner at any time, except when the medical officer in charge of the patient is of opinion that it would involve risk to the patient or to others by his being 'dangerous and unfit to be at large' (see p. 172).

Emergency Cases

Certification, as has been shown, is a somewhat cumbersome and difficult procedure which does not lend itself easily to the management of emergency cases. For these it may be possible to arrange a direct admission to a mental observation ward by a special arrangement with the Medical Superintendent or with the help of the Duly Authorized Officer of the Local Health Authority. Failing this there are three other methods which may be appropriate to the case:

(1) on an Urgency Order;
(2) as a temporary patient;
(3) as a voluntary patient.

Observation—The Three Day Order

This is used when urgent restraint is necessary as in an acute anxiety which is combined with depression making it necessary to place the patient under supervision on account of suicidal tendencies. The practitioner should seek the help of the Duly Authorized Officer. He, being a lay officer, will normally accept the opinion of the practitioner but the decision as to whether the patient should be placed under restraint on account of mental illness rests with him. If he so decides he will issue a 'Three Day Order' and will arrange admission of the patient to an observation ward in a hospital designated for the purpose, or will send him on an urgency order to a mental hospital.

The Urgency Order

The Urgency Order is made on request from a near relative or the Duly Authorized Officer on Forms Lunacy 4 and 2, obtainable from any law stationer, and is accompanied by a medical certificate (Forms 8 and 9). The certificate should be couched in non-technical language and should not include a diagnosis. Although commonly completed by the psychiatrist called in, it may be completed by any practitioner. Whoever does so is protected legally so long as he acts with care and in good faith. It is wise to avoid sedating the patient prior to the arrival of the Duly Authorized Officer lest he should fail to appreciate the nature of the case because the psychotic features of the case are masked.

If the patient is to be admitted to a private institution the Duly Authorized Officer's services are not required and the Urgency Order is signed by the nearest relative.

Only one medical certificate is required and the patient must be admitted within two days of the medical examination. At the expiry of seven days the order is no longer valid and the patient must be released, or, alternatively, certified.

In Scotland a three day emergency admission to a mental hospital may be arranged on a request from a person, who need not be related to the patient. The request must be supported by a certificate signed by a doctor who must not be the Medical Superintendent or his son, brother or father, or any medical officer of the institution. Neither must he have any pecuniary or patrimonial interest in the institution. During the three days the patient may be examined in the usual way with a view to certification.

As a Temporary Patient (Mental Treatment Act, 1930, *Section* 5)

Temporary treatment is a procedure which enables a patient to be detained who has a prospect of early recovery. Detention is for a maximum of six months in the first place and may be extended by the Board of Control for two periods of three months each if the prospect of recovery in that time remains. A patient who regains his volition may only be detained for twenty-eight days after this event, so long as he does not lose his volition in the interim.

The procedure is intended as a means of giving treatment without certification to incipient mental patients who otherwise might have to be certified and whose illness, for example acute confusion, is likely to be of short duration. The official description is a patient 'who is suffering from mental illness and is likely to benefit by temporary treatment, but is for the time being incapable of expressing himself as willing or unwilling to receive such treatment'. The application requires two supporting recommendations by medical practitioners, one of whom must be the patient's usual medical attendant, if practicable, and the other a member approved by the Board of Control for the purpose. Specialists in mental disorders are normally so approved. The application by a relative and the two medical statements are entered on a Form A.1 which is obtainable from law stationers.

For this purpose there is no objection to the two practitioners examining the patient together but if they examine the patient separately the examinations must take place within five days of each other and the admission must be within two weeks of the examination or of the second of two examinations.

Voluntary Treatment (*Mental Treatment Act*, 1930, *Section* 1)

The patient who needs care and treatment and yet is capable of making a choice in the matter may make application to the hospital or institution to be received in the institution for the purpose. He obtains a form of application from the officer in charge of the institution, which may be a place approved for the purpose by the Board of Control, or from a person so approved should he prefer to place himself under single care.

An application respecting a person under sixteen years of age must be made by the parent or guardian and, in this case, must be supported by a medical recommendation stating that he is likely to benefit from admission as a voluntary patient and giving the date of that examination.

Once admitted he (or the parent or guardian) requires to give three days' written notice of his intention to leave and once he has left, even if it be before the expiry of his notice, he cannot be brought back without a fresh application. If while in the institution he loses his volition for twenty-eight days continually he must be discharged, unless he is certified or detained as a temporary patient.

The person in charge of the institution is required to notify the Board of Control of the reception, departure or death of a voluntary patient. Doctors are advised to use this method of admission only if they are reasonably confident that the patient will stay under care. If this is in doubt an Urgency Order is probably preferable.

Voluntary Treatment in Scotland

In Scotland the Mental Treatment Act, 1930, does not apply but voluntary treatment is provided for under the Lunacy (Scotland) Amendment Act, 1866 (Section 15) and the Mental Deficiency and Lunacy (Scotland) Act, 1913 (Section 59). The signed application must be submitted to the General Board of Control, St Andrew's House, Edinburgh, and if immediate admission is desired an application must also be submitted to the Superintendent of the Institution. The approval of the General Board of Control must be obtained within three days of the admission.

Summary Reception Order (*Lunacy Act*, 1890, *Section* 14, *amended by Ninth Schedule of National Health Service Act*, 1946)

A Summary Reception Order is a form of certification without petition from a relative or person having charge of the patient. The Duly Authorized Officer sets the procedure in motion by application to a Justice of the Peace who arranges for the examination of the patient by a medical practitioner and completion of a certificate on Form 8. The considerations to be borne in mind in the examination and completion of the certificate are the same as those described under certification associated with a reception order on petition.

Inquisition

An application by an interested person to the Chancery Division for an inquiry into a person's mental state and its bearing upon the administration of his property, requires to be supported by sworn affidavits by two medical men that the patient is of unsound mind. If the Judge in Chancery, to whom application is made, decides to hold an inquisition its object is to determine whether or not the patient is capable of managing either himself or his affairs, or both. If he is found incapable his affairs may then be administered by a 'Committee (pronounced Komité) of the person' appointed for the purpose, which reports to the Judge in Lunacy as trustee of the property.

Discharge from Certificate

This may be effected by:

(1) A direction in writing from the petitioner, or, if he is dead, the nearest relative or the person who made the last payment on the patient's account.

(2) By the Local Authority in the case of a rate-aided patient.

(3) By the Board of Control.

(4) As a consequence of representations made by commissioners of the Board of Control or visitors of the hospital.

There is due provision for the raising of objections to the discharge by the Medical Superintendent.

A discharged patient believing himself to have been improperly confined is entitled to obtain from the Secretary of the Board copies of the relevant documents.

The Mental Patient as a Witness

A mental patient may be regarded as a competent witness in a Court so long as he understands the nature of an oath and can appreciate the purpose of the proceedings. The decision as to the admissibility of his evidence rests with the Judge who may require medical assistance, as, for example, from a medical officer at a mental hospital where the patient is detained. A practitioner attending the Courts to assist the Judge should be prepared to speak from his knowledge of the case and from the patient's medical notes.

Mental Deficiency

The definition of mental deficiency in the Mental Deficiency Acts, 1913–27 is as follows:

> 'A mental defective is one in whom there is a condition of arrested or incomplete development of mind existing before

the age of eighteen, whether arising from inherent causes or induced by disease or injury.'

There are the following four classes of mental defectives:

Idiots, those incapable of guarding themselves against common dangers.

Imbeciles, those unable to learn to manage their affairs or themselves.

Feeble-minded persons, those requiring care, supervision and control for protection of themselves or of others, or as children appear incapable of benefiting from normal education.

Moral defectives, those who possess also some vice or criminal tendencies and require supervision and control for the protection of others.

Certification of a mental defective requires the completion of a special certificate by each of two registered medical practitioners, one of whom is approved for the purpose. Copies of the forms are held at mental deficiency institutions. The considerations to be borne in mind by the practitioner are similar to those in the certification of unsound mind. He must exercise the same discipline and care. He may not examine the alleged mental defective without his consent or, if under age, the consent of the parent or guardian. The medical certificate must state the facts upon which the opinion is formed. Each practitioner must have personally examined the alleged defective within twenty-one days before the presentation of the petition. Neither practitioner must be a near relative, partner or assistant of the petitioner or of the other practitioner.

There are various circumstances laid down in which the Local Authority may have a defective or alleged defective, who appears to be in trouble or need, removed to a mental institution as a 'place of safety'. Under certain conditions the Duly Authorized Officer may obtain a warrant on which a policeman may enter otherwise private premises and search for a defective with a view to placing him in a place of safety. In this search he is accompanied by a medical practitioner.

Petitions relating to mental defectiveness require to be supported by two medical certificates. If a medical examination is impracticable the reason must be fully stated on the petition.

If this is the case and the petition is not dismissed the judicial authority must then order a medical examination. If he decides to postpone the decision on the petition by adjournment of the case, pending further evidence, he may order the alleged defective to undergo a medical examination. An order for the detention of a mental defective is valid for one year, after which the case is reviewed at stated intervals according to the regulations.

Admission to a mental deficiency institution may be arranged without the formality of certification in a parallel manner to the admission of voluntary patients to mental hospitals (see page 170). Application should be made to the Medical Superintendent.

20

MEDICAL ASPECTS OF DIVORCE

Medical evidence may sometimes constitute an important part of the proceedings in a divorce case. Cases in which cruelty is alleged may require factual evidence of mental or physical trauma which should be given as in other Court cases. Similarly evidence may be required as to the presence or absence of venereal disease. Special considerations apply to petitions for divorce on grounds of incurable insanity and in nullity cases.

Insanity—in Divorce (Medical Evidence)

The Matrimonial Causes Act, 1937, provides for divorce by reason of incurable unsoundness of mind involving care and treatment for five years immediately preceding presentation of the petition for divorce. The evidence is usually that of a medical attendant with personal knowledge of the patient, having been in regular attendance on him over a long time. It must be an expression of an unqualified belief in incurable unsoundness of mind and reasons on which opinions are based must be quoted. Although the future cannot be foretold with certainty, opinion based on all known facts is acceptable. He may, if able to express a firm and unqualified belief in the respondent's incurability, give his evidence by affidavit.

He may have to state whether the petitioner by his neglect, cruelty or other misbehaviour has caused or aided the onset of the mental illness, or by failing to co-operate in treatment has aggravated the condition, caused it to persist or interfered with the chances of recovery. Examples of this might be refusal to visit the patient or have the patient out on trial, and refusal to consent to some treatment that is recommended.

The medical history must be disclosed to the Court. The Ministry of Health has authorized the Board of Control to grant bona fide applicants permission to obtain copies of reception documents and statutory medical reports. The file of the Board of Control should be before the Court.

The Court usually appoints a guardian *ad litem*. A practitioner should give information only to the guardian *ad litem* and to no other person without his authority. The evidence he gives in Court or to solicitors in preparation of the case is covered by absolute privilege but is not protected, in divorce cases, by the protection afforded to the practitioner by the Lunacy and Mental Treatment Acts. By the latter an action for wrongful certification can only be brought to Court if a good prima facie case is ruled and leave given.

'Care and Treatment'

Section 3 of Matrimonial Causes Act gives the definition of 'under care and treatment'.

'Care and treatment' is briefly described as detention under an order or inquisition under the Lunacy and Mental Treatment Acts, 1890–1930, under any order or warrant, under Army Act, Air Force Act, Naval Discipline Act and Naval Establishment Act, 1884, and Yarmouth Naval Hospital Act, 1931; or detention as a criminal lunatic, or in pursuance of an order under the Criminal Lunatics Act, 1884, and treatment as voluntary patient under the Mental Treatment Act, 1930, if it be treatment following, without any interval, a period of such detention. The period of detention must be continuous but is not broken by being released on trial, or holiday in a home under the control of the mental authority.

The question of what constitutes continuous care and treatment and what breaks the continuity for the purposes of the Matrimonial Causes Act is complicated and requires careful attention in each individual case. Frequent and long absences and the transfer of a patient to another institution without the certificate of the medical officer, under Section 25 of the Act, certifying that the patient has not recovered, have been held by the Courts to represent a cessation of 'continuous care and treatment'. The original period of temporary treatment does not count for divorce purposes, but any extended period does. The Act applying to Scotland (The Divorce (Scotland) Act, 1938) has certain differences in that all that need be shown is the continuous operation of the reception order for the previous five years. In England evidence of five years' detention requires to be backed by medical opinion. In Scotland evidence of five years' detention is enough.

Insanity may, of course, be used as a defence by the respondent in a divorce case, it being held that, being insane, he was not responsible for the act, for example, of desertion or cruelty.

Medical Aspects of Divorce for Nullity

Divorce for Nullity requires a declaration by the Court that the marriage was void from the start. The reasons for which the Court may so declare are set out below, subject to the petitioner being in ignorance of the facts at the time of the marriage.

(1) That one of the parties was so insane as not to know what he or she was doing.

(2) That one of the parties was so drunk as not to know what he or she was doing.

(3) That the marriage was never consummated, either by reason of the sexual impotence of one of the parties, or the wilful refusal of the respondent to consummate or allow consummation of the marriage.

(4) That either party, at the time of the marriage, was of unsound mind or a mental defective (as defined in the Mental Defectives Acts, 1913–38) or subject to recurrent fits of epilepsy or insanity.

(5) That the respondent at the time of the marriage was suffering from venereal disease in communicable form (see also under Venereal Disease, Chapter 32).

(6) That the respondent at the time of the marriage was pregnant by some other person.

Medical evidence may be required if the petition is based on any of the above cases. The importance of clinical notes taken at about the time of the marriage can hardly be overemphasized.

21

DRUGS

That the incidence of addiction to and abuse of drugs in this country is comparatively small must be due in no small measure to the very stringent laws and regulations applying to Dangerous Drugs and Poisons. These laws are strictly enforced and penalties for infringement are severe. As mentioned in Chapter 4, the registered medical practitioner is in a specially privileged position regarding Dangerous Drugs and Poisons and any abuse of his privileges is most seriously regarded. Any infringement of the law may result in a heavy fine or imprisonment and in the withdrawal of his authority under the Acts, which will seriously hamper him in the practice of his profession. He may have his name erased from the Medical Register. A knowledge of the law, a careful study of the memorandum issued by the Home Office*, and the exercise of continual care will enable him to avoid running any risk of these penalties.

The Pharmacy and Poisons Act, 1933

The Pharmacy and Poisons Act, 1933, sets out the arrangements under which pharmaceutical chemists require to be members of the Pharmaceutical Society by virtue of being registered as such. It lays down the powers of the Society and the Statutory Committee and governs the selling of poisons.

Part II of the Act establishes the Poisons Board on which there is considerable medical representation among its sixteen members. Its constitution is set down in the Second Schedule to the Act. The Board prepares and maintains a list of substances to be treated as poisons for the purposes of the Act. The list is in two parts. It is subject to approval by the Secretary of State

* 'The Duties of Doctors and Dentists under the Dangerous Drugs Act and Regulations' (D.D.101). H.M.S.O.

for the Home Department, and to variation from time to time. The list is known as 'the poisons list'.

Part I consists of poisons to be sold only by authorized sellers of poisons. Part II contains the commoner articles which may also be sold by any person whose name is on a special list maintained by the Local Authority for the area.

Section 18 of the Act provides for prohibitions and regulations in respect of the sale of poisons, but the supply of medicines by a duly qualified medical practitioner for the purposes of medical treatment is excluded from the restrictions (Section 19), so long as the following provisions are satisfied:

(i) The medicine must be distinctly labelled with the name and address of the person by whom it is supplied or dispensed.

(ii) On the day of supply or dispensing or, if not reasonably practicable, on the next day the following particulars must be entered in a book kept regularly, but not necessarily exclusively, for the purpose. Thus entry in a day book will suffice:

(*a*) Date.
(*b*) Ingredients and quantity of medicine supplied.
(*c*) The name of the person to whom it is supplied.

Contravention of these provisions renders the offender liable, on summary conviction, to a fine not exceeding £50 in respect of each offence. These latter restrictions do not apply in respect of a prescription given by duly qualified medical practitioners in accordance with the National Health Service Acts.

The Act restricts the sale of poisons but sale to a duly qualified medical practitioner is specifically exempt from the restrictions.

Section 25 of the Act provides for inspection and for enforcement of the Act but inspectors appointed to inspect premises of registered pharmaceutical chemists and authorized sellers of poisons for this purpose are not authorized to enter or inspect the premises, not being a shop, of a duly qualified medical practitioner.

Further provisions regarding poisons, largely affecting pharmaceutical chemists, are to be found in The Pharmacy and Medicines Act, 1941. It is of interest to medical practitioners to know that in this Act are prohibitions against the advertisement of any article leading to its use for the treatment of Bright's disease, cataract, diabetes, epilepsy or fits, glaucoma, locomotor ataxy, paralysis or tuberculosis. The exceptions are that certain bodies or persons may so advertise under certain conditions and also where it can be shown that such advertising was only so far as it was reasonably necessary to bring it to the notice of certain classes of persons, of which medical practitioners are one. Advertising of articles leading to their use for procuring miscarriage is forbidden.

Section 11 of the Act deals with the requirements for labelling and disclosure of contents of medicine for sale and offered as samples but specifically excludes from the requirements a medicine or article prescribed and supplied for the use of a particular person. There are restrictions in Section 12 on the sale of medicines by unauthorized persons, but medical practitioners are specifically excluded from the restrictions.

The Poisons Rules

The Poisons Rules* are made by the Secretary of State under the powers given to him by Section 23 in Part III of the Pharmacy and Poisons Act, 1933. He is thereby empowered to make rules on many matters relating to poisons, for example the sale and supply, storage, transport, labelling, records and prescribing. The Rules may be revoked, altered or added to from time to time by the Secretary of State.

There are sixteen Schedules to the Poisons Rules, which are briefly described below. Of these Schedules four are of particular importance to doctors. These are the First, the Third, the Fourth and the Seventh.

The First Schedule

Poisons listed in this Schedule are those substances in the poisons list to which special restrictions apply as to those to whom or by whom they may be supplied or sold. They may be supplied to registered medical practitioners for the purpose of medical treatment, subject to proper labelling and record keeping. The list is long. Examples are opium, morphine, cocaine and strychnine and their derivatives.

* See Appendix D.

The Third Schedule

This contains two lists of substances and preparations which, though containing First Schedule poisons, are exempt from the restrictions applying to such poisons. The first list contains substances commonly used in industry and the second is of substances in which the content of poison is sufficiently small as to constitute no danger. Examples are tobacco (nicotine being a First Schedule Poison), soaps and lotions containing alkaloids of stavesacre and polishes containing chlorides of antimony. The exemptions also apply to machine spread plasters, surgical dressings and certain corn paints.

The Fourth Schedule

Fourth Schedule poisons are substances permitted to be sold by retail only upon a prescription given by a duly qualified medical practitioner (also registered dentist and registered veterinary surgeon or practitioner). The list includes barbituric acid and derivatives, amidopyrine, chlorpromazine, etc., and is reproduced in Appendix G.

Prescriptions for Fourth Schedule Poisons

A prescription for Fourth Schedule poisons must be in writing and signed and dated by the doctor, and his address must be appended (except when on Form E.C.10). The name and address of the patient must be included as also must a statement of the total amount to be supplied and the dose (except where it is for external treatment only). Where the prescription is for ampoules either the total amount to be supplied or the total amount intended to be administered or injected must be stated, together with the amount to be administered or injected in each dose. In an emergency the chemist may dispense the medicine on an undertaking by the practitioner to furnish a prescription within twenty-four hours, failure to honour such an undertaking being a contravention of the Rules.

Except when on Form E.C.10, a prescription for a Fourth Schedule poison may make provision for the prescription to be repeated a stated number of times or at stated intervals. If the prescription states the intervals but not the number of times the chemist is not permitted to dispense it more than three times in all. If it states the number of times but not the intervals it may not be dispensed more than once in three days.

The Seventh Schedule

The Seventh Schedule to the Rules gives the labelling to be used instead of the word 'poison' for certain substances which are noted in the Schedule. The wording to be used is:

(1) '*Caution. It is dangerous to take this preparation except under medical supervison.*'

Includes beta aminopropylbenzene and certain derivatives. Beta-aminoisopropylbenzene and certain derivatives. Insulin. Pituitary. Thyroid. Phenylethylhydantoin and certain derivatives.

(2) '*Caution. It is dangerous to exceed the stated dose.*'

Medicines (including injections) for internal treatment, other than those above or Schedule I poisons.

(3) '*Poison. For animal treatment only.*'

(4) '*Caution. This preparation may cause serious inflammation of the skin in certain persons and should be used only in accordance with expert advice.*'

Certain preparations for hair dyeing.

(5) '*Caution. This substance is caustic.*'

Potassium hydroxide and sodium hydroxide and articles containing either of these.

(6) '*Caution. This substance is poisonous. The inhalation of its vapour, mist spray or dust may have harmful consequences. It may also be dangerous to let it come into contact with the skin or clothing.*'

Includes dinitrocresol, phosphorus compounds, etc., used in agriculture and horticulture.

(7) '*Caution. This preparation should be administered only under medical supervision. The vapour is dangerous.*'

Preparations for internal or external treatment containing di-isopropyl fluorophosphate.

The remaining Schedules are briefly described below.

The Second Schedule lists poisons exempted from the labelling provisions when sold or supplied in certain circumstances (e.g. chloroform, formaldehyde, nitrobenzene).

The Fifth Schedule shows the restricted forms in which certain poisons may be sold by persons on the Local Authority's special list (listed sellers) and covers substances used for agricultural, horticultural and photographic purposes (e.g. sheep-dips, vermin poisons, photographic solutions).

The Sixth Schedule is a statement of particulars permitted in certain cases as to the proportion of poison in the substance. It is, in effect, a permissive simplification of the labelling requirements of certain substances containing poisons. For example, a preparation containing opium may be labelled to show the proportion of morphia it contains; one containing salts of barium may be labelled to show the proportion of one particular barium salt which the preparation would contain were all the barium in the preparation converted into that salt.

The Eighth Schedule lists poisons required to be specially labelled for transport.

The Ninth and Tenth Schedules relate to the list of authorized persons (listed sellers) entitled to sell poisons in Part II of the Poisons List kept by the Local Authority.

The remainder (*Eleventh to Sixteenth Schedules*) relate to the certificates for purchase of poison to be signed by a householder, forms of authority for purchase of strychnine for killing moles and seals, form of entry in the book to be kept by sellers of poisons, exemption of nicotine in insecticides and the colouring of certain poisons.

The Labelling of Poisons

Section 18 of the Pharmacy and Poisons Act, 1933, requires the containers of poisons to be labelled with one word 'Poison', or other prescribed indication of character (see above under the Seventh Schedule to the Rules).

The label 'Poison' or, alternatively, the appropriate wording as in the Seventh Schedule must be either on a separate label or be surrounded by a line within which there must be no other words.

The 'Poison' label, on First Schedule poisons, must either be in red lettering or on a red background.

Embrocations, liniments, lotions, liquid antiseptics or other liquid medicine for external application must be labelled with the name of the article and the words '*For external use only*'.

The container in which a poison is supplied must be impervious to the poison and sufficiently stout to prevent leakage. The same requirements apply to storage of poisons. Poisons should be stored separately in a cupboard or drawer reserved solely for the purpose.

Rules 27, 28 and 29 of the Poisons Rules make special provisions as to storage in and supply of medicines for hospitals and for supply to out-patients.

Dangerous Drugs

The Dangerous Drugs Act, 1951, contains the main legal requirements controlling the issue and prescription of Dangerous Drugs and further details of these requirements are to be found in the Dangerous Drugs Regulations. The chief drugs covered by the Act are crude drugs (raw opium, coca leaves and Indian hemp), medicinal derivatives and certain synthetic drugs of addiction such as pethidine.

The Act is administered by the Home Office and the Department of Health for Scotland. The Home Office 'Memorandum on the duties of Doctors and Dentists under the Dangerous Drugs Act' is obtained from Her Majesty's Stationery Office and should be studied by all practitioners. In appendices to this Memorandum are to be found a list of drugs controlled and a list of preparations which are exempted from the requirements.* New drugs or preparations coming under control are notified from time to time in the medical press.

Registered medical practitioners are authorized to possess, but not to prescribe, crude drugs and to possess, prescribe and supply the controlled manufactured drugs so far as may be necessary for the exercise and practice of their profession. Practitioners may not go beyond this, for example, by supplying the drugs solely for the gratification of addiction, which is not regarded as a 'medical need'.

Practitioners who find themselves worried as to how much they may do in the treatment of addiction without contravening the regulations will find some useful observations on the subject at the end of the Home Office Memorandum. From this they will be able to infer what course of action is considered

* See also Appendix G.

reasonable. Further doubt may be resolved by obtaining a second opinion.

Practitioners have been convicted for offence against the Act for using drugs obtained by them under this authority for the gratification of their own addiction. Practitioners must in their own interests keep always within the strict confines of this authority as any abuse of it, however slight, will be most seriously regarded.

By prescribing a Dangerous Drug to a patient a practitioner is causing that patient to be deemed a person authorized to be in possession of the drug. There is no law limiting the quantities that a practitioner may prescribe for a patient, except that the quantity is limited by what is the 'medical need' of the patient. Nevertheless a practitioner needs to exercise the utmost care in ensuring that he is not prescribing drugs for a patient who is already receiving a supply from another practitioner. The new patient asking for supplies of a drug, with the aid of whatever subterfuge, should always arouse the practitioner's suspicions. Occasionally the request is not so veiled but is supported by a statement that the patient is 'on the Home Office Register'. This patient is immediately suspect for there is no such register. Any person not disclosing to a practitioner that he is obtaining supplies from another source is committing an offence.

In a recent case in the Courts, where a patient was charged with being in unlawful possession of a drug (heroin) under the Dangerous Drugs Regulations as he had not disclosed that he had obtained drugs on the prescription of another practitioner, the practitioner was also charged by invocation of the Accessories and Abettors Act which states that 'whosoever shall aid, abet, counsel or procure the commission of an offence shall be liable to be tried and punished as a principal offender."

The magistrate dismissed the charge against the practitioner of aiding and abetting another person to be in possession of the drug as he considered that the object of the regulations was manifest, to ensure that the second practitioner approached should not be misled, by the withholding of information, into prescribing the drug in excess of quantities which he in his absolute discretion thought proper.

The authority may be withdrawn from a practitioner convicted of an offence under the Dangerous Drugs Act or under certain sections of the Customs and Excise Act in connexion with drugs. It may also be withdrawn under certain conditions of mental illness in the practitioner. Withdrawals and restorations of authority are published in the *London Gazette* and in the *Edinburgh Gazette*.

Prescriptions for Dangerous Drugs

There is need for strict observation of the requirements for the writing of prescriptions for Dangerous Drugs. Prescriptions must be in writing and must include, when the prescription is one for a preparation contained in the *British Pharmacopoeia*, the *British Pharmaceutical Codex* or the *National Formulary*, a statement of the total amount of *the preparation* to be dispensed. Full instructions as to the use of the drug must be included, as also must the date and the name and address of the patient and the practitioner. Prescriptions on Form E.C.10 do not require the inclusion of the practitioner's address. The practitioner must sign with his usual signature. When the prescription is not for a recognized drug (*B.P.*, *B.P.C.* or *National Formulary*) the total amount of *the drug* must be specified. When the prescription is for ampoules either the total amount to be supplied or the total amount intended to be administered or injected must be specified. There are some modifications to these requirements when prescriptions are given in the course of hospital practice.

If the practitioner wishes the prescription to be dispensed more than once he must indicate this on the prescription, but no prescription may be dispensed more than three times altogether. He may, if he wishes, indicate the dates before which the second and third dispensing is not to be carried out. Such repeatable prescriptions, however, are not permitted on Form E.C.10.

A chemist is required to abide strictly by the law and regulations and is forbidden to dispense a prescription which does not conform to the requirements. For example, he may not dispense a prescription dictated over the telephone for it does not so conform. In case of genuine emergency, however, he may do so provided that an undertaking is given by the practitioner to provide a signed order within twenty-four hours.

Failure on the part of a practitioner to honour this undertaking is an offence.

Failure on the part of a practitioner to comply with the exact requirements inevitably causes difficulties for the chemist and for the patient because the former, necessarily observing the rules, is forced to withhold supplies from the latter. Any irritation felt by the practitioner from this cause is of his own making.

Drugs or preparations may only be used for the treatment of the patient for whom they are prescribed, and where an unwanted surplus remains the surplus drugs should be destroyed. The onus for this lies with the patient or, if he has died, with the relatives and not with the practitioner. He may not take the drugs back on to his own charge for the patient is not an authorized supplier of drugs. He should, however, encourage the destruction of the drugs.

Obtaining Supplies of Dangerous Drugs

A practitioner must not be dismayed if a chemist, to whom he is not known, refuses to supply Dangerous Drugs to him. He may only obtain these drugs from authorized chemists or licensed wholesalers (Pharmacy and Poisons Act, 1933). The practitioner must either be personally known to the supplier or be 'introduced by a person so known' before he can be supplied. In addition he must either sign the entry in the Poisons Book or give a signed order with full details. The order or entry must comply with the requirements for prescriptions set out on page 187. So long as the order is properly completed and signed, difficulties are unlikely to be experienced by the practitioner except where he is in a locality where he is a stranger or is seeking to obtain supplies from a wholesaler with whom he has not dealt previously.

Records and Storage of Dangerous Drugs

Registers must be kept by practitioners of drugs obtained and of drugs supplied. Full details of the forms which these registers must take are set out in the Memorandum. There is insistence in the Regulations upon the registers being in the form of bound books, separate books for each professional address and upon the entries therein being in chronological order. There are special requirements to be observed regarding alterations and deletions and provision is made for detailed entries to be in a day book instead of in the register, another book providing cross references in chronological order. All books must be available for inspection without notice by authorized inspectors of the Ministry of Health and Department of Health for Scotland and in certain cases by Home Office Inspectors and the police. The record books must be retained for two years after completion. Suitable books which enable the practitioner easily to conform to the regulations are obtainable from suppliers of medical stationery.

The Dangerous Drugs must be kept in a locked receptacle inaccessible to other than authorized persons. Any losses should be reported to the police. A locked car is not regarded as a 'locked receptacle' for this purpose. Consequently Dangerous Drugs left in a car in the absence from the vehicle of the practitioner must be in a locked case. Whether a special compartment in the car with a separate lock is to be regarded as 'a locked receptacle' has never been decided and presumably the question must await a ruling of the Courts.

Penalties

If any emphasis is necessary on the desirability of conforming strictly to the Regulations or of not attempting to obtain or obtaining drugs for wrongful purposes this is provided by a consideration of the penalties which may be imposed on conviction of an offence. Firstly there is the danger of withdrawal of the authority and the possibility of consideration of the offence by the General Medical Council. Secondly, there is the possibility of a fine of from £250–£1,000 or imprisonment from twelve months to ten years, or both. For an isolated offence relating to record keeping or prescribing which is shown to have been committed through inadvertence, the maximum penalty is a fine of £50.

Hospitals and Nursing Homes

There are special provisions for the custody of Dangerous Drugs in hospitals by which matrons, ward sisters and dispensers are given limited authority. The provisions do not apply to private hospitals, sanatoria and nursing homes.

Export of Drugs

Export of Dangerous Drugs out of the country is only permitted under licence and a practitioner must not prescribe drugs for a patient to take out of the country with him. The patient must arrange to obtain supplies from a practitioner in the country to which he is travelling or from the ship's doctor. The usual professional courtesy of a letter to the doctor concerned, in the ship or overseas, will serve to overcome the patient's difficulty.

There are a considerable number of other drugs, which are listed in the Export of Goods (Control) (Consolidated) Order* which may not be exported without a licence from the Board of Trade. Licences are not required, however, for reasonable quantities of these drugs which a patient may take with him for personal use, or which a practitioner may take for his professional use abroad. This concession does not apply to travellers to China, Hong Kong, Macao, Tibet and North Korea.

The Therapeutic Substances Act, 1956

This Act was passed to consolidate previous Acts. Part I refers to the control of the manufacture and importation of certain therapeutic substances which, at the time of the passing of the Act included vaccines, sera, toxins, anti-toxins and antigens, arsphenamine and analogous substances, insulin and posterior pituitary preparations.

A licence is required for the manufacture of these substances, but this does not apply to the preparation of any of these substances by a duly qualified medical practitioner, either for the individual use of one of his own patients, or on a request from another duly qualified practitioner for a similar purpose.

Part II of this Act applies to penicillin, streptomycin, aureomycin and chloramphenicol, isoniazid and salts thereof, erythromycin, neomycin, oxytetracycline, tetracycline, bacitracin, viomycin, polymyxins, or their salts, cortisone, hydrocortisone, or their esters, corticotrophin. Further substances may be added by Regulations from time to time.

The Act prohibits the sale, and dispensing or administration of these substances except by duly qualified medical practi-

* See Appendix D.

tioners, registered dental practitioners, veterinary surgeons or practitioners or persons acting in accordance with their directions.

A registered pharmaceutical chemist or authorized seller of poisons may sell or supply these substances on the authority of a prescription signed and dated by any of the above-mentioned persons.

The restrictions do not apply to sale or supply for certain specified purposes, including wholesale dealing, to a qualified medical practitioner and to a hospital clinic.

A prescription signed by a medical practitioner must not be dispensed more than once or more than three months after the date of signature, unless the prescription contains express directions as to the number of occasions or the intervals at which it may be dispensed.

Contravention of the Act is liable to penalties of a heavy fine (up to £100) or, on a second or subsequent conviction, fine or imprisonment, or both.

The Radioactive Substances Act, 1948

The purpose of this Act is to enable control of radioactive substances and certain apparatus producing radiation. There is prohibition of the sale or supply of radioactive substances, containing more than a prescribed quantity of a radioactive chemical element, intended for application to a human being, except by a medical practitioner or dentist specially licensed, or a pharmaceutical chemist acting on their prescriptions, or a person acting according to the directions of a licensed medical practitioner or dentist. Similar prohibitions apply to the administration of such substances by way of treatment. Applications for a licence are made to the Minister of Health or the Secretary of State for Scotland as appropriate. Restrictions as to the dispensing of prescriptions are similar to those under Part II of the Therapeutic Substances Act (q.v.).

The use of irradiating apparatus for treatment is restricted in a similar way to the persons licensed under the Act. It is also provided that the appropriate Minister may extend these restrictions to the use of such apparatus for diagnosis, but no such restriction has as yet been imposed.

The present position is that only those licensed may prescribe radioactive substances or use irradiating apparatus for treatment, but irradiating apparatus may be used by anyone for diagnosis.

The appropriate Minister has powers of inspection of premises, vehicles, etc., for the purpose of detecting offences against the Act which are punishable by fine or, in the case of a second or subsequent offence, fine or imprisonment or both.

22

ABORTION, STERILIZATION AND ARTIFICIAL INSEMINATION

Abortion

Section 58 of the Offences Against the Person Act, 1861, states that:

'Every woman, being with child, who with intent to procure her own miscarriage shall unlawfully administer to herself any poison or other noxious thing, or shall unlawfully use any instrument or other means whatsoever with the like intent and whosoever with intent to procure the miscarriage of any woman whether she be or be not with child shall unlawfully administer to her or cause to be taken by her any poison or other noxious thing, or shall unlawfully use any instrument or any other means whatsoever with the like intent, shall be guilty of felony and being convicted thereof shall be liable, at the discretion of the Court, to be kept in imprisonment for life.'

The words poison or noxious thing may be taken to mean anything which is given with intent to procure miscarriage and is not confined to the definition of Poisons in the Poisons List. Conviction is unlikely to follow, however, when substances not in the Poisons List are given in normal medicinal dosage which are unlikely to cause any harm.

The Infant Life (Preservation) Act, 1929, prohibits the destruction of a child before it has attained an independent existence but after it is viable, but provides that:

'No person shall be found guilty of an offence under this

section unless it is proved that the Act which caused the death of the child was not done in good faith for the purpose only of preserving the life of the mother.'

Decision as to the dividing line between preserving the life and preserving the health of the mother is extremely difficult and, it might well be held that it is the practitioner's duty to perform an abortion where failure to do so will seriously affect the mental or physical condition of the mother.

In the case of *Rex* v. *Bourne*, 1938, in which a practitioner carried out an abortion on a young girl who had been the victim of rape, it was allowed that an abortion considered necessary in the interests of the mother's mental health was lawful.

The law is not precise regarding therapeutic abortion, there being no statutory provision permitting it. The *Bourne* case has tended to clarify the matter to some extent. The institution of criminal proceedings is likely to depend upon the distinction between the proper practice of therapeutic medicine and the activities of the abortionist as such. The operative word in the 1861 Act is probably 'unlawfully', which was originally regarded as excluding from the provisions of the Act an abortion carried out in good faith to preserve the life of the mother. The *Bourne* case would seem to have extended this to preserving the mental or physical health of the mother. This places upon the doctor a deep responsibility to ensure that an abortion is carried out only when the continuance of the pregnancy is likely to endanger the life of the mother, or to lead to serious impairment of her mental or physical health.

Reasons of eugenics or the fact that the mother has been the victim of rape cannot by themselves justify abortion.

A practitioner faced with a situation of this sort should not take action, or advise abortion, without consultation with a practitioner of acknowledged high standing and, if in any doubt, with the secretary of his medical defence organization.

Consent by the patient to the abortion is no defence. The clinical indication for the abortion must be clear. Neither does consent by the patient vindicate in any way the practitioner's carrying out an abortion for eugenic or other non-clinical reasons.

A medical practitioner who contravenes the Act without good therapeutic reasons may expect a heavy sentence from the Courts, and erasure from the Medical Register.

A practitioner called to a patient upon whom he suspects a criminal abortion has been attempted or committed should, if her condition allows, as well as affording her all necessary medical care, endeavour to obtain from her a statement which may be used as evidence against the abortionist. It may be that all he can do is to obtain a dying declaration (q.v.), but if there is time he should consult his defence organization in order to protect himself. There is always the dangerous possibility of the practitioner called in being suspected of having performed the abortion. Glaister* advises calling in a colleague and a nurse or neighbour of the patient who will then be able to give evidence as to the onset of the abortion, especially if self-induced.

A general practitioner having a suspicion that a woman who consults him has a threatened or incomplete abortion as a consequence of the attentions of an abortionist should advise specialist treatment. Such patients are inclined to practise deception and concealment as to the cause of their bleeding, and a general practitioner may find himself caught up in a train of awkward circumstances if he endeavours to handle the case on his own.

The following resolutions published by the Royal College of Physicians in 1916, after taking legal opinions, serve as a useful guide to practitioners having to deal with a case of abortion:

'The College is of opinion:

1. That a moral obligation rests upon every medical practitioner to respect the confidence of his patients and that without her consent he is not justified in disclosing information obtained in the course of his professional attendance on her.

2. That every medical practitioner who is convinced that criminal abortion has been practised on his patient, should urge her, especially when she is likely to die, to make a

* *Medical Jurisprudence and Toxicology.* Glaister. E. and S. Livingstone Ltd., 9th edition, 1950.

statement which may be taken as evidence against the person who has performed the operation, provided always that her chances of recovery are not thereby prejudiced.

3. That in the event of her refusal to make such a statement, he is under no legal obligation (so the College is advised) to take further action, but he should continue to attend the patient to the best of his ability.

4. That before taking any action which may lead to legal proceedings, a medical practitioner will be wise to obtain the best medical and legal advice available, both to ensure that the patient's statement may have value as legal evidence, and to safeguard his own interest, since in the present state of the law there is no certainty that he will be protected against subsequent litigation.

5. That if the patient should die, he should refuse to give a certificate of the cause of death, and should communicate with the Coroner.'

Under Section 59 of the Offences Against the Person Act, 1861, procuring or supplying poisons or instruments for procuring a miscarriage is regarded as a misdemeanour, and the Pharmacy and Medicines Act, 1941 (Section 9), prohibits the advertisement of goods in terms calculated to lead to their use in procuring a miscarriage except where it can be shown that the advertisement was published only in a technical publication intended principally for medical practitioners, nurses, pharmaceutical chemists and the like.

Child Destruction

A child carried by a mother who is proved to be twenty-eight weeks pregnant or more is normally presumed to be capable of being born alive. The Infant Life (Preservation) Act of 1929 lays down that the destruction of such a child is a felony. It is not so, however, if the destruction is effected by an act which is done in good faith solely for the purpose of preserving the life of the mother.

Infanticide (Infanticide Act, 1938), Concealment of Birth (Offences Against the Person Act, 1861, Section 60) and the causing of an infant's death by overlying while under the influence of drink (Children and Young Persons Act, 1933) are covered by the Acts mentioned. The Infanticide Act, 1938, takes account of the woman whose balance of mind is disturbed but in the opinion of some does not provide for the possibility of her being treated as a sick person rather than being brought to trial.

Sterilization

As reported in the Annual Report of the Medical Defence Union for 1948, consideration was given by the Union to the legal and ethical position of practitioners approached by patients with a request for sterilization. The defence bodies sought the opinion of Counsel on the matter. The opinion given was that sterilization on eugenic grounds alone is illegal, but that it is not so if there are therapeutic reasons. Such reasons are that there are present conditions which, if sterilization is not performed, may imperil the health and/or life of the patient. A practitioner in whatever branch of the profession should therefore satisfy himself as to the conditions, before either advising or performing an operation or other procedure for this purpose, just as he must in the case of a therapeutic abortion. A decision to undertake such an operation should not be taken without a confirmatory second opinion and the written consent of the patient, given in full understanding of the nature of the operation and of its irreversible consequences. The patient's written consent is a *sine qua non* and an advisable additional precaution is that of the patient's spouse. The spouse probably has no right to forbid the patient to undergo sterilization, but it is wise to seek the patient's permission to consult his or her spouse.

A practitioner having doubts as to the legality of performing the operation is advised to consult the secretary of his medical defence organization.

Sterilization of the Male

There is no direct authority in law on the question of whether sterilization of the male is legal or illegal. It has been stated by a learned Judge (*Stephen's Digest of Criminal Law*) that castration is mayhem.

Cases have occurred in English law in which persons have been found guilty of a criminal offence for allowing themselves to be maimed in order to avoid work or duty. In 1604 a man persuaded a companion to cut off his left hand so that he could in future avoid work and beg instead. Both the man and his companion were found guilty. Lord Justice Denning has indicated (*Bravery* v. *Bravery*, 1954) that he would regard sterilization of the male performed for the sole purpose of avoiding parenthood, there being no medical reason for such avoidance, as being in the same category and therefore illegal. He stated that in his view sterilization for a just cause is lawful, when performed with the man's consent, but in the absence of a just cause it is unlawful whether or not consent is given. It seems likely that the Courts would always take a similar view.

There is no certainty that the Courts would decide that an operation for sterilization is a legal operation in every instance. There is, however, probably little or nothing to fear from the performance of such an operation where there are sound therapeutic reasons for it as for example the preservation of the man's health or the danger of transmission of disease to the offspring.

The Roman Catholic View on Abortion and Sterilization

Abortion

Therapeutic abortion and sterilization are regarded by Roman Catholics as wrong not because the Church forbids them, but because they offend against the natural law of God. A hospital doctor is not obliged to resign his position because such operations are performed in the hospital, but no Roman Catholic may perform these operations. If called upon to give an anaesthetic to a patient for the purpose of such an operation, he need not refuse if he allows it to be known that he has religious objections to the operation and knows that the operation would be performed in any case.

The Canon Law of the Roman Catholic Church states that all who effectively procure abortion, the mother included, incur excommunication reserved to the ordinary (Canon 2350 (1)). All who perpetrate voluntary homicide and who effectively procure abortion of a human foetus and all who co-operate thereto incur criminal irregularity (Canon 985.40). The Canon Law makes no distinction between a viable foetus and one that is not viable, and the law includes being a party to the abortion.

Therapeutic abortion is explicitly condemned by the

decree of the Holy Office of July 24th, 1895. Craniotomy and embryotomy were also condemned. Bonnar in *The Catholic Doctor* states that in cases of rape the extraction of semen before conception has taken place, said to be before ten hours have elapsed, is permissible.

Sterilization

The Roman Catholic Church regards sterilization as a serious mutilation of the human body. The teaching is that it is wrong and never permissible, with the exception that it is permissible when medically necessary as a remedy for a serious or fatal condition. Sterilization to prevent a pregnancy which may be expected to bring dangers is not accepted by the Roman Catholic Church as permissible.

Artificial Insemination

Artificial Insemination by Husband (A.I.H.)

The practitioner asked to carry out artificial insemination will be faced with no particular legal problems if the donor is to be the husband.

The Roman Catholic Church has been said to permit artificial insemination only so long as it is insemination from the post-coital vaginal pool. Any other method of artificial insemination whether from the husband or an outside donor is considered by the Roman Catholic Church to be 'immoral and absolutely illicit'.

Artificial Insemination by Donor (A.I.D.)

Precautions are, however, necessary if the donor is someone other than the husband. The doctor will be wise in the first place to recommend the fullest investigation of both wife and husband in order to ensure that all possibility of a normal conception has been excluded. This being done he should explain to both parties the nature of the insemination so that it is fully understood. The legal implications should also be explained, although this is by no means easy. There is as yet no legal guidance as to the position with regard to grounds for divorce, either by the husband of the patient, or by the wife of the donor if he happens to be a married man. Nor is the position of the doctor clear. He might be cited in divorce proceedings which conceivably might lead to action being taken by the General Medical Council.

In the absence of any pronouncement on the subject the medical ethics of carrying out such a procedure must presumably be a matter for the doctor's individual conscience.

Any doctor contemplating advising a patient to undergo A.I.D. may find it helpful to seek the advice of his medical defence organization, in order that he may know in advance the up-to-date legal and ethical implications.

Being satisfied that all is understood the practitioner should obtain a request and consent signed by both husband and wife. It is strongly advised that the identity of the donor is not disclosed to either party, nor should the identity of the parents be disclosed to the donor. The fullest secrecy should be observed and at the same time the fullest care in selection of donor. The possibilities of innocent disregard of all conventions by A.I.D. are staggering. Conceptions can occur which would never occur by the operations of nature. There are the later dangers of unsuspected consanguineous marriages involving individuals conceived by A.I.D.

Legitimacy

It remains to be seen what legal complications may ensue. It is a presumption in English law that a child born in marriage is legitimate. This presumption can be set aside if it can be proved that it was impossible for the husband to have been the father, by reason, for example, of impotence or absence at the material time. Already in America it has been authoritatively stated, that a child born as a result of A.I.D. is illegitimate whether with or without the husband's consent. The possibilities of legal adoption, however, may be the means of overcoming this difficulty.

Nullity and Divorce

It has usually been held that the birth of a child in wedlock was evidence of consummation. Since the introduction of artificial insemination, however, it is possible that, though the offspring remains legitimate (i.e. A.I.H.), the parents' marriage can subsequently be annulled on the grounds that it has never been consummated, even though the donor is the husband.

A child may be conceived by A.I.D., but even if it can be proved that the husband was not the father, there is nothing in English law which defines the act of A.I.D. as adultery. Nevertheless some authorities would regard it as coming within this definition. It seems probable that if the husband had consented to the procedure he could not thereafter obtain a divorce on the grounds of adultery, for it was carried out with his consent or connivance. Lord Wheatley, a Judge of the Court of Session, reached the conclusion (*Maclennan* v *Shortland or Maclennan* 10. i. 58) that artificial insemination did not come within the definition of sexual intercourse as understood by Scots law. He ruled in the case that A.I.D. without her husband's consent was not adultery on the part of the wife.

A request from a single woman for artificial insemination should be treated with care. There is always the possibility that an apparently altruistic display of the maternal instinct covers some hidden motive of lesser quality, such as the forcing of a marriage on a man.

23

MEDICAL DEFENCE AND ALLIED MATTERS

Even apart from its vast clinical field the content of general practice is very wide and very full. By the very frequency of their occurrence a number of problems are familiar. Other problems and situations, however, present themselves only occasionally and the answers to them do not come so readily to mind.

In the following three chapters information and guidance will be found on a number of unrelated matters, any one of which may at some time or other present a problem to the doctor in general practice.

Medical Defence

The most fleeting contemplation of the nature of medical practice, in whatever form, should be sufficient to awaken any doctor to a realization of the legal hazards which surround him in his daily work. What is so surprising is that there are always a few doctors who seem careless of the dangers involved and take no steps to ensure in advance that, when trouble comes, whether after days or after years of practice, they can call to their aid and protection the services of a medical defence organization. These organizations are, in fact, an insurance to protect the reputation and the pocket for not only do they offer advice and give assistance in combating accusations and accusations against their members but also provide legal defence and pay the damages. The organizations do not, of course, undertake to foot the bill in every case and they reserve the right to act in their member's defence only in those cases in which they decide it is fitting and proper to do so. In other words, they will normally come to the aid of a member in the fullest possible manner when he is in trouble which arises from the usual hazards of practice, but membership does not give a free hand to a doctor to misbehave in the certain knowledge that, whatever his actions or misdemeanours, his defence organization will rally to his side and pay up. Defence organizations have always shown themselves to be more than reasonable and will always help where it is at all possible and proper for them to do so.

The British Medical Association objects to any requirement by an employing body that a doctor employed by them shall be a member of a professional organization, but makes the one exception that it takes no objection to a requirement that a doctor should belong to a medical defence organization, thus emphasizing its view of the importance of such membership.

The defence organizations will assist a doctor only in professional matters and not in matters arising in other contexts. Even so the range of these professional matters is wide, from the accusation of negligence or wrong treatment accompanying refusal to pay an account to a charge of unprofessional conduct laid before the General Medical Council. Numerous examples of the wide range of services provided by the defence organizations are to be found in their annual reports.

All doctors are strongly urged to join a defence organization immediately on qualifying and to maintain their membership all through their professional life. At the first sign of trouble, on the first inkling of an accusation, the secretary of the organization should be informed and his advice acted upon. As is mentioned elsewhere and cannot sufficiently be emphasized a threatening or accusing letter, for example, should be acknowledged formally only and be forwarded immediately to the secretary for advice and instructions. Long experience has shown that any attempt by a doctor to deal with the matter by himself, without advice, seriously hampers the subsequent handling of the matter by the defence organization and may ruin the chances of a successful outcome. An unhappy choice of words in a doctor's home-composed reply may play right into the hands of his accuser, and his letter may subsequently and disastrously be used against him.

It is nowadays quite normal for partnership and assistantship agreements to include a clause requiring all the parties to belong to a defence organization. As partners in a partnership are responsible collectively for the actions of one of them and as a principal is responsible for the actions of his assistant, such a provision should be a *sine qua non* to any such arrangement. Similarly it is wise for a doctor to ensure that any person he employs as a locum tenens is a member, in benefit, of one of the defence organizations. The benefits of membership of a defence organization are obtainable for a modest annual subscription. There are three such organizations in the United Kingdom and their names and addresses are as follows:

The Medical Defence Union, Tavistock House, South, Tavistock Square, London, W.C.1.

The Medical Protection Society, Victory House, Leicester Square, London, W.C.2.

The Medical and Dental Defence Union of Scotland, 105 St Vincent Street, Glasgow, C.2.

Libel and Slander

An indiscreet remark or expression of opinion, either by word of mouth or written in a certificate or report, may lay a practitioner open to an action for damages for slander or libel. So also may he be the subject of defamatory statements from others who criticize him or give expression to some grudge they bear against him.

The essential feature of defamation which is actionable is that damage is threatened or done to a man's reputation. Libel is a defamatory statement in writing or other visible form, and is a criminal offence if sufficiently gross. Slander is not a criminal offence, but may be a misdemeanour and is committed by word of mouth or gesture.

As to what is and what is not defamation requires a considerable research into legal rulings. Abusive language and untrue statements which, while possibly damaging, yet do not cause a loss of reputation, are distinguished in law from defamation.

To be actionable a defamatory statement must have been made or brought to the notice of a third person, even if made 'in confidence'. A defamatory statement made to a wife about her husband may be actionable, as may be also a statement dictated to a secretary. In view of this, there will be occasions when a statement possibly defamatory to the person to whom it is addressed is better written by the practitioner himself.

The fact that a statement can be proved to be true may be used as a defence for, though a defamation, it is not actionable if it is true. Nevertheless, such a defence is a possible danger, as if the action is lost the defence itself may be held to be an aggravation of the defamation and result in heavier damages.

Statements made by a practitioner in the course of judicial proceedings or preparation for them are protected by absolute privilege and cannot be regarded as actionable. Absolute privilege probably applies to statements made before the Disciplinary Committee of the General Medical Council.

Another form of privilege is known as qualified privilege. Simply expressed this is a privilege covering a statement made, by reason of a legal or moral duty, to someone who has a similar duty to receive it. If the statement can be shown to be actuated by malice the qualified privilege will no longer obtain. What constitutes a duty in this respect is a question which can usually only be decided on the merits of the particular case and is certainly not one to be decided by a practitioner himself. He should seek the guidance of his medical defence organization before making any statement which may conceivably come in this category. Similarly he should seek advice should he believe himself to be the subject of an actionable defamation, for it may prove to have been made in circumstances covered by qualified privilege.

The wise guidance of his defence organization, based upon experience of many cases and a detailed knowledge of the many intricacies of the law of defamation, will prove of the utmost value to a practitioner, and may well save him from making matters worse by gaining greater publicity for the alleged defamation.

The above statement of the law applies equally in Scotland subject to the following differences:

(1) The distinction between libel (written defamation) and slander (oral defamation) is not of importance. Both are classified under the general name of defamation.

(2) To be actionable the defamation must be untrue.

(3) Defamation, no matter how gross, is never a criminal

offence with one exception under the Representation of the People Act, 1949.

(4) To be defamatory it is not essential that a statement be published to a third party. An action will lie for injured feelings though reflecting damages of lesser amount than if the statement had been published to third parties. A statement, however, is not published merely by being dictated to a secretary or, in the case of a telegram, being read by Post Office officials.

Abusive Letters

The receipt of an abusive letter, either anonymous or signed, is an annoyance to a practitioner, but it is doubtful whether, in the majority of instances, it is worth his while to initiate action. If in doubt his medical defence organization will offer him suitable advice on this point. Such a letter can be held to be a criminal libel especially if expressed in terms which would denigrate the practitioner in the mind of an average person.

Medical Records, Radiological and Pathology Reports and X-ray Films

A doctor should always bear in mind the wisdom, and sometimes the necessity, of keeping clinical records about his patients. Apart from the obvious advantages to the conduct of his clinical practice and the usefulness to a colleague who succeeds him in the treatment of the patient or acts as locum tenens in his practice, he never knows when he will be required to give evidence in a Court of any kind as to the patient's health, for example before and after an injury. The advisability of adequate records demonstrates itself also in other contexts besides injury where evidence of health before some occurrence is called for. The doctor will cut a sorry figure in Court if he is unable to give useful evidence because of his omission to record his findings at any material time. The use of records in Court is referred to on page 103 and the requirements regarding record keeping, under the terms of service of general practitioners in the National Health Service, are set down on p. 238.

Medical case notes made in private practice should be regarded as being the property of the doctor compiling them, whether in general practice or in specialist practice (including in private nursing homes and pay beds in hospitals). The specialist will, of course, pass on his views and recommendations to the family doctor, possibly with copies of reports of investigations.

Case notes made in a general ward of a hospital are the property of the Hospital Management Committee, but the usual exchanges of information between specialist and general practitioner take place. Access to the notes are permitted to doctors concerned with the treatment of the patient and to any persons authorized by the Hospital Management Committee. They are normally not made available to any person or body outside the hospital without the consent of the patient and the concurrence of the doctor concerned.

The medical record cards in general practice in the National Health Service are the property of the Ministry of Health or of the Secretary of State for Scotland. The patient has no right to see them or retain them. They are handled only by the general practitioner himself and by officials of the Executive Councils concerned. The notes are passed, through the Executive Council, from one doctor to another when the patient changes his doctor.

X-ray Films

There is no precedent in the Courts declaring who is the owner of an X-ray film. Medical opinion would regard the proper owner of the film as being the radiologist (or, in the case of a hospital, the hospital). Where a fee is paid by the patient, perhaps it could be held that the fee is paid for an opinion and that the film remains the property of the radiologist, as being a part of the evidence on which the opinion is formed. Cases have been decided in the American Courts to the effect that the film is the property of the radiologist.

It seems likely that should a case arise the Courts would hold that it was customary for the films to be retained by the radiologist and must be regarded as his property. He might hand them over to the general practitioner, but the patient would have no claim on them. They would probably be regarded as part and parcel of the clinical record and notes. In the absence of an express contract to the contrary, it seems likely that the usual custom of retention by the radiologist would constitute ownership.

It is the view of the British Medical Association that a radiograph taken in a hospital is the property of the hospital. Neither the radiograph nor the report should be passed to any other person without the consent of the hospital, the radiologist and the patient. The same general considerations should apply also when a radiograph is taken by a radiologist acting as a private practitioner. When a patient is referred to the hospital for investigation and treatment, or to a private radiologist, then it must be assumed that a report may be passed to the patient's own doctor.

A radiologist may be subpoenaed to appear in Court and give evidence as to his findings, but he should not disclose his findings to others without the consent of the patient unless he is subpoenaed. Frequently a radiologist is called upon to undertake an examination specifically for legal purposes, in which case he will be expected, if he accepts the case, to provide a report and to give evidence in Court if asked to do so.

Reports on Pathological Examinations

The same considerations apply to reports on pathological examinations as apply to radiological examinations and reports.

The Administration of Anaesthetics

The responsibilities of a general practitioner in the National Health Service concerning the provision of an anaesthetic for a patient under his care and the procedure for claiming fees, are referred to in Chapter 26. Here are set out general considerations for any doctor called upon to administer an anaesthetic.

All practitioners are trained in the administration of anaesthetics but, as in other branches of medicine, a practitioner is not bound to attempt or undertake anaesthetic procedures which are beyond his competence. Should he elect to do so he might be held responsible for any untoward consequences. The dangers to himself of assuming such responsibilities will, of course, be mitigated if he has had to do so in an emergency when more expert help was not available. In coming to the decision he must be the judge of his own competence, but if he over-reaches himself and attempts too much his action may well come to be judged by others after the event. He must take into account the possible lessening of his skill due to being out of practice in the art of anaesthesia.

Consent

Having decided to administer the anaesthetic, the practitioner should, before proceeding, ensure that the patient has consented to the administration, which consent is not necessarily to be assumed because the patient has consented to submit to an operation. The consent form used in hospitals often contains the additional phrase 'for which I understand an anaesthetic is necessary'. It is normally unwise for the same practitioner to anaesthetise and operate, and always unwise to administer an anaesthetic unless someone else is present.

Precautions

His clinical training will have made him aware of the necessity for examining the patient in order to assess his fitness for the administration and of satisfying himself that the patient has an empty stomach and is suitably prepared. If he considers that the administration of an anaesthetic constitutes a special risk owing to the unfitness of the patient, he should discuss the matter with the surgeon and, if it is decided that for surgical reasons the operation must be proceeded with, the relatives should be warned. The anaesthetist may withdraw from the case and ask, for example, that the services of a more experienced anaesthetist should be obtained.

He must satisfy himself that the apparatus is in working order and correctly assembled, with special regard to the contents of the cylinders and their correct coupling. He must ensure, by careful checking, that he is using the drug he intends to use. He should be constantly on guard against such dangers as injuries by gags, including those hot from the steriliser, the swallowing or inhaling of foreign bodies, including dentures, the possibility of other injuries to an unconscious patient, burns, overdose and asphyxia. Equally thorough precautions are called for in the administration of local anaesthetics, the needles being carefully examined so as to reduce to a minimum the possibility of breakage.

The protection of the patient from damage (e.g. anaesthetic agents in liquid form on skin or mucous membranes) and precaution against explosions are part of the anaesthetist's training and should ever be borne in mind. While legally no part of his responsibility, it is as well that he should ascertain beforehand which side is to be operated upon (e.g. which eye, which limb, which tooth) and warn the surgeon in good time if he appears to be starting to operate on the wrong side.

Sometimes packs placed in the throat by the operator may give rise to trouble. The anaesthetist must, of course, do whatever is in the interest of the patient should any difficulty arise from this cause. In general, however, it is probably wiser to persuade the operator to remove the swab rather than for the anaesthetist to incur a joint responsibility for any harm by interfering with it himself.

All deaths occurring under anaesthesia, including those after the administration has ceased, are reported to the Coroner. An anaesthetist who has the misfortune to preside over such an event is advised to report the matter to the Coroner, and in any case to give all the information to the Coroner should he ask for it.

The wise practitioner will approach the administration of every anaesthetic with a personal discipline or routine which will enable him to give satisfactory answers, should the need arise, on the series of points listed in *Taylor's Principles and Practice of Medical Jurisprudence**. These relate to the necessity for the anaesthetic and the suitability to the circumstances of the method chosen, proper and full prior examination of the patient, contra-indications, preparation, care in administration, the type, amount and duration of the anaesthesia, the immediate availability, at hand, of all resuscitative methods, and the measures adopted if danger should threaten.

The Choice of the Anaesthetist

The normal custom is for the choice of anaesthetist to rest with the surgeon who is to do the operation. The patient's own doctor has no right to insist on giving the anaesthetic himself but he can reasonably expect the surgeon to extend to him the

* *Taylor's Principles and Practice of Medical Jurisprudence*. J. and A. Churchill. 11th Edition, 1957, p. 72.

courtesy of an invitation to be present at the operation. It is hardly practicable to extend this courtesy in respect of operations on hospital patients. Long operating lists make it difficult to predict the exact time of the operation and the general practitioner is unlikely to be able to leave his work for a long enough period to attend, possibly at some distance. If, however, he should inform the surgeon of his wish to attend he will usually be invited to do so if mutually convenient arrangements can be made.

Attempted Suicide

The practitioner called in to treat a patient whose condition suggests an attempted suicide will often be very exercised in his mind as to what is the best and correct course to adopt. The doctor is bound as a citizen to aid the law, but when a doctor/patient relationship has been entered into the situation of the doctor is different. He has his duty to the patient. His duty may well extend beyond the immediate treatment of the injuries or poisoning for he may judge that it is necessary to take steps to protect the patient against his own further attempt. If the patient is deemed to require care and supervision in the home the relatives should be so informed and the duty handed over to them. In this there is likely to be involved some infringement of strict professional secrecy, but a reasonable degree of disclosure may well be justified in order to ensure that the patient has necessary care and supervision. Alternatively, the mental welfare officer could be asked to arrange admission for observation in an observation ward or mental hospital.

If none of the above solutions apply or if the patient is likely to die then the authorities should be notified, the proper authority being the local Superintendent of Police.

The question as to whether, in a particular case, his public duty in respect of the criminal law transcends his duty of professional secrecy must be decided by the practitioner according to his conscience. The advice of a colleague will always be of help. He must consider what is in the public good and what is in his patient's interest and he may well decide that the latter is best served by a suitable warning to the relatives. If death follows the attempt he will, of course, ensure that the Coroner is made aware of the circumstances.

The Views of the Roman Catholic Church on Various Matters of Medical Importance

Caesarean Section

The Roman Catholic Church considers that the operation of Caesarean Section, when a pregnant woman is gravely ill, should only be done when vaginal delivery constitutes a serious hazard to the woman's life or to the life of the child. If the woman seems certain to die uterine baptism may be carried out if possible. If the woman dies and the foetus is alive, post-mortem section should be performed and the foetus baptized either absolutely or conditionally. The head or other presenting part should be baptized (see Chapter 16).

Euthanasia

The Church disapproves entirely of euthanasia.

Leucotomy and Electro-Convulsive Therapy

Leucotomy and electro-convulsive therapy are special treatments which may alter personality. The Roman Catholic Church disapproves of altering personality and, therefore, these treatments are allowed only for grave reasons. The matter is left to the conscience of the Catholic doctor who is advised to act only when there are strong positive indications in accordance with the best neuro-psychiatric teaching.

Other Matters

The views of the Roman Catholic Church on professional secrecy, baptism, bequest of eyes, artificial insemination and sterilization are to be found under those headings.

24

SOME OTHER PROFESSIONAL ACTIVITIES

Appointed Factory Doctors

A general practitioner may obtain an appointment as Appointed Factory Doctor for an area. Vacant appointments are normally advertised in the medical press and are made by the Chief Inspector of Factories, Ministry of Labour and National Service, under the Factories Act, 1948.

The duties include the carrying out of certain statutory medical examinations, particularly in regard to young persons employed in industry and workers engaged in certain dangerous processes. The Appointed Factory Doctor is required to investigate and report on certain cases of gassing and certain industrial diseases. He may also act for the Ministry of Pensions and National Insurance in connexion with claims for Industrial Injury Benefit under the National Insurance (Industrial Injuries) Act, 1946.

Fees are payable for the work done on an item of service basis according to an agreed scale, paid by the employer in the factory concerned.

The work of Appointed Factory Doctors is supervised by Medical Inspectors who act under the Chief Inspector of Factories. In large industrial concerns employing whole-time Industrial Medical Officers the Medical Officer is often the Appointed Factory Doctor.

Fees

The law does not recognize that a medical colleague or his family can expect to be treated free, though the time-honoured custom of giving free treatment to a widow and family of a colleague has been recognized in at least one Court case.*

With free medical treatment being available to all the community under the National Health Service, these considerations are to some extent obsolete. Nevertheless, now and again, it will be found for various reasons that treatment is recommended outside the National Health Service. The practitioner is advised to inform the widow of a practitioner if he intends to charge, so that she may go elsewhere to obtain treatment free of charge if she so wishes. Occasionally, in the past, practitioners have chosen to treat certain medical auxiliaries without charge. There has never been any entitlement to free treatment for such persons and in any case this point is also obsolescent.

In treating a fee-paying patient it is not often that the amount of a fee is agreed beforehand or even discussed. A patient applying for private treatment will expect to be charged and will be expected to pay reasonable fees. If the practitioner has to sue for his fees at some later date, he is unlikely to obtain the full amount if the amount charged is not reasonable. The practitioner has no right to put a patient to expense, for example, for some expensive examination or for the paid services of a consultant, without ensuring that the patient knows firstly that he will have to pay and secondly that he has some idea of what amount is involved.

Sometimes the submission of a bill to a patient is followed by a claim for negligence. The practitioner faced with this situation should make no attempt to reply to a charge, except to send a formal acknowledgment of the letter, but he should place the correspondence in the hands of his medical defence organization.

There is a presumption in law that medical practitioners give their services for payment. Therefore, they are entitled to claim in the Courts reasonable fees. Under the National Health Service payment direct by the patient to the practitioner is not permitted and the point does not arise. This presumption, nevertheless, still remains where there is not some other contractual basis such as the National Health Service.

In the days before the National Health Service, difficulty was sometimes encountered because in emergency a third party

* *Corbin* v. *Stewart* (1911), 28 T.L.R. 99.

had called in the doctor, who gave necessary treatment and was subsequently denied payment by the patient on the ground that he had not attended on the patient's authority or request. Arrangements for emergency treatment under the National Health Service have largely caused the disappearance of this difficulty, and thus it is not one likely to be encountered except rarely.

Road Traffic Act, 1934

There is special provision, however, in the case of treatment rendered in a road accident. The Road Traffic Act, 1934, gives a medical practitioner summoned in an emergency to treat a person injured in a motor accident the right to a fee (see Appendix F). The fee is recoverable from the user of the car and the claim must be made within seven days. It is only payable to the first practitioner to render treatment. He may claim by word of mouth at the time of the accident or, failing that, by submitting his claim in writing to the user of the vehicle by hand or by registered letter, stating his name and address, the circumstances and the fact that he was the first to give treatment.

Sometimes, in the press of the circumstances, a practitioner more concerned with the care of his patient may omit to ascertain the identity of the user of the car. Should this happen he can always remedy the oversight by obtaining information from the local police. In order to qualify for a fee under this Act the treatment must be immediately required. Payment has been successfully resisted by an insurance company in a case in which the practitioner was not called in for treatment until the patient had been conveyed home, involving a lapse of time.

It frequently happens that, in a road accident, more than one person is found to require treatment. A fee may be claimed for each person examined and treated in this way.

General practitioners in the National Health Service are not debarred under their terms of service from claiming and accepting fees under this heading.

A doctor even well away from his practice may witness the results of a motor accident. Humanity demands that he should render assistance unless he is satisfied that other assistance is at hand. The International Code of Ethics (see Chapter 7) states that a doctor must give necessary treatment in an emergency, unless he is assured that it can and will be given by another. If, however, he chooses to pass the accident by he cannot be deemed to feel in any obligation to the patient. Should he go to the patient's assistance, a doctor/patient relationship is at once established and he is under obligation to render all possible treatment to the patient (see also Chapter 15).

Services Rendered to the Police

A practitioner may at any time be called in by the police to examine and report upon a person charged, or liable to be charged, with various offences or witnesses or victims of the offence. The types of case likely to be encountered are common assault, sexual offences, murder, manslaughter, committing grievous bodily harm and being drunk or under the influence of drink or drugs while in charge of a motor vehicle. In addition, there may be required by the police confirmation of death, a report on injuries, an opinion on the cause of death, medical assistance in the execution of duty or examination of or emergency treatment to a prisoner confined in the cells. Minimum fees for these services are laid down by the British Medical Association. Emergency treatment to a patient taken ill in the street will normally fall under the emergency arrangements under the National Health Service but, where the police call a practitioner who is not in the National Health Service, a fee may be charged to the patient or the police. Full particulars of the entitlement to fees for general practitioners in the National Health Service are to be found on p. 247.

The risk of being called in by the police in these circumstances is ever present, and practitioners would be wise to arm themselves against such an eventuality by ensuring a sound knowledge of the special points of evidence to be looked for, and without which an opinion cannot be formed. The evidence and opinion of the practitioner will frequently be required later in the Courts. A study of a textbook on Forensic Medicine will provide practitioners with a sound foreknowledge of the requirements and is to be regarded as essential.

Persons in Custody

Distinction should be made between an apprehended person and a prisoner. An apprehended person may only be examined with his consent and the doctor must not disclose the findings to the police or anyone else without the person's consent.

A practitioner called upon to examine a person who is in custody should, therefore, before proceeding, ascertain whether or not that person is in custody before conviction or after conviction. If before conviction, examination should not take place without his consent. In obtaining the consent, the practitioner should inform the individual of his right to refuse and also of the fact that his report may be used against him at trial. It is a wise precaution to have a reliable witness to this consent.

If the individual is a prisoner already convicted his consent to examination is not necessary. All that is required is an order by the authority in charge of the prisoner.

It occasionally happens that a patient is detained at a police station following a road accident, or on suspicion of being under the influence of alcohol or drugs and in charge of a motor vehicle. Normally this patient will be examined by the police surgeon, but he is entitled to refuse the examination and to ask that his own medical adviser should be called to conduct his examination and report on him.

The practitioner should record his findings and his assessment of the patient's appreciation of the circumstances. He should note also the time at which the examination is made. All this should be done at the time of the examination, but no comment or opinion should be made to any police officer. He should record in the police station book no more than a statement that he has examined the patient, with the time and date. He will, of course, address himself to the task of determining whether the patient is ill, or under the influence of alcohol, or both. The practitioner should inform the patient of his findings and obtain his consent before disclosing them to the police authorities, pointing out to him the implications of so doing.

A difficulty will arise if, by the time the practitioner arrives, the patient is found to be unconscious. If he has sent for the doctor it is reasonable to assume that he would have consented to an ordinary clinical examination, but withdrawal of blood for a blood alcohol estimation is not advised in these circumstances.

Nursing Homes

The Public Health Act, 1936 (Sections 187–195), requires registration with the County Council or County Borough Council of all nursing homes by the person who carries on the home. The authority has powers of inspection and may lay down certain records that are to be kept. Ordinary hospitals and mental institutions are excluded, but otherwise a nursing home is held to be any premises for the reception and nursing of the sick, including also maternity homes. Exemption may be granted to Christian Science nursing homes and hospitals or institutions not carried on for profit. For the ethical relationships of doctors to nursing homes, see Chapter 10.

Venereal Disease

The Venereal Diseases Act, 1917, lays down that only registered medical practitioners may treat venereal disease for reward, or prescribe any remedy or give any advice in connexion with treatment of a venereal disease.

Any offer of treatment by advertisement or any claim regarding prevention or treatment in any way is prohibited.

Regulations made under the N.H.S. Acts order that Board of Governors and Regional Hospital Boards shall take all necessary steps to secure that any information obtained by officers of the Board with respect to persons examined or treated for venereal disease, shall be treated as confidential.

To state or write falsely that a person is suffering or has suffered from venereal disease is actionable, but a statement to a solicitor, in connexion with inquiries relating to legal proceedings, that a person has venereal disease is protected by absolute privilege. If true, such a statement made in other circumstances where it may be considered clearly warranted (as, for example, for the protection of some other person) may well be a breach of professional confidence but is likely to be regarded as defensible by a Court as being a moral duty.

The most likely occasions in the Courts to concern a doctor are cases of divorce and nullity. If it is shown that a petitioner contracted venereal disease from the partner during marriage, then this is normally accepted as a presumption of adultery. In nullity cases, evidence may be required of a doctor to show that the respondent had venereal disease at the time of marriage. Clearly, therefore, careful notes should always be kept. Disclosure should never be made without the written consent of the patient. It is likely that a subpoena will be issued to the doctor and in Court he is likely to be required to disclose what is within his knowledge. This raises what is really an undecided conflict between the statutory rules of secrecy in cases of venereal disease and the demands of a Court of Law. It seems probable, however, that the requirements of a Court of Law will always be held to overrule the regulations.

Veterinary Work

A medical practitioner is not permitted to practise veterinary surgery or medicine without being qualified to do so, and registered as a veterinary surgeon or practitioner. His name must appear in the Register of Veterinary Surgeons or in the Supplementary Veterinary Register.

The specific circumstances in which it is permissible for one not so registered to give treatment to animals are as follows:

(1) Treatment to an animal given by its owner or a member of his household, or his employee.

(2) Treatment to an agricultural animal by a farmer or agricultural worker ('a person engaged in agriculture') so long as the treatment is not given for reward.

(3) First-aid in emergency to save life or to relieve pain.

(4) Destruction of any animal by a painless method.

(5) Castration of certain young animals.

(6) Tailing a lamb, docking a dog's tail or removing its dew claws before its eyes are open.

Vivisection

Under The Cruelty to Animals Act, 1876, vivisection may only be carried out under licence which is obtained from the Home Office, and if granted bears the signature of the Home Secretary. Licences are not easy to obtain. The application requires the endorsement of two eminent medical men in high positions. The applicant is required to state the precise nature of experiments it is proposed to conduct and the kind of knowledge he hopes to attain as a result. The work must be

25

THE DOCTOR AND SOME OTHER PUBLIC SERVICES

Adoption

Adoption of children is effected in accordance with the Adoption Act, 1950, which for Scotland still preserves certain former differences, and the Adoption of Children (Northern Ireland) Act, 1950. In Jersey the procedure is governed by Adoption of Children (Jersey) Law, 1947, though the remainder of the Channel Islands are not covered by any adoption law. The Isle of Man has an adoption law based on a former British Act.

Adoption may be carried out through an adoption society whose work is usually concerned with finding a child for would-be adopters, or through the children's officer of the Local Authority, who, having responsibility for a child, is concerned with finding suitable adopters.

An adoption order is irrevocable and deprives the natural parents of all rights in respect of the maintenance and upbringing of the child. Although a baby may be placed, with a view to adoption, at birth, yet the mother cannot give legal consent until it is six weeks' old.

Under the Adoption of Children Rules the guardian *ad litem*, appointed to watch over the interests of the child, is required to investigate all circumstances relevant to the proposed adoption, including whether either of the prospective adopters suffers or has suffered from any serious illness and whether there is any history of tuberculosis, epilepsy or mental illness in their families.

Under the Adoption Societies Regulations adoption societies are required to obtain a medical report on the child, signed by a duly qualified medical practitioner. The form of report is to be found in a Schedule to the Regulations. The medical examination and report are not required to be made or issued free of charge under the National Health Service.

The following is a list of some of the adoption societies. In addition adoptions are arranged by many local societies, religious and other bodies:

The Church Adoption Society, 4a Bloomsbury Square, London, W.C.1.

The National Adoption Society, 47a Manchester Street, London, W.1.

The National Children Adoption Association, 71 Knightsbridge, London, S.W.1.

The National Vigilance Association of Scotland, 262 Renfrew Street, Glasgow.

The Scottish Association for the Adoption of Children, Child Welfare Department, Johnston Terrace, Edinburgh.

Boarded Out Children

Regulations regarding Boarded out Children are made under the Childrens Act, 1948. A useful Memorandum on this subject is issued by H.M. Stationery Office.

The Regulations require that there shall be a medical examination and a report in writing on the physical and mental condition of the child before boarding out. The examination must be within three months before the boarding out, except in an emergency. The Local Authority, or organization concerned, expresses an opinion as to the child's suitability for boarding out and the medical practitioner is not required to do so.

Boarded out children must be medically examined at least once a year. The examination is arranged by the Local Authority and, as in the initial instance, a written report on the physical and mental condition is called for. If the child is under two years, or is boarded out in emergency without the medical examination within three months he is required to be examined within one month after being boarded out.

Fees for the initial and subsequent examinations and report are laid down and are to be found in Appendix F.

Registration of Blindness

The Register of Blind Persons is established under the National Assistance Act, 1948. To be included in the Register a person must be 'so blind as to be unable to perform any work for which eyesight is essential'. The test applied is not to decide whether the person is unable to pursue his ordinary or any particular occupation. Only the visual condition is taken into account in certifying. The test is by Snellens type with the focus properly corrected and classification is into three groups:

Group I—below 3/60. It is sometimes desirable to test for this group at one metre. It is not usual to classify a person having a visual acuity of 1/18 as blind unless there is considerable contraction of the visual field.

Group II—3/60 but less than 6/60. These are categorized as blind if the visual field is considerably contracted, but not if the visual defect is of long standing without material contraction of the field as for example in albinism or congenital nystagmus.

Group III—6/60 or above. These are categorized as blind only if the field is markedly contracted in the greater part of its extent, and particularly in the lower part of the field. Cases of homonymous or bitemporal hemianopia retaining a central visual acuity of 6/18 are not so categorized.

Three months after a cataract operation is regarded as being required for readjustment so that a patient formerly certified as blind remains so for three months. Also if, after the operation, the visual acuity is less than 6/60 the added limitations of two pairs of strong glasses (near and distance) and no clear vision in the range 16 to 20 ft. may justify a certification of blindness.

The foregoing gives some indication of the type of defect in visual acuity which would justify a patient's application for blind certification. The certification is carried out by a practitioner who devotes his whole time to the practice of ophthalmology, in all its branches, or who is in charge of the ophthalmic department of a general hospital of not less than 100 beds, and in special circumstances by other holders of a diploma in ophthalmology. Patients having these defects will normally be referred to or be under the care of an ophthalmologist who can carry out the necessary certification.

A classified Register of Blind Persons is maintained by the Local Authority or by a voluntary organization acting for the Authority. Registration is voluntary but is desirable. Special educational treatment is available for those on the Register. Registration is essential if the individual wishes to claim a pension at the age of forty, a wireless set and a free wireless licence, special training and lessons in Braille.

Habitual Drunkards

A habitual drunkard may voluntarily make application for admission to a licensed retreat, wherein he may be retained for a specified period not exceeding two years, subject to being released on licence in certain circumstances. His signature to the application requires to be attested by two Justices of the Peace and to be supported by a statutory declaration by two persons stating that he is known by them to be a habitual drunkard within the meaning of the Act. The Act is the Habitual Drunkards Act, 1879, which defines a habitual drunkard as a person who, not being amenable to any jurisdiction in lunacy is, notwithstanding, by reason of habitual intemperate drinking of intoxicating liquor, at times dangerous to himself or herself or to others or incapable of managing himself or herself and his or her affairs.

The person in charge of a habitual drunkard who dies must forward to the Coroner, to the Registrar, to the Clerk of the Local Authority and to the person by whom the last payment for the deceased was made (or to one of the signatories to the statutory declaration made above) certified copies of a certificate of the cause of death with the name of anyone present at the death.

Industrial Injuries

The provisions of the National Insurance (Industrial Injuries) Act, 1946, replaced the Workmen's Compensation Act. Nowadays a lump sum in compensation for loss of wages cannot be claimed from the employer unless a successful Common Law action is brought on grounds of negligence.

To qualify for benefit under the National Insurance (Industrial Injuries) Act the accident must arise out of, and in the course of, the employment. Injury benefit is paid for a period up to twenty-six weeks. Thereafter, the workman may be awarded a disablement pension, or a gratuity, depending upon the degree of disablement.

The time limit for claiming under these provisions is twenty-one days, though extension of this period is allowed where good cause is shown for the delay.

The benefits are also payable for prescribed industrial diseases. It must be shown that the claimant is suffering from the disease, that he has been employed since July 5th, 1948 in a scheduled occupation known to give rise to the disease and that the disease is due to the nature of the employment. There are supplementary schemes for pneumoconiosis and byssinosis.*

National Insurance Contributions

National Insurance contributions, payable weekly by means of stamps affixed to the National Insurance card, are compulsory. In the case of a self-employed person (Class 2) the stamps, purchased from the Post Office, are required to be affixed weekly by the individual, who is subject to penalties for non-observance of the requirement. The card when completely filled with stamps (every fifty-two weeks) is passed to the local office of the Ministry of National Insurance and a fresh card is issued. The weekly contribution for self-employed persons differs for men and for women.†

An employed person (Class 1) has his stamps affixed by his employer who is responsible for so doing. The cost is divided into the employers' contribution and the employees' contribution.†

Principals in general practice are, for this purpose, self-employed and thus are responsible for the whole of the contribution.

An assistant is an employed person. In his case the principal is responsible for seeing that the weekly contributions are paid and the cards stamped. He pays the employer's contribution and the assistant pays the employee's.

Members of hospital medical staffs are regarded as employed persons if they are employed by one or more Regional Hospital Boards, Boards of Governors or Hospital Management Com-

* See Appendix D.
† See Appendix F.

mittees to an aggregate of more than five notional half-days. Otherwise these are regarded as self-employed. Notwithstanding that a practitioner may be employed for, say, four notional half-days and yet has no other employment such as private practice, he is regarded as a self-employed person who is responsible for the full contributions.

Even a practitioner who is employed for five notional half-days by a Regional Hospital Board, and for the rest of his time is undertaking regular medical board work for the Ministry of Pensions and National Insurance, is regarded as a self-employed person as he does not fulfil the precise conditions required for being categorized as 'employed'.

A practitioner who is unemployed, as for example in a period between leaving one appointment and starting another, is responsible for affixing the stamps on his card for the whole period, unless he has registered as unemployed by application to the labour exchange. If he fails to affix the stamps he will be called upon to complete his contributions at a later date.

A doctor is similarly responsible for stamping the cards of other employees such as receptionists, chauffeurs, gardeners and domestic servants. The liability for National Insurance contributions only exists when the employment is for at least four hours a week, or eight hours in the case of those engaged in cleaning or other domestic work. Neither does it apply to a caretaker who receives no wage or other money payment. The employer remains liable for Industrial Injuries contributions in these instances.

The application of these schemes to married women is exceptional and somewhat complicated. A woman married before the commencement of the scheme (July 5th, 1948) can only become insured if she becomes employed or gainfully occupied. Otherwise a married woman has an option as to whether she contributes or not for National Insurance. Where applicable she must contribute for Industrial Injuries benefits. A doctor's wife employed by him as receptionist, for example, may be insured as a self-employed person (twenty-four hours per week or more) or as a non-employed person (less than twenty-four hours per week). If she herself is a doctor and in practice with her husband she is in a similar position. Fuller information about insurance for married women is to be found in a leaflet

(N.I.1) which may be obtained from the local Pensions and National Insurance Office.

For a comprehensive description of the National Insurance Schemes doctors are advised to consult a Ministry of Pensions and National Insurance booklet entitled *Everybody's Guide to National Insurance* (H.M.S.O., price 6*d*.).

Benefits

Self-employed persons are entitled to all National Insurance benefits except Unemployment benefit. Employed persons are entitled to all National Insurance and Industrial Injuries benefits. For sickness and industrial injury benefit claims are made on the National Insurance medical certificate, which should be completed and taken to the local office of the Ministry of Pensions and National Insurance. Notification of incapacity must be made within three days, even if there is delay in obtaining the actual medical certificate which, however, must be forwarded within ten days for sickness benefit and twenty-one days for Industrial Injury benefit. Weekly certificates are required to be submitted unless the medical attendant has issued a certificate for a longer period.

Marriage Guidance Councils

These Councils are voluntary bodies in the work of which a doctor may participate as member, officer or lecturer, as marriage counsellor or as medical consultant.

When acting as marriage counsellor the doctor should avoid using his position to promote his professional advantage.

Marriage counsellors encourage applicants to consult their own family doctor when medical advice is deemed necessary. The counsellor may obtain the applicant's permission to ask the doctor to co-operate in treating him or her or in arranging reference to a specialist. If the doctor declines co-operation or if the applicant prefers to be referred to another doctor for the purpose, it has been agreed with the British Medical Association that it is proper for the counsellor to give the applicant the names of other doctors who will provide the necessary medical advice and assistance. A list of such doctors may be kept by the local Marriage Guidance Council in conjunction with the local Division of the British Medical Association, and any doctor willing to undertake this work may apply for inclusion in the list. They may give voluntary service or see applicants on a fee paying basis (other than for patients on their National Health Service list). In their association with patients of other doctors in this context doctors should be careful to conform to the relevant ethical rules of the profession (Chapter 8 and Appendix C).

S.O.S. Messages

For Relatives

Arrangements can be made with the British Broadcasting Corporation (Telephone: Langham 4468) for messages to be broadcast, free of charge, to relatives to go to the bedside of a sick person. Such messages can only be accepted when the doctor in attendance (or the hospital authority) certifies that the patient is dangerously ill, and when it has proved impossible to deliver the message to the relative by all other means. Messages to relatives after death has occurred are not accepted for broadcasting.

Stolen or Lost Dangerous Drugs

Messages regarding these will only be broadcast at the request of the police. Doctors whose drugs are missing should, therefore, report the matter to the police.

26

THE GENERAL PRACTITIONER IN THE NATIONAL HEALTH SERVICE

Detailed particulars relating to all the circumstances of practice and terms of service of general practitioners in the National Health Service, are to be found in an excellent booklet entitled *Handbook for General Medical Practitioners*, a copy of which is provided by the Ministry of Health or the Department of Health for Scotland for each general practitioner whose name is on the list of an Executive Council. In the following pages reference is made to many of the points that are of interest to general practitioners. They are, however, advised to consult the Handbook for the detailed information in which it abounds. The Terms of Service are reproduced in full in an appendix and there are other appendices giving the Model Allocation Scheme, the Model Distribution Scheme, lists of drugs, appliances and reagents in the various categories, classification lists of foods, drugs, toilet preparations and disinfectants, certification rules and lists of certificates to be given free of charge, a list of forms used in the Service and addresses of Laboratories and Transfusion Centres.

The National Health Service in Scotland is operated under The National Health Service (Scotland) Act, 1947. Basically this Act and the English Act are the same, but there are some differences to which reference is made in the following pages where relevant. The Act is administered by the Secretary of State for Scotland so that references to 'The Minister' or 'The Minister of Health' are to be regarded as references to the Secretary of State insofar as they apply to Scotland.

The Terms of Service of general practitioners under the National Service are set out in the First Schedule to the National Health Service (General Medical and Pharmaceutical Services) Regulations, to which are added Part II of the National Health Service (Service Committees and Tribunal) Regulations, and any allocation scheme or distribution scheme in force under these Regulations in the area in which the practitioner practises.

Revision of Terms of Service

The Executive Council may alter the Terms of Service with approval of the Minister by giving notice of the proposed alteration to the practitioner. Except when the alteration is brought about by an Act of Parliament or when the Minister has approved, after consultation with representatives of general practitioners, the Executive Council shall first consult with the Local Medical Committee and give three months' notice to practitioners of the alteration unless the Minister directs that the notice shall be given to the Local Medical Committee only.

Responsibility for Treatment

The practitioner is responsible for the treatment of all those on his list and all those that he has agreed to accept on his list, unless and until the Executive Council has notified the practitioner that a patient is not on his list. He is also responsible for treatment of temporary residents accepted by him as such and patients assigned to him by the allocation scheme. He must also treat any person whom he is required to treat under the terms of the allocation scheme, pending his acceptance by or assignment to a practitioner. In addition he is required to treat any patient in a case of accident or in emergency.

If a practitioner is uncertain as to the identity of a person claiming to be on his list, he may ask him for his medical card (Form E.C.4). The patient may not be able to produce this but, even so, the practitioner must give the necessary treatment and supply any drugs or appliances, or give a prescription, as for a patient on his list. He may charge a reasonable fee for his services thus given and must render an account or give a receipt. The patient may then apply to the Executive Council for a refund. Normally this must be done within fourteen days, though exceptionally, where good reason is given, this may be extended to one month. If the Executive Council is satisfied that the patient is on the list of the practitioner, the fee is refunded to him and the amount is deducted from the remuneration of the practitioner, who is, however, credited with payment for any drug or appliance he has supplied if so entitled in the ordinary way for a patient on his list.

A further responsibility of the practitioner is the provision of maternity medical services for all those for whom he has undertaken to provide such services.

Hospital treatment of the patient in a hospital is specifically excluded from the terms of service, unless the practitioner is required to treat him by virtue of the fact that he is also a member of the medical staff of the hospital.

The Doctor's Medical List

Acceptance of Patients

There is free choice of doctors by patients, subject to the doctor's acceptance. Section 45 of the Act (Scottish Act, Section 46) provides for Regulations allowing the choice of doctor to be exercised by someone other than the patient. This may be done in the case of a child under sixteen by the mother, or in her absence the father, or in the absence of both the guardian or other person having care of the child; by a relative of or a person having care of one who on account of old age, sickness, or other infirmity is incapable of choosing a doctor; or in the case of a person at an approved school by the managers or a person authorized by them.

The patient applies to the practitioner to accept him on his list by presenting his medical card or form of application for acceptance (Form E.C.1 Rev.). If the patient is not already on the list of a practitioner in the area this is all that he need do. The practitioner indicates his acceptance of the patient by appending his signature, and forwarding the medical card to the Executive Council within seven days for the necessary transfer of the patient's name to his list. Thereafter, his responsibilities to the patient are as laid down in the Terms of Service.

The practitioner applied to is at liberty to decline the application of the patient for inclusion in his list. If the patient is accepted by a partner, deputy or assistant on behalf of a practitioner, the practitioner's name must be added.

Arrangements for Changing Doctors

Arrangements for changing to another general practitioner are fairly simple in the National Health Service. The patient is required to obtain the signature of his former practitioner on his medical card consenting to the change. If this is forthcoming then the patient may be accepted on the list without further ado. The medical card is signed by the accepting practitioner and forwarded to the Clerk to the Executive Council for registration.

A patient may change his doctor without obtaining the consent of his present doctor. In order to do this he must notify the Executive Council of his wish to do so and send his card to the Clerk. The Clerk will return his card to him indicating to him the date on which he may change, which will be fourteen days after the receipt of the request. Thereafter, he will obtain acceptance by the new doctor in the usual way.

Removal from List

A practitioner has the right to have a patient's name removed from his list. To exercise this right he may give notice at any time to the Executive Council and, at the expiration of seven days from the receipt of such notice, the name is removed from the practitioner's list. If the patient is under treatment at the time the practitioner should, of course, be satisfied that the patient can obtain treatment from another practitioner and should offer to communicate details of the treatment to the other practitioner, especially where there may be some little delay in the transfer of the patient's medical record card.

Provision is also made for the removal from the list of a practitioner of the name of any person under the following circumstances:

(*a*) death;
(*b*) absence abroad, or intended absence, for three months;
(*c*) enlistment in Her Majesty's Forces;

(*d*) transfer to the list of another practitioner;
(*e*) cessation of residence in the area;
(*f*) whereabouts of the person not known to the Council;
(*g*) request by the patient (after fourteen days);
(*h*) failure to provide particulars of inmates in a residential institution (see p. 249).

The name is deleted from the list on the date on which the Executive Council receives notification of the relevant event.

Range of Service

The Regulations require the practitioner to render to his patients 'all proper and necessary treatment'. This includes, for example, the administration of an anaesthetic or assistance of some other kind at an operation performed by, and of a kind usually performed by, a general practitioner unless the service performed involves skill and experience beyond what a general practitioner can reasonably be expected to possess. An anaesthetic given for an operation by a dental practitioner is not included and for this service a fee may be accepted.

Other services which involve such special skill and experience are excluded except that a practitioner is expected to render, in an emergency, whatever services are, in the circumstances, in the best interests of the patient.

The exact dividing line between what is and what is not accepted as being within the scope of a general practitioner is not defined. It is probably impossible to define it, but the Regulations do call for regard to be paid to whether the service in question is, or is not, usually undertaken by general practitioners in the area.

There are also excluded the administration of an anaesthetic at an operation performed by a practitioner providing maternity medical services and the provision of maternity medical services unless the practitioner has, by arrangement with the patient, undertaken to provide her with such services under the National Health Service. A practitioner who has not arranged with the patient to undertake the medical supervision of her pregnancy, confinement and postnatal period is not required to do so just because she is a patient on his list for ordinary general medical services. On the other hand her being, for maternity medical services, under the care of another practitioner does not alter the fact that she remains on her own doctor's list and his responsibility for providing her with general medical treatment remains.

If the patient requires treatment which is outwith the scope of the general practitioner's obligations under the Terms of Service, he has a duty to tell the patient so and, if the patient wishes, to do all that is necessary to enable him to receive the treatment required. Thus he is required to refer him to hospital if this is what is necessary and in doing so he should give full particulars to the hospital, in writing, either beforehand or as soon as possible afterwards.

He should also give his patients what advice and assistance he thinks they require to take advantage of the local health authority service, maternity medical service and supplementary ophthalmic services, including in this last case a recommendation on the form provided by the Executive Council for the purpose (Form O.S.C.1).

Visiting

The practitioner is required to visit his patients in the area where he has undertaken to provide general medical services and if the patient's condition requires it. The Terms of Service do not state who decides if the condition requires it but if the practitioner has not seen the patient he can hardly be the one to decide. He will never be in the wrong if he visits on receipt of a message but he may well be if he does not.

Maternity Medical Services

'All proper and necessary treatment' in respect of maternity medical services is definitely stated to include an initial medical and obstetric examination, and an examination at or about the thirty-sixth week of pregnancy. In Scotland an additional examination at or about the thirty-eighth week is required. Such other examinations and antenatal care are called for as the practitioner considers necessary. He is required to attend at the confinement only if he thinks it necessary or if the midwife summons him. He is responsible for the medical care of the mother and the child for fourteen days after the confinement and, later, a postnatal, including a pelvic, examination. He is responsible for providing the services of an anaesthetist when necessary, for which a fee is claimed on Form E.C.31 unless the anaesthetist is his own or his partner's trainee assistant.

The Obstetric List

The Executive Council maintains a list known as the Obstetric Part of the Medical List. In England and Wales applications by practitioners to be included in the list are referred to a professional committee called the Local Obstetric Committee for approval, whereas in Scotland this approval is not required. If his name is included in the list the practitioner is recognized as a general practitioner obstetrician.

If an expectant mother, whether on his list or not, applies to him for maternity medical care and he accepts her he asks her to sign Part II of Form E.C.24, for which he claims payment from the Executive Council* when his services to her (which are indicated above) are completed. He signs Part I and hands it to the patient.

A doctor who is not a general practitioner obstetrician may undertake maternity services under the National Health Service and under the same conditions, but only for patients who are on his list. The form to be completed in this case is Form E.C.24A, and the fee payable is less than that payable to a general practitioner obstetrician.*

The completion of the form places an obligation on the doctor to carry out the services outlined above, though provision is made for the termination of the arrangement, for example when the patient moves to another area. A doctor may also be called upon to attend an expectant mother who is temporarily away from home, usually for the purpose of a single antenatal examination which falls due during her temporary absence.

A general practitioner obstetrician may not employ as his deputy for this work anyone but another general practitioner obstetrician, except when special approval has been given by the Executive Council.

The doctor may call in a consultant obstetrician or paediatri-

* See Appendix F.

cian in connexion with the services under the domiciliary consultation scheme, including to a patient or her child in a nursing home, which is an exception to the rule regarding domiciliary consultations in any other circumstances. He may also call in the Emergency Obstetric Unit where one is available.

A doctor called in by a midwife to a patient who has not made arrangements with him for services under this scheme is paid by the Local Health Authority to whom his claim must be submitted within three months (see p. 294).

Certificates in the National Health Service

The requirements for medical certification are set down in the National Insurance (Medical Certification) Regulations.* Failure to observe these Regulations creates three possibilities which are likely to bring the practitioner into danger. There may result a summons to appear before the Medical Disciplinary Committee of the General Medical Council, the possibility of an action for negligence or, with National Health Service patients, the imposition of a fine after inquiry by the Minister of Health. (For general observations on certification, see Chapter 10.)

Care and accuracy in certification is essential. To certify incapacity for work when the patient is capable is a breach of the Regulations, as also is the reverse. Each certificate must be based on an examination of the patient and only one National Insurance certificate must be issued in respect of each examination, unless as a duplicate in which case it should be so marked. Further examinations must be made before the issue of each intermediate certificate and of the final certificate.

The cause of incapacity must be stated as precisely as possible. Occasionally, in the patient's interest, the practitioner deems it desirable to write in a 'diagnosis' unlikely to disclose to the patient the true nature of his illness. If he wishes to act in this way he should also complete Form Med. 6 (which is to be found at the back of the book of First Certificates) and forward it in an envelope marked 'Confidential' to the Divisional Medical Officer, Ministry of Health, London (or Cardiff, Manchester or Leeds as appropriate), or in Scotland

* See Appendix D.

to the Regional Medical Officer, Department of Health for Scotland, Edinburgh.

The certificate must be signed by the practitioner with his own signature and not by means of initials or a rubber stamp. The certificate must not be signed until the diagnosis and the patient's name have been entered. This makes it clear that the practice of signing 'blank' certificates for others to complete is a breach of the Regulations. Clearly such a practice is also unwise in respect of any form of certificate.

The certificate must be issued not later than the day after the examination though a supplementary certificate (Form Med. 5) may be used when for some reason it is not possible to comply with this rule.

In issuing a Final Certificate, the practitioner must not certify the patient as being fit to resume work later than the third day after the examination.

A practitioner may not certify in respect of himself on a National Insurance Certificate. The Rules for Medical Certification are to be found in Appendix VIII of the *Handbook for General Medical Practitioners* issued by the Ministry of Health, and in Appendix V to the corresponding publication of the Department of Health for Scotland.

A practitioner asked for a certificate by a patient who is receiving treatment, otherwise than from or under the supervision of a registered medical practitioner, has no responsibility for issuing him with such certificates. The certificates which must be issued free of charge are laid down in a Schedule to the Terms of Service and the list is to be found in Appendix E.

Anaesthetics

If the practitioner in the course of his treatment of one of his patients requires the administration of an anaesthetic, he is responsible for providing the services of another practitioner to give the anaesthetic, if the administration is within the accepted scope of a general practitioner (see p. 233). A claim for a fee for the anaesthetist should be made on Form E.C.31 to the Executive Council within twenty-one days.*

* See Appendix F.

Records

The practitioner is required to keep records (in the prescribed form) of the illnesses of his patients and his treatment of them. The medical record forms are forms E.C.5 and 6 with continuation cards, E.C.7 and 8. The records are the property of the Ministry of Health (or of the Department of Health for Scotland) and must be forwarded to the Executive Council when called for, or within seven days of the death of the patient, or on removal from the list.

Emergency Treatment in the National Health Service

Any general practitioner in the National Service, except those whose contract specifically excludes the liability, is required to attend a patient not on his list (or that of his partner) where emergency treatment is required. For this service he may submit a claim on Form E.C.32 to the Executive Council (normally within twenty-one days) for payment of an emergency fee according to a scale of fees laid down in the Regulations.* The amount of the fee may sometimes be recovered by the Executive Council from the practitioner on whose list the patient is unless there was reasonable cause for his non-attendance. The practitioner concerned has a right of appeal to the Minister.

The above does not apply in an area in which the Local Medical Committee and the Executive Council have agreed that no fees for emergency treatment shall be paid. The Schedule to the Regulations, however, does provide for payments in special and exceptional circumstances.

Temporary Residents

A patient temporarily residing in an area away from his home and consequently unable to apply for treatment to his own doctor is, nevertheless, entitled to apply to a N.H.S. general practitioner in the area for treatment as a temporary resident. Care, treatment and the provision of necessary medicines is undertaken in the same way as in the case of a person on that doctor's list and mileage is claimed if appropriate. The doctor accepts the patient by completing Form E.C.19,

* See Appendix F.

which also, subsequently, serves as a claim for payment when he submits it to the Executive Council. Formerly use was made of a special section on the patient's medical card for this purpose but the use of this section is now obsolete.

A patient can only be accepted as a temporary resident when he requires treatment. If his stay in the area is to be less than twenty-four hours, he should not be treated as a temporary resident but as a case requiring emergency treatment. If his stay is to be more than three months he should be accepted on to the new doctor's list in the ordinary way.

Medical notes relating to the treatment of a temporary resident are entered on a continuation card which is forwarded to the Executive Council, on completion of treatment, for onward transmission to the patient's own doctor at his home. A special fee is payable to the doctor for the whole of his attendance on the temporary resident. If the patient is in a convalescent home or other institution where arrangements are made for the treatment of a substantial number of patients (including some holiday camps), as locally agreed by the Local Medical Committee, the fee in respect of each individual is halved. If the doctor is dissatisfied with the placing of an institution or camp in this category he may apply to the Minister for a ruling.

Any person requiring treatment may apply for it as a temporary resident, even though he is not on a doctor's list elsewhere and has never received treatment under the National Health Service.

Children and others residing at boarding schools for the greater part of the year should be on the list of the doctor in that area and, if required, should be treated as temporary residents when at home by their family doctor.

Treatment of Visitors from Abroad

The National Health Service is available to any person in the United Kingdom. Thus Commonwealth and foreign nationals temporarily resident in this country, whether on holiday or business, are entitled to apply to a practitioner for treatment as a temporary resident or, if in the area for a period longer than three months, for inclusion in his list. These facilities are not intended to cover persons who enter the

United Kingdom for the specific purpose of obtaining treatment, although there are certain exceptions in respect of inhabitants of the Channel Islands, where the National Health Service does not operate.

Treatment of Seamen

British or foreign merchant seamen in port, whether on board or on shore, may obtain treatment under the National Health Service. Normally they will receive treatment as temporary residents, though where a number of seamen are treated at one time arrangements are made for a lower temporary resident fee for each case. In some ports, however, special arrangements are made for their treatment by doctors employed by the Shipping Federation.

Treatment of Service Personnel

Service personnel on leave or temporarily away from their unit are normally required to apply for treatment from the nearest service hospital or unit or Admiralty surgeon and agent. If, however, they are more than two miles from such medical attention they may apply to a general practitioner in the National Health Service for acceptance as temporary residents. If their absence is for a period of longer than three months they may in certain circumstances be placed on the doctor's list.

When they are accepted as temporary residents, their service rank and number should be entered on the form in lieu of a National Health Service number. Claims for payment are made in the ordinary way as for temporary residents.

A doctor wishing to apply for the service medical report of a patient invalided from the service and joining his list may apply to the Executive Council. Unless the patient states that he has already given consent Form E.C.53 should be completed by the patient and forwarded to the Executive Council by the doctor with the application.

If information is required from service medical records relating to an ex-service patient not invalided, a request should be forwarded to the relevant service department giving the patient's service number and other particulars, an undertaking that the information will be used solely to assist medical treatment, and the written consent of the patient.

The addresses of the Service Departments are:

The Under Secretary of State, War Office (AMD7), London, S.W.1.

The Under Secretary of State, Air Ministry (S7(b)), Theobalds Road, London, W.C.1.

The Medical Director General of the Navy, Admiralty, London, S.W.1.

27

THE GENERAL PRACTITIONER IN THE NATIONAL HEALTH SERVICE

(continued)

Arrangements for Practice

The practitioner must carry on practice either from his residence or from a health centre, unless he has permission from the Executive Council (or, on appeal, from the Minister) to do otherwise. The Council (or the Minister) will need to be satisfied that the alternative arrangements are under conditions which enable the practitioner to carry out his obligations under the Terms of Service, particularly the visiting of his patients. The practitioner may be required to notify patients at his own expense of any special arrangements.

When a practice is declared vacant and a successor has been or is to be appointed, no other practitioner may carry on practice from the premises formerly occupied or used for practice by the retiring or deceased practitioner, without the consent of the Council or, on appeal, the Medical Practices Committee.

The exceptions to this are as follows:

(1) When a successor has been offered the practice vacancy but has not accepted after one month.

(2) When an offer has been made to and accepted by the successor and the Medical Practices Committee has approved the terms of agreement for such practice.

(3) When twelve months have elapsed from the date of appointment of the successor.

(4) When a partner of the retiring or deceased practitioner acquires the premises in pursuance of an agreement which has been in operation for twelve months before the date of retirement or death.

(5) When premises are used in consequence of temporary arrangements, or by agreement, between the 'owner or Executor' and the successor pending approval by the Medical Practices Committee.

The date on which the successor is appointed is the date on which the successor is notified that there is no appeal, or, alternatively, the date on which the decision on any appeal is notified to him. For precise details of these conditions reference should be made to paragraph 9 of the Terms of Service.

Surgery Hours and Premises

The practitioner is required to attend and treat his patients at the times and places agreed by the Council.

The surgery and waiting room premises must be proper and sufficient, having regard to the circumstances of the practice (see also p. 73). On receipt of a written request a member or officer of the Executive Council or Local Medical Committee authorized for the purpose by the Executive Council must be admitted, at all reasonable times, so that he may inspect the surgery and waiting room premises.

A practitioner may wish to vary his place of residence or his surgery, or the times of attendance at his surgery. He will require to obtain the approval of the Executive Council of any change. The practitioner has the responsibility for notifying the change to all of the patients on his list. Normally the Executive Council will undertake the circularization for him, but at his expense. Supplementary methods of familiarizing patients of the new arrangements by notices placed in the surgery can also be used but such methods as announcements in the local press or notices on public premises are to be avoided as being unethical (see p. 71). If the Executive Council refuses permission for any change the practitioner has a right of appeal to the Minister.

Deputies, Assistants and Partners: Absences from Practice

The practitioner is required to provide all treatment personally unless prevented by temporary absence from home, other professional duties or other reasonable cause. He must make all necessary arrangements for securing the treatment of his patients when he is so prevented. The Executive Council must be informed of the arrangements. He must not be away from his practice for more than a week without informing the Executive Council of his proposed absence, and of the arrangements made for deputies.

He is, however, permitted to arrange for treatment to be given at any time by his partner or assistant acting in his place so long as reasonable steps are taken to secure continuity of treatment and subject to the right of the patient to require the services, when available, of the principal instead of the assistant. The patient, however, cannot insist on this if the principal is prevented by reasonable cause, as for example by temporary absence from home or by illness.

He is responsible for all acts and omissions of any practitioner acting for him as deputy or assistant in relation to his obligations as a general practitioner under the Terms of Service, unless the deputy's name is included in the medical list, in which case the deputy is himself responsible.

He shall not employ an assistant, except for a period of less than three months, without the consent of the Executive Council. If the consent of the Executive Council is withheld he may appeal to the Medical Practices Committee. He must notify the name of any assistant employed by him to the Council.

Neither must he, without the consent of the Executive Council, employ as deputy or assistant any practitioner who is disqualified for inclusion in the medical list of the Council by decision of the Tribunal. The assistant, or deputy, may treat patients at places and times other than those arranged by the practitioner for whom he is acting, due regard being paid, however, to the convenience of the patients. Unless his name is included in the medical list, he must put the name of the practitioner for whom he is deputizing on any certificate, prescription or other document issued by him under the

Terms of Service, as well as his own signature. If the principal's name is already on the document as, for example, on the certificates of incapacity for work (Forms Med. 1, 2a, 2b and c), this will suffice.

Trainee Assistants

A limited number of doctors are recognized on application to the Executive Councils, which consult the Local Medical Committees, as trainer general practitioners. The selection of the trainer is made by the Local Medical Committee, or a Sub-committee to whom the task is delegated, together with two persons nominated by the University. The training period is for one year. The trainer receives a training grant plus the salary of the trainee and boarding expenses (together not exceeding a fixed figure including the employer's share of National Insurance Contributions for the assistant) and an allowance for a motor car if an additional car is necessary. The training grant is paid quarterly. The form of application is Form E.C.45. Training grants are not normally given to a doctor with less than 2,000 persons on his list (1,500 in rural areas) and he is not entitled to increase his list of patients beyond the usual maximum (e.g. 3,500 for a single-handed doctor) in respect of a trainee for whom a grant is paid.

Normally the number of practitioners recognized as trainers under the scheme is limited to about 5 per cent. in each area. A high standard is expected before the application is granted, and also the suitability of the circumstances of the doctor's practice and the opportunities presented thereby for training a young doctor are taken into account. Once authority has been granted, the selection of the trainee practitioner is a matter for the trainer. The trainee must not be liable and medically fit for military service and must not have had previous experience in general practice in the British Isles, except for short periods as a locum.

Acceptance of Fees

Subject to certain exceptions, examples of which are mentioned below, the practitioner is not permitted to demand or to accept fees or remuneration from, or on behalf of, patients in respect of any service (whether under the Terms of Service or not and including maternity medical services) rendered to patients on his medical list or on the list of his partner or assistant, or of a practitioner for whom he is acting as deputy. Treatment in this connexion includes advice. A practitioner is expected to take all practicable steps to ensure that any practitioner deputizing for him observes these rules in respect of his patients. Examples of the exceptions are:

(*a*) Where he has reasonable doubts as to identity and the medical card is not produced (see p. 231).

(*b*) The acceptance of payment from a statutory body in respect of services rendered for the purpose of that body's statutory functions.

(*c*) For certificates and reports of vaccination and immunization.

(*d*) For notification of infectious disease.

(*e*) From a school or employer or other body for medical services rendered for their purposes, as opposed to services rendered for the patients.

(*f*) Treatment not in the range of service (see paragraph 6 of Terms of Service):

(i) in Section 5 accommodation for private patients (pay beds in hospital);

(ii) in a registered nursing home not being a hospital under the Act.

If the practitioner is on the staff of a hospital as a specialist providing treatment of the kind given in the hospital, he must notify the Executive Council within seven days on a form supplied for the purpose (Form E.C.33).

(*g*) Fees under Section 16 of the Road Traffic Act, 1934 (see p. 215).

(*h*) Fees from a dental practitioner:

(i) for an anaesthetic given at a dentist's request;

(ii) for treatment for arrest of bleeding following dental extraction (see Appendix F).

(*i*) For private certificates.

(*j*) Appointment as part-time Industrial Medical Officer for examinations.

(*k*) Certificates under the Lunacy, Mental Treatment or Mental Deficiency Acts, except:

(i) Certifying that detention of a person absent on trial is no longer necessary (Lunacy Act, 1890, Section 55 (8));

(ii) Certifying that a person is incapable of managing his own affairs (Lunacy Act, 1890, Section 33).

Contraceptive Advice

No fee may be demanded by a general practitioner or accepted for contraceptive advice to patients on his, or his partner's list, but appliances and chemicals required for eugenic reasons must be purchased by the patient and not prescribed on Form E.C.10.

Acceptance of Fees for Police Calls

The question as to whether or not a National Health Service practitioner is entitled to accept fees for examining and attending persons as a result of police calls is fraught with difficulty. Appended below is a list of the usual reasons for which a doctor may be called by the police, together with an indication of whether fees may be claimed and from whom. Reference to claims for emergency treatment fees will, of course, not apply in those areas where it has been agreed that emergency fees will not be payable.

(1) Emergency treatment.	
(*a*) Road traffic accidents	A fee may be claimed under the Road Traffic Act, 1934 (see p. 215).
(*b*) Other accident or illness occurring in the street or elsewhere.	If the patient is on the doctor's list, no fee is payable. Otherwise an emergency treatment fee may be claimed from the Executive Council.
(2) Medical treatment or examination, at the request of the police, of persons in police custody, or	Fee may be claimed from the police.

examination for police purposes.

(3) Examination of a victim of an offence.

The fee for the examination may be claimed from the police. For any treatment that may be required to a patient who is not on the doctor's list an emergency fee may be claimed from the Executive Council. In areas where emergency fees are not payable it might reasonably be claimed, in this instance, that the treatment qualifies for a special payment.

(4) Examination of a person charged or likely to be charged with drunkenness or some other offence.

If the examination is at the request of the police, a fee may be charged to the police. If at the request of the 'patient' he may be charged a fee whether or not he is on the doctor's list. If a patient who is held in custody on a charge of being drunk claims that his doctor should attend him because he considers he is ill, then if, in fact, he is found to be ill the treatment should come under the National Health Service. What the doctor may charge for, however, is any report that the patient asks for which has to be passed to the police or is used in connexion with the patient's defence.

(5) Dead Bodies.

A patient said to be ill and found dead on arrival.	If the patient is on the doctor's list, no fee may be charged. If not, an emergency treatment fee may be claimed from the Executive Council.
If the doctor is called to confirm death, or to give an opinion or furnish a report for the police.	A fee may be claimed from the police.

For general considerations relating to Services rendered to the Police, see Chapter 24.

Regional Medical Officer

The practitioner must provide the Regional Medical Officer, within such reasonable period as the Regional Medical Officer may specify, clinical information in writing about the case of any patient to whom the practitioner has issued or has declined to issue a medical certificate.

If the practitioner seeks the advice of the R.M.O. regarding a patient he should comply with any reasonable request by the R.M.O. to meet him for the purpose of examining the patient in consultation.

He must allow the R.M.O. access at reasonable times to his surgery or elsewhere where medical record cards are kept, notice being given, and he must furnish such records or necessary information with regard to any entry in the records as the R.M.O. may request. Also he is required to answer the inquiries of the R.M.O. relating to any prescription or certificate he has issued or to any statement made in any report furnished by him under the Terms of Service.

Residential Institutions and Schools

If a practitioner provides general medical services for pupils, inmates or staff of a residential school or institution the Executive Council may require him to provide the names and addresses of all those for whom he is providing the services on a specified date. If so requested he must comply within two months (see p. 233).

Withdrawal from Medical List

The practitioner may give notice at any time of withdrawal from the medical list or from the list as a practitioner providing maternity medical services. His name will then be withdrawn at the end of three months from the date of the notice, or earlier if the Executive Council agrees. If representations are made to the Tribunal that the continued inclusion of the practitioner on the medical list would be prejudicial to the efficiency of the general medical services, he shall not be entitled to have his name removed pending the termination of the proceedings inquiring into the matter.

Continued Absence or Disability of Practitioner

When the Executive Council, after consultation with the Local Medical Committee, is satisfied that owing to continued absence or bodily or mental disability his obligations under the Terms of Service are not being adequately carried out it can, with the consent of the Minister, notify the patients on a practitioner's list that he is, for the time being, in the opinion of the Council, not in a position to carry out his obligations under the Terms of Service.

Practice Compensation

Section IV of both the original National Health Service Acts provided for compensation for the loss of goodwill of their practice to general practitioners in the National Health Service. The sum of £66 million was allotted by Parliament for this purpose and after examination of all claims, each practice was allotted a portion of this sum amounting to approximately 1·56 year's purchase of the agreed value of the practice. Each partner in a partnership is entitled to compensation in proportion to the share of the goodwill that he held on the appointed day in 1948.

Subsequently the National Health Service Amendment Act, 1949, made provision for variations in the amount of compensation payable to partners whose proportionate shares alter on the implementation of partnership agreements made before the appointed day and the inclusion of partners who, having remained outside the National Health Service on July 5th, 1948, decided to come into the Service by a new appointed day (February 16th, 1950). The partner disposing of some of his goodwill in pursuance of a partnership agreement made before the appointed day is entitled to immediate payment of the compensation in relation to the proportion of his share of the goodwill with which he has parted.

Payment of Compensation

Practice compensation is normally payable only on retirement from the Service or death. Provision is made, however, for part payment of compensation in certain cases of hardship. This provision has been applied to some practitioners experiencing hardship as a result of debts, or commitments entered into before the appointed day, but not to hardship from causes arising since that day such as arrears of tax, overdrafts, house purchase and other financial difficulties. Application may be made to the Minister (or Secretary of State) for whole or part payment but with the passage of years it seems likely that there can be few, if any, practitioners who could now show cause for a claim which would be met.

Retirement and receipt of compensation does not preclude a practitioner from engaging in other fields of practice or in giving general medical services under the Act in another area.

General Practitioners Employed in the Hospital Service

Practitioners are employed in the Hospital Services under the Terms and Conditions of Service of Hospital, Medical and Dental Staff. Therein are laid down the conditions of appointment and remuneration of Hospital Medical Staff of all grades. General practitioners working part-time in hospital may be graded as Consultants or in one of the junior grades, or may be employed under paragraph 10 of the Terms.

Paragraph 10 (*a*) provides for the remuneration of general practitioners in general practitioner ('cottage') hospitals other than maternity hospitals, over and above their remuneration from Executive Councils in respect of persons on their lists. A staff fund is created by making a payment* per annum for each occupied bed (except pay beds and maternity beds) as averaged out over the year. This fund is divided among the general

* See Appendix F.

practitioners on the staff of the hospital as they themselves determine.

Paragraph 10 (*b*) provides for a rate* per annum per weekly half-day to be paid to practitioners working at convalescent homes, general practitioner maternity hospitals or other types of hospital where no other rate is appropriate. The weekly 'half-day' is assessed, as in the case of all other hospital medical staff, by determining the average number of hours per week required by an average practitioner to perform the duties of the post and dividing it by three and a half. Any fraction is regarded as a 'half-day' and remunerated as such. Thus seven hours is two half-days and twelve hours is regarded as four half-days. Smaller sums are paid where the time spent per week is not more than two hours. The maximum remuneration permitted under this heading is for the equivalent of nine half-days.

Provision is made for leave which is at the rate of six weeks' per annum for those in receipt of a salary under paragraph 10 (*b*). Many other points are covered in the 'Terms and Conditions of Service', including sick leave and claims for expenses. Provisions regarding superannuation in respect of these posts are considered in Chapter 34.

Postgraduate Courses

Section 48 of each of the National Health Service Acts allows for payment to be made for provision of refresher courses for general practitioner principals in the Service. Courses are specially arranged with Universities and Medical Schools and they vary from a minimum of three half-day sessions to a maximum of twenty-two sessions. Fees for a practitioner's attendance are paid direct to the University by the Ministry up to a maximum of twenty-two sessions in any one academic year (September 1st to August 31st). Only those practitioners with a N.H.S. list of not less than 500 (in a rural practice 250) are eligible.

For attendance at an intensive course of up to twenty-two sessions prior approval is necessary. This is obtained by making application, well in advance, on Form G.P.R.C.2 (revised) to the Postgraduate Dean by whom it will be submitted to the

* See Appendix F.

Ministry if the University is prepared to accept the applicant. The applicant will be notified of the outcome.

For short weekend courses and for courses spread over a number of weeks no such prior approval of the Ministry is necessary, but the doctor may be called upon to pay the University for the course if he proves to be ineligible (see above). The exception to this is the occasional instance in which a locum tenens is required to cover the practitioner's absence. In such a case prior application for approval must be made as for an intensive course.

A circular known as Memo. G.P.R.C.1 (revised November, 1951) gives the full details including what subsistence allowances, travelling expenses, and payments for locum tenens may be claimed. Full particulars and the necessary forms for completion may be obtained from the Postgraduate Dean or the Director of the University or Medical School.

28

DRUGS AND PRESCRIPTIONS IN THE NATIONAL HEALTH SERVICE

Drugs

The general practitioner in the National Health Service, who has not arranged to dispense and provide the necessary drugs himself, prescribes on Form E.C.10. The form may not be used for persons other than the patients who are under treatment by him. A patient for this purpose is a person for whose treatment a practitioner is responsible under his Terms of Service. Separate forms must be used for each patient and more than two prescriptions should not be written on one form. The form must bear the name of the practitioner on whose list the patient is. An assistant or other practitioner deputizing for another must, therefore, append the name of the principal concerned as well as his own signature unless it is already stamped on the form.

A practitioner is entitled to prescribe whatever drug he considers necessary for the treatment of the patient. He is naturally expected to exercise care in not prescribing excessive quantities, and in not prescribing expensive preparations where a less costly prescription would have the same therapeutic value for the particular patient. His prescriptions are scrutinized on behalf of the Joint Pricing Committee which may refer instances of costly prescribing to the Executive Council for investigation. As a result of this the practitioner may be charged the cost of the preparation and, in some instances, required to pay a fine. Consequently, when he finds it necessary to prescribe a preparation which is more costly than an alternative which is generally regarded as a therapeutic equivalent, a practitioner should satisfy himself that he could justify the use of the more costly preparation should he be called upon to do so. His responsibility remains the same even when the item has been recommended by a specialist.

It is not permissible for an Executive Council to authorize in advance the prescribing of any particular preparation so that practitioners cannot cover themselves in advance.

Practitioners should do their best to be acquainted with the cost of preparations, both proprietary and otherwise, so that, where possible, they can prescribe the less costly therapeutic equivalent. Information regarding equivalents and other information which help the prescriber are to be found in the National Formulary (Appendix) and the Prescribers' Notes which are issued from time to time.

In coming to a decision regarding the prescription of proprietary preparations, the practitioner will be helped by a booklet issued to all practitioners (with a later list of amendments), which gives the classification of proprietaries according to the Joint Committee on Prescribing of the Central and Scottish Health Services Councils. Proprietary preparations are listed as: (*a*) those which may be freely prescribed, (*b*) those which should not be prescribed and (*c*) those which may be prescribed in certain circumstances. Any preparation not listed should be regarded as being in the last category.

The practitioner must supply (in a suitable container unless he administers it himself) any drug or appliance necessary before a supply can be obtained by the patient. If he has undertaken to supply drugs and appliances in any case he must do so.

If he has not so undertaken he must prescribe them on Form E.C.10. He must order what is necessary for the patient. Each order must be signed by the practitioner himself and must be an order in itself. An order to repeat a previous mixture or prescription of any kind must not be given. Although more than one prescription may be placed on a form a separate form must be used for each patient. The only exception to this is the special arrangement for stock orders for schools or institutions. Generally speaking only drugs included in the National Formulary can be so prescribed as stock orders, Dangerous Drugs and Fourth Schedule poisons being of course excluded.

Test Prescriptions

From time to time drugs and appliances are tested, and in order that this may be done the practitioner is required to comply with any reasonable request by the Executive Council to furnish orders for this purpose.

Prescribing of Appliances

A list of appliances which a general practitioner may prescribe is to be found at Appendix IV of the *Handbook for General Medical Practitioners* (Appendix IX of the Scottish Handbook). For the provision of other appliances the patient should be referred to a hospital for examination. Nursing and aftercare requisites are provided through the Local Health Authority. Renewal and repair of artificial limbs, invalid tricycles or wheelchairs are dealt with through the local Artificial Limb and Appliance Centre of the Ministry of Health.

Dispensing and Delivery of Medicines

Many general practitioners make arrangements of one kind or another for the delivery of medicines to patients' homes and thus help their patients. There is no legal obligation upon a doctor to do this, the obligation of a dispensing doctor being only to supply medicines at his surgery.

Subject to an appeal to the Minister, a practitioner under the National Health Service may be required by the Executive Council to supply drugs and appliances for patients on his list who live at least one mile from the nearest chemist, or otherwise would have difficulty in obtaining them from a chemist, unless he can show that he is not in the habit of supplying them for patients.

For this service he may receive a capitation payment in respect of each patient for whom he dispenses. This payment covers all drugs and appliances except those on a special list (*Handbook for General Medical Practitioners*, Appendix III (England and Wales), Appendix X (Scotland)). For these he either applies for additional payment or, if the patient agrees, gives a prescription on a special green Form E.C.10 (D).

The other method of payment for dispensing is for the doctor to choose to be paid for each of his prescriptions on the same basis as a chemist is paid.

Dispensing doctors are responsible for the collection from patients of the charges for prescriptions, and for elastic hosiery and for paying over the charges for prescriptions to the Executive Council. The prescribed payments for elastic hoisery are retained by the doctor and the amounts subsequently deducted from the payment made to him for supplying.

Joint Pricing Committee

The Joint Pricing Committees are set up under the National Health Service Act. There is a Joint Pricing Committee for the Executive Councils in England. It consists of eighteen members. On the Committee are four registered pharmacists and one medical practitioner. The Welsh Pricing Committee consists of fourteen members and includes three pharmacists and one medical practitioner.

In Scotland the equivalent Committee is the Drug Accounts Committee which consists of fifteen members and includes two pharmacists and two medical practitioners. These Committees receive reports from the various pricing bureaux in the country and from these reports, among other things, there may arise a request by the Joint Pricing Committee for investigation of excessive prescribing, either of an individual prescription or of the total prescribing costs.

Investigation of Excessive Prescribing

Inquiry as to excessive prescribing may be related to a single prescription or to a practitioner's total prescribing costs on the ground that they are substantially above the average of the area. Periodic reviews are made of the total cost of each practitioner's prescribing for a month and these are compared with the area average. His own figures and the area average are notified from time to time to every practitioner.

If there is deemed to be, prima facie, extravagant or unnecessary prescribing in that, by reason of the character or quantity of the drugs or appliances supplied, it is in excess of what was reasonably necessary for treatment the matter is referred to the Local Medical Committee for investigation.

The same considerations apply whether the practitioner is issuing prescriptions to be dispensed by a chemist or is supplying the drugs himself and furnishing accounts.

The Local Medical Committee notifies the practitioner as to the matters under inquiry and invites a statement from him, giving him also reasonable opportunity to appear before the Committee. The Committee has to decide whether the cost of prescribing has been more than was necessary and by what amount. The decision of the Committee is notified to the practitioner, the Executive Council and the Minister, with any statement it desires to make as to factors which should be borne in mind in deciding or recommending the withholding of any money from the practitioner's remuneration.

The practitioner may appeal within one month to the Minister who will then appoint referees to hear the appeal. If the Minister himself is dissatisfied with the findings of the Committee he may also appoint referees to hear the case. On hearing the findings of the Local Medical Committee or the result of the appeal the Executive Council may, if appropriate, recommend what sum of money should be withheld from the practitioner and the Minister will direct the withholding of whatever sum he thinks fit. The practitioner is entitled to appeal orally or in writing, to the Minister, against the amount to be withheld.

Visits by the Regional Medical Officer

When the prescribing of a practitioner, whose total prescribing costs are substantially above those of the average in the area, is called into question, the first step may be for the Regional Medical Officer to visit the practitioner by appointment to discuss the details of the doctor's prescribing for the month selected for review. The outcome of this interview may be that the practitioner is able to satisfy the Regional Medical Officer that the high cost was justified or unavoidable or, alternatively, the Regional Medical Officer may help by suggesting methods of reducing the costs without detriment to treatment and the matter is left for the time being. It may, however, be necessary to refer the matter to the Local Medical Committee at this stage for investigation as above.

Further Review

The practitioner's prescribing costs are reviewed some months later and a further, and probably more formal, visit is made by the Regional Medical Officer. The practitioner may invite a member of the Local Medical Committee to be present at this interview. Explanations given by the practitioner are subsequently set down and sent to him for amendment and signature. If further improvement seems likely, a suitable letter is addressed to the practitioner. If not, and the costs remain high, the matter is referred to the Local Medical Committee for formal investigation.

In Scotland these inquiries are not undertaken by the Regional Medical Officer, but steps are taken with a similar purpose by the Local Medical Committee.

The Prescribing of Foods and Toilet Preparations

The prescription of foods and toilet preparations, as such, is not permitted on Form E.C.10, and if a practitioner prescribes such a substance he is liable to be charged for the cost of the preparation. There are, however, substances which under some circumstances may be regarded as drugs, whereas normally they are regarded as foods or toilet preparations. A useful guide classifying a representative selection of preparations into Foods, Drugs and Toilet preparations is to be found in Appendix VIA of the *Handbook for General Medical Practitioners* (Appendix XI of the Scottish Handbook).

If the Executive Council considers that something which the practitioner has prescribed is not a drug, the practitioner will be notified that its cost will be recovered from him.

If he objects, the matter is referred to the Local Medical Committee. The practitioner, the Executive Council or the Local Medical Committee may, after the investigation, appeal to referees appointed by the Minister of Health. These referees cannot be officials of the Ministry.

Whether the investigation refers to costly prescribing or to the prescribing of a food, the practitioner has the right to defend himself either in person or in writing. He will need to justify the use of the costly preparation in the treatment of the patient, or to show that the alleged food was, in fact, to be regarded as a drug in the treatment of the particular patient. Whereas in the case of excessive prescribing of drugs a fine may be imposed in addition to the cost of the drug, only the cost of the food or toilet preparation that he has prescribed may be recovered from the practitioner, and not a fine.

The National Health Service (Medical Administration)

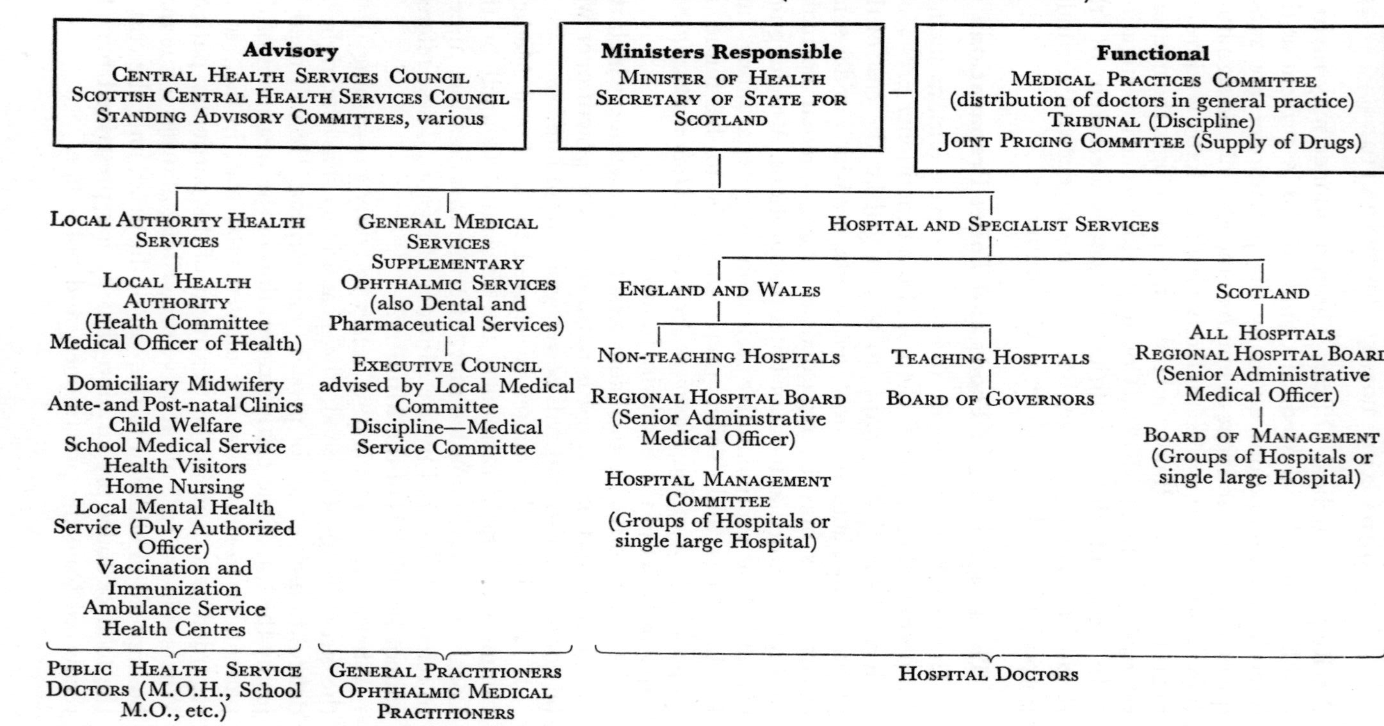

Geographical Administration of the National Health Service

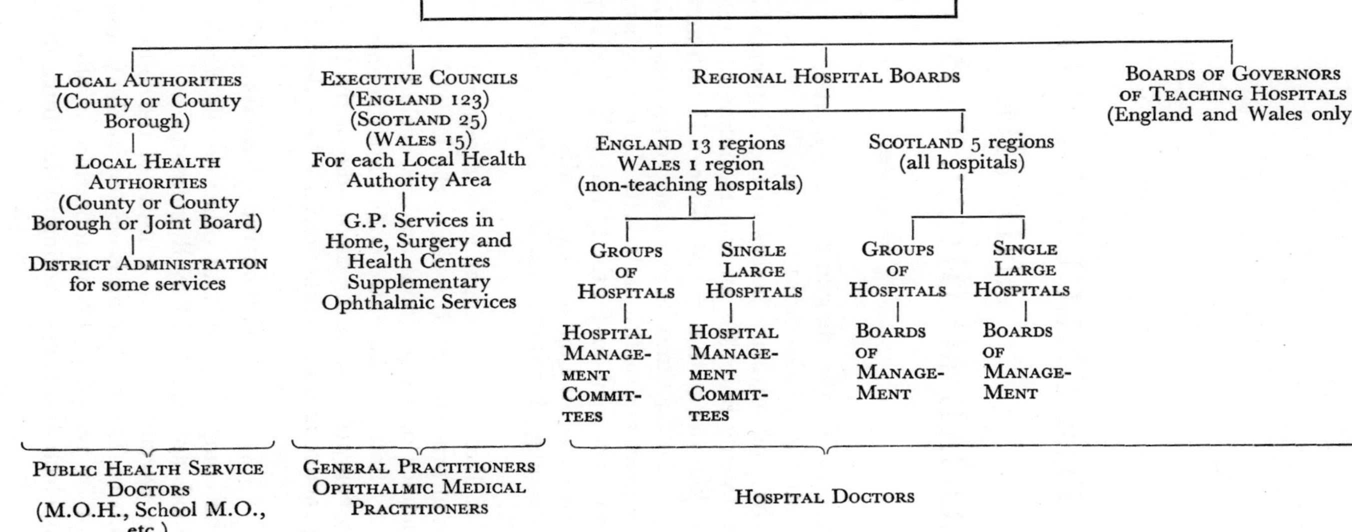

29

THE EXECUTIVE COUNCIL AND THE LOCAL MEDICAL COMMITTEE

Reference to the diagrams (on pp. 260, 261) will serve to indicate the relationship to one another of the various administrative and advisory bodies in the National Health Service. The starting point for an understanding of these relationships is the knowledge that the Minister of Health and the Secretary of State for Scotland have a duty to provide a hospital service and a general practitioner service. The administration of these services is carried out for the Ministers by the Regional Hospital Boards (and, in England and Wales, the Boards of Governors of Teaching Hospitals) and by the Executive Councils respectively.

The Executive Council is in direct relationship with the general practitioner. It looks to the Local Medical Committee for advice on professional matters, including those of a disciplinary nature. These two bodies are the ones that are principally concerned with the day-to-day activities of the doctor in his practice and their functions are here described.

Executive Councils

The composition of and other details respecting Executive Councils are laid down by Regulations.

An Executive Council consists of the following twenty-five members. The Chairman is elected by the Council. A member is not by reason of his membership or office debarred from being elected, sitting or voting in the House of Commons:

8 members appointed by the Local Health Authority;
5 members appointed by the Minister of Health;
7 members appointed by the Local Medical Committee;
3 members appointed by the Local Dental Committee;
2 members appointed by the Local Pharmaceutical Committee.

The Regulations are specially modified in some details as they apply to the Isles of Scilly. In Scotland also there are variations in numbers composing an Executive Council.

Members are appointed for three years and are eligible for reappointment. The Local Health Authority, the Local Medical Committee, the Local Pharmaceutical Committee and the Local Dental Committee are required to notify the Clerk to the Executive Council, who in his turn notifies the Minister of Health, of the name and address of any person appointed by them to the Executive Council.

Chairman

When the chair becomes vacant the Executive Council elects a Chairman at a special meeting called for the purpose.

Vice-Chairman

The Vice-Chairman is appointed by the Council and holds the office, so long as he remains a member, for whatever period is specified in the resolution appointing him.

Resignation of Member

A member may resign by giving notice in writing to the Clerk. The seat of a member is declared vacant if he has not attended a meeting for a period of six months without reasonable cause.

Vacation of Office

A member appointed by the Local Health Authority ceases to be a member of the Council upon ceasing to be a member or officer of the Local Health Authority, unless he is immediately re-elected to the Local Health Authority not later than the day of his retirement.

Disqualification from Membership

The Local Government Act, 1933 (Section 59, Sub-section 1, sub-paragraphs (*b*) and (*e*) subject to paragraphs ii, iii and v) are held to apply as if the section related to membership of an Executive Council. The effect of this section is to disqualify from membership by reason of bankruptcy, composition or arrangement with creditors or a sentence of imprisonment for three months without option of a fine.

Casual Vacancy

A casual vacancy is to be notified to the body which appointed the person whose membership has lapsed. This body fills the vacancy, the person so appointed holding office for the remainder of the term of his predecessor.

The Regulations lay down the procedure regarding meetings, officers, committees, standing orders and the like, and the requirements for the Supplementary Ophthalmic Services, including the appointment of the Ophthalmic Services Committee under Section 41 of the National Health Service Act (Scottish Act, Section 42).

Functions of the Executive Councils

The Acts require Executive Councils to keep lists of practitioners and of patients and to make arrangements for General Medical Services either at health centres or otherwise. Although the setting up of health centres is a function of the Local Health Authority, the provision of general medical services therefrom is the responsibility of the Executive Council. The Executive Councils are required to make arrangements for patients to choose a medical practitioner, subject to the consent of the medical practitioner or the limitation of his list. They must arrange for an allocation scheme so that patients unable to obtain acceptance on any practitioner's list may be allocated to one. They must also arrange for the issue, free of charge, by medical practitioners of certificates reasonably required by patients or required for the purposes of any enactment. A list of certificates under this head is to be found in Appendix E. The Council is also required to arrange for general dental and pharmaceutical services and to administer the Supplementary Ophthalmic Service.

Health Centres

The National Health Service Act (Section 21) states that it is the duty of Local Health Authorities to provide Health Centres for General Medical, Dental, Pharmaceutical and Local Health Authority Services, for out-patient and specialist services and for the exercise of their powers under the Public Health Act, 1936 (Section 179) and the Public Health (London) Act, 1936 (Section 298), which cover information on questions of health and disease, lectures, pictures and films. The preceding section of the Act leaves it to the Minister when to insist on the duty being carried out. In Scotland a similar duty is laid upon the Secretary of State who may delegate all or part of the function to Local Health Authorities, but only after consultation with the profession. In the Isles of Scilly the provision of Health Centres is permissive with the approval of the Minister and not a duty.

Section 46 of the Act lays down that in England and Wales, Health Centres shall be made available on such terms as may be agreed between the Executive Council and the Local Authority, or in default as determined by the Minister. The Executive Council may make such charges to practitioners using Health Centres as are necessary to defray what the Council pays to the Local Health Authority. Although the Local Health Authority administers the Health Centres and provides the staff, it does not employ medical practitioners for providing general medical services. These are in contract with the Executive Council in the ordinary way.

In Scotland (N.H.S. (Scotland) Act, 1947, Section 15), the corresponding Terms and Conditions are determined by the Secretary of State.

Default Powers of Minister

If the Minister, following a complaint or otherwise, is of opinion that one of the statutory bodies in the National Health Service, for example the Executive Council, the Ophthalmic Services Committee or the Medical Practices Committee, has failed to carry out its functions or to comply with the Regulations or Directions, he is empowered under the National Health Service Act to make an order declaring the body to be in default. The members thereupon vacate their office and new members are appointed. The Minister can order someone to act for the body pending the appointment of new members.

The Local Medical Committee

The National Health Service Act, 1946, Section 32 (N.H.S. (Scotland) Act, 1947, Section 33) provides for the setting up of a committee of doctors corresponding to the area of each Executive Council and known as the Local Medical Committee. The Committee is officially recognized as the body representing the N.H.S. general practitioners in the area.

The Committee is consulted, in some instances compulsorily, by the Executive Council on a large number of matters affecting general practitioners and their work. Not only does it act thus in an advisory capacity to the Executive Council, but it is also a useful source of advice and help to the general practitioners themselves.

Functions

It has powers, in certain instances, of considering a complaint by one practitioner against another. It may be required to investigate a practitioner's prescribing, his keeping of records or his certification.

The Local Medical Committee nominates the seven medical members of the Executive Council and, often, members of other Committees.

Representatives of Local Medical Committees meet at least once a year in a Conference of Local Medical Committees where much of the policy of general medical practitioners in the National Health Service is formulated. Instructions are given by the Conference to its executive which is the General Medical Services Committee. This Committee, while autonomous in the field of N.H.S. general practice, is a Committee of the Council of the British Medical Association and reports to it as well as conducting negotiations with the Government on matters affecting general practitioners in the National Health Service.

In order to meet the costs of the Local Medical Committee, deductions may be made by the Executive Council from the remuneration of general practitioners. This is done either at the request of the Local Medical Committee, subject to the approval of the Minister or the Secretary of State, or by voluntary authorizations by the practitioners. The deductions are usually made in proportion to the numbers on the practitioners' lists.

30

DISTRIBUTION OF DOCTORS: THE MEDICAL PRACTICES COMMITTEES

A reference to the diagram on p. 260 will show that in addition to the Executive Council and the Local Medical Committee, whose interest in the general practitioner is a continuing affair, there are other bodies within whose orbit the general practitioner may occasionally come.

Firstly there is the Medical Practices Committee whose duty it is to watch over the distribution of doctors, and generally to ensure that the requirements of the Acts and Regulations relating to entry into general practice are observed. Secondly there is the disciplinary machinery of the Medical Services Committees and the Tribunal with whom the general practitioner will be concerned only when allegations have been made that his conduct has been contrary to his Terms of Service. The machinery by which these bodies work is described below.

The Medical Practices Committee

Constitution and Functions

The Medical Practices Committee is set up under Section 34 of the Act and its constitution is laid down in the Sixth Schedule to the Act. The Committee is appointed by the Minister after consultation with representatives of the profession, and consists of a Chairman, who is a medical practitioner, and eight other members, of which six are medical practitioners. Of the six at least five must be actively engaged in medical practice. Members are appointed for a period of three years and are eligible for reappointment. A member appointed as a person actively engaged in practice who ceases to be so engaged is deemed to have resigned his membership of the Committee.

The Medical Practices Committee is charged with the duty of securing the necessary distribution of doctors by considering and determining applications for inclusion in the list of an Executive Council.

Applications to Practise

The application must first go to the Executive Council which refers the matter to the Medical Practices Committee, which must not refuse the application unless there are already sufficient doctors providing general medical services in the area (restricted area), or if the number of applicants for a vacancy exceeds the number required to provide an adequate number in the area. In the latter case the Medical Practices Committee shall select the most suitable applicant after consultation with the Executive Council, which in its turn shall have consulted the Local Medical Committee. An unsuccessful applicant has a right of appeal to the Minister. Notice of appeal must be sent to the Minister normally within seven days of the receipt of the decision of the Medical Practices Committee. If this right is exercised a successful applicant may not be included in the list until the appeal has been heard and decided. The Minister may grant the appeal unconditionally or subject to conditions. The decision may be that both the successful applicant and the appellant are, as a result of a decision by the Minister, included in the list, or either one of them.

If the successful applicant is not to be included in the list should the appellant win his appeal, then the successful applicant must be a party to the appeal and can thereafter bring no further appeal in respect of the application in question.

Designation of Areas

For the purposes of ensuring the best distribution of doctors all areas of England and Wales are categorized by the Medical Practices Committee as belonging for the time being to one of the following categories:

(*a*) Restricted—additional doctors not necessary.
(*b*) Intermediate or doubtful.

(*c*) Designated—additional doctors needed. Initial Practice Allowances may be paid.

An application to practise in a restricted area except by being appointed to a vacancy will, as has been pointed out above, probably be refused. If the area is an intermediate one the application will be considered on its merits, and if a designated area the application will normally be granted unless more doctors than are necessary apply at the same time.

The Medical Practices Committee is constantly revising the categorization of areas and any changes are announced in the medical press. Categorization is normally of comparatively small areas and the whole area of an Executive Council will not necessarily be in the same category.

Partnerships

There is a special provision that the Medical Practices Committee, and on appeal the Minister, shall have special regard to a desire expressed by an applicant to practise in partnership with a doctor or doctors already providing general medical services in the area. Generally speaking this means that when a partner in a bona fide partnership resigns the remaining partner or partners shall be permitted to choose his successor. For this purpose it is generally required that a bona fide partnership shall have existed for at least one year before the outgoing practitioner retires.

The Scottish Medical Practices Committee

The Scottish Medical Practices Committee is appointed by the Secretary of State for Scotland and consists of a Chairman, who is a medical practitioner, and five other members of whom three must be medical practitioners actively engaged in medical practice. In other respects the conditions regarding membership are similar to those of the Medical Practices Committee (England and Wales).

In Scotland, appointments to vacancies are made by the Executive Council, from whose decision there is a right of appeal to the Scottish Medical Practices Committee. The appeal may be against a decision to appoint no successor to a practice as well as against the appointment of a particular successor.

The Scottish Medical Practices Committee also hears appeals

from doctors against decisions of the Executive Council about the employment of assistants and on various other points. The Committee has other functions similar to the English Medical Practices Committee but it does not categorize the areas as is done in England and Wales. Each application to practise is considered on its merits. In its Annual Report the Committee gives a list of areas where additional doctors appear to be required. A doctor starting in practice in one of these areas could expect to receive the Initial Practice Allowance, if he qualifies in other respects.

Applications to start a new practice are referred by the Executive Council to the Scottish Medical Practices Committee with whom the decision rests. The doctor may appeal against the decision to the Secretary of State.

Goodwill and Doctors' Houses

The Acts specifically prohibit the sale or purchase of the goodwill or any part of the goodwill of a National Health Service practice. The intention of the Acts is quite clear. It is to prohibit the proffering or acceptance of any consideration or benefit in return for a practice or part of a practice. It is not only a question of the passage of money from one party to the other. The Acts are so worded as to make it clear that the net is spread very widely indeed. In fact it is a total prohibition on the bartering of practices in the Service.

The restriction is absolute and any attempt to evade it by such subterfuges as the incoming practitioner working for a time as assistant or partner for an unreasonably small salary or share, or the payment of a sum of money for an allegedly distinct private practice, will be regarded as meriting the same penalty as would be merited by a straightforward sale of the goodwill.

If, for example, for a valuable consideration A does, or refrains from doing, any act or allows any act to be done for the purpose of facilitating the succession of B to the practice, they may be guilty of an offence.

If B, or his representative, whether before or after succession gives any consideration to A it will be regarded as a purchase of goodwill unless it can be shown that no part of the consideration is in respect of the goodwill.

These considerations do not apply to anything properly done in the acquisition of premises, in pursuance of a partnership agreement made before the appointed day or to performance of services as an assistant. The rights under a partnership agreement made before the appointed day may not be sold to anyone else.

Touching this matter of concealed sale, the *British Medical Journal* has warned that "the sale of goodwill is prohibited no matter how indirect that sale may be. The performance of services for an unreasonably low return is deemed to constitute the sale of goodwill whatever the intention of the parties may be." The prohibition is not confined to the goodwill of the National Health Service part of the practice. A practitioner can, however, sell a practice in an area of an Executive Council on whose list his name has never been entered.

Penalties

The penalty for contravention is a fine not exceeding an amount which will secure that the offender derives no benefit from the offence, together with an additional sum of £500, or to imprisonment not exceeding three months, or both fine and imprisonment. An offence is regarded as committed whether by the practitioner himself, be he purchaser or vendor, or any person acting on his behalf, or an executor, and whether it is effected by a single transaction or by a series of transactions. On conviction penalties may be imposed accordingly.

The Sale of the Doctor's House

The possibility of evasion of the restriction by the sale or letting of the doctor's house for an inflated figure, is excluded by specific mention of this point in Section 35 of the Act (Scottish Act, Section 36).

A practitioner may not purchase or rent another practitioner's house for a sum substantially in excess of its normal value for residential purposes if it is to be used for practice purposes. A retiring doctor, or the widow of a doctor, may dispose of the practice house that he or she owns to whomsoever he or she wishes and the restriction on the purchase price only applies if the house is to be used for practice purposes. Under certain conditions the house may not be used for practice under the National Health Service other than by the doctor appointed as the successor to the National Health Service practice (see p. 269). The Executive Council, however, has no powers of acquisition of any practice premises. Under the Acts the Minister (or Secretary of State) has power to acquire premises for the purposes of the Health Service, but it has been officially stated that such power is unlikely to be used in respect of general practitioners' houses.

In a case heard before Mr Justice Vaisey (*Brown* v. *King*, Chancery Division, December 12th, 1955) the Judge distinguished between the value of a house being enhanced because it was suitable and equipped for the purposes of medical practice and a price inflated by reason of the goodwill of the practice. In the former case he saw no contravention of Section 35 of the National Health Service Act, 1946.

> 'The criterion,' said the Judge, 'is not the fact that the premises are fit for use or are especially fit for use as the residence or place of business of a medical practitioner; the criterion is the premises having been previously used "for the purposes of a medical practice". The criterion is whether that fact enhances the value—that is to say, if the consideration takes that into account—it is not the fact that the premises are used "for the purposes of a medical practice" nor the fact that the premises are well suited "for the purposes of a medical practice". The criterion is as to whether the premises are sold for more than they would have realized if the premises had not previously been used for the purposes of a medical practice.'

A practitioner, or his representative, who is in doubt as to whether or not any proposed transaction involves the sale of goodwill, may apply to the Medical Practices Committee or, the Scottish Medical Practices Committee which, if satisfied that there is no contravention of the relevant section of the Acts, will issue a certificate to that effect. Such certificate constitutes a defence to any charge of contravention of the provisions, unless it can be shown that the Medical Practices Committee was not informed of all the material circumstances, or that there was misrepresentation.

In any scrutiny by either Medical Practices Committee of

any transaction in this context, inquiry will be made into the allocation of shares in a partnership. If the incoming partner's share falls below a reasonable proportion the approval of the Committee is not likely to be forthcoming. The usual view held is that the initial share of the junior partner should be at least a quarter of the total profits; in a two-doctor partnership and in a multiple partnership at least one-third of the share held by the partner with the maximum share. There should be adequate provision for the share to increase with a view to reaching approximate parity within five to ten years.

31

MEDICAL SERVICE COMMITTEES AND THE TRIBUNAL

Medical Service Committees

Any complaint against a general practitioner alleging a failure to comply with the Terms of Service falls to be investigated by a Medical Service Committee. This Committee consists of a Chairman and six members, of whom three are doctors selected by the Local Medical Committee and three laymen appointed by and from the lay members of the Executive Council. The Chairman is a lay person appointed at a special meeting of the Medical Services Committee or, should they fail to elect a Chairman (or should a statement be submitted by members of the Committee objecting to the Chairman that has been appointed), a person appointed by the Executive Council or by the Minister.

The complaint may, for example, be by a patient regarding his treatment or by the Ministry of Pensions and National Insurance alleging improper certification. The right of complaint from an individual is restricted to the patient, the patient's spouse, someone acting with the authority of the patient or a person acting on behalf of a patient who is incapable or is under eighteen. The complaint must be made in writing to the Clerk of the Executive Council within six weeks of the alleged offence. If reasonable cause is given the complaint can be received within eight weeks or, if either the practitioner agrees or the Minister's consent has been obtained, at an even later date. In the case of consent being obtained from the Minister, full reasons for delay have to be furnished to the

Minister and to the practitioner and the latter may send to the Minister a statement as to why he considers the investigation should not take place.

Where a complaint is made against a general practitioner in respect of the acts and commissions of a deputy whose name is also included in the medical list, the complaint shall be deemed to have been made against both practitioners. A practitioner on the list of an Executive Council is himself responsible for failure to comply with the Terms of Service in relation to another doctor's patient. Both principal and deputy come within the jurisdiction of the Executive Council, but the Medical Service Committee may dismiss the case against the principal without hearing if, in the opinion of the Chairman, there are no prima facie grounds of complaint against him personally and he has made all proper and necessary deputizing arrangements.

Before replying to the letter from the Executive Council embodying the complaint the practitioner is advised to consult the Local Medical Committee or his medical defence organization, by whom he should be guided as to the conduct of his case.

The hearing before the Committee is private. A practitioner appearing before a Medical Service Committee may be assisted in the presentation of his case by some other person, except that he must not be a Counsel, solicitor or other paid advocate.

The Committee reports its findings to the Executive Council which may, as a result of an adverse finding, recommend the withholding of money from the doctor's remuneration or the imposition of a special limit on the size of his list. Both practitioner and complainant have a right of appeal to the Minister which must be notified within one month of receiving the decision of the Executive Council. The Executive Council may also make representations to the Tribunal to the effect that the practitioner's name should not remain on the Council's list.

There are Dental Service Committees and Pharmaceutical Service Committees as well. The corresponding Committee in respect of the Supplementary Ophthalmic Service is known as the Ophthalmic Investigation Committee. In addition, cases in which there are concerned, for example, a doctor and a chemist, are heard by a Joint Services Committee, which is constituted suitably for the purpose.

Tribunals

Section 42 of the National Health Service Act (Section 43 of the Scottish Act) provides for the setting up of a Tribunal for the purpose of inquiring into cases in which representations are made, in a prescribed manner, by an Executive Council or by an individual to the effect that the continued inclusion of any person in any Executive Council list would be prejudicial to the efficiency of the Service. The representations may refer to general practitioners, pharmacists, dentists or to medical practitioners, ophthalmic opticians or dispensing opticians undertaking Supplementary Ophthalmic Services.

The Chairman of the Tribunal must be a practising barrister, advocate or solicitor of not less than ten years standing and he is appointed by the Lord Chancellor (in Scotland, by the Lord President of the Court of Session). There are two members, other than the Chairman; one is appointed by the Minister of Health or Secretary of State after consultation with representatives of Executive Councils and the other, known as 'the practitioner member', is one of a panel of six which is appointed by the Minister after consultation with the several professional organizations concerned. The panel consists of a medical practitioner, a dental practitioner, a medical practitioner practising as an oculist, an ophthalmic optician, a dispensing optician and a registered pharmaceutical chemist. The professional member appropriate to the case in question is selected. If he is unable to act, a deputy of similar qualifications may be appointed.

The Tribunal is bound to hear a case about which representations have been made by an Executive Council, but is not compelled to do so where the representations come from any other source. There are regulations for procedure in the inquiry which, among other things, allow for an opportunity for the individual to appear in person and to be represented if he so wishes by Counsel, solicitor, or some other person.

If, having heard the inquiry, the Tribunal finds that continued inclusion in the Executive Council list would be prejudicial to the Service, the Tribunal directs that the name of the individual shall be removed from the list and may also direct exclusion of the name from or removal from any other corresponding list. Thus an adverse verdict following a complaint by one Executive Council may result in removal from other Executive Council lists, nor may the offender be accepted on these other lists until such time as the Tribunal or the Minister may direct otherwise.

The Executive Council must remove the name at the end of the period allowed for appeal; there being provision for appeal (but by the respondent only) to the Minister who may confirm or revoke the findings of the Tribunal. The appeal will be heard by a person appointed by the Minister before whom the appellant may appear and may call witnesses or other evidence. The hearing either before the Tribunal or on appeal may be in public if the accused so requests. The procedure in Scotland is similar, the Secretary of State acting in place of the Minister of Health. There is provision for reciprocity between the two countries.

Regulations also provide for publication of decisions of the Tribunal or the Minister to disqualify a name from any list, and also for a decision effecting the removal of any disqualification imposed.

Any disqualification imposed under similar regulations before the appointed day (National Health Insurance Act, 1936, and Acts repealed by it) remains valid until the Tribunal or the Minister directs to the contrary.

The inquiry of the Tribunal relates to the National Health Service and to the effect upon its efficiency of the practitioner's remaining in the service. It differs, therefore, from an inquiry of the Disciplinary Committee of the General Medical Council which inquires into the conduct of a doctor as a doctor and not necessarily as one engaged in the National Health Service. Removal from the register as the result of such an inquiry will automatically bar the doctor from further participation in the National Health Service as a medical practitioner.

32

REMUNERATION IN THE NATIONAL HEALTH SERVICE

Before the inception of the National Health Service a Committee under Sir Will Spens was set up with terms of reference which called upon it to state what should be the average net remuneration, from all sources, of general practitioners in order that the correct rates of remuneration in the National Health Service could be determined.

The Committee reported its views on net remuneration in terms of the 1939 value of money and 'left it to others' to determine what the rate should be having regard to the change in the value of money since 1939. The method of payment by capitation fee was retained as a result of the Spens Report, which was accepted by the Government and by the profession before they entered the National Health Service.

The general principles applying to the various sources of remuneration are here described. A detailed description of the exact provisions and requirements under each heading is to be found in the *Handbook for General Medical Practitioners*, together with the current rates of payment.*

Method of Payment by Capitation Fee

The payment of general practitioners in the National Health Service is derived from a sum of money known as the Global Pool, the amount of which is determined centrally. From this sum certain deductions are made to allow for other sources of income such as private practice and appointments and fees outwith the National Health Service. The net figure, after these deductions, is called the Central Pool.

The Central Pool, after deduction of the mileage fund and

* In 1957 an interim increase of 5% on basic rates was applied.

sums for such services as temporary residents and maternity services and loadings, is distributed to the Executive Councils in proportion to the numbers on lists in each Executive Council area. The Local Pool thus formed is used by the Executive Council for the remuneration of the individual practitioners on the Council's list, and must be fully expended by them for that purpose. Each practitioner receives, broadly, a proportion of this Pool corresponding to the proportion of patients in the area that are on his list. Each patient brings to the practitioner a capitation fee. A practitioner having more than 500 patients on his list, receives from the Central Pool an additional sum, known as a 'loading', for each patient between 501 and 1,500. Thus a practitioner having 1,250 patients will receive 1,250 capitation fees and, in addition, a 'loading' for 750 patients. A practitioner having more than 1,500 patients on his list receives 'loading' for 1,000 patients and a capitation fee for each patient up to the maximum permitted (3,500, with a small permitted tolerance).

When an assistant is employed, which is with permission of the Executive Council, an additional number of 2,000 patients is permitted, the remuneration of the assistant being the responsibility of the principal. An assistant cannot attract further 'loadings'.

Notional Lists in Partnerships

The total permitted list of a partnership (without an assistant) must not exceed the aggregate of the maxima allowed to each partner. Thus a partnership of three may have an aggregate list of 10,500. It is permissible for one of these partners to have more than the maximum on his list up to 4,500, provided that the partnership aggregate does not exceed the total permitted to the three. All three may qualify for the loadings. Whatever the aggregate numbers on the lists of the partners they may be so adjusted to form notional lists in order that the partnership may claim the maximum benefit from the loadings.

An example from a partnership with smaller numbers will make this point clear. Dr A has a list of 1,200, Dr B. 700 and Dr C. 2,000. Taken individually their entitlement to loadings would be 700, 200 and 1,000 respectively, making a total of 1,900 loadings for the partnership. For this purpose, however, a notional adjustment of lists can be made so that the fullest advantage may be obtained and the largest possible number of loadings accrue to the partnership.

	Actual lists	*Notional lists*
Dr A	1,200	1,500
Dr B	700	900
Dr C	2,000	1,500
	3,900	3,900

The total number of patients is the same but the loadings are now 1,000, 400 and 1,000, a total of 2,400 and a definite advantage over the previous figure.

In order to claim the number of loadings which is most advantageous to the partnership, each practitioner must be in practice as a principal and must be entitled to a share of the profits which is not less than one-third of the share of any other partner. For a partnership to qualify for loadings in respect of a salaried partner, his salary must be at least one-third of the net income of any other partner and there must be provision for him to receive a proportionate addition, should the net earnings of the practice exceed a sum sufficient to provide the guaranteed minimum income.

The Mileage Fund

The mileage fund, which in reality is a rural practices fund, is a sum of money deducted from the Central Pool and distributed to those Executive Councils in whose areas mileage schemes operate. Payments are made to practitioners, by Executive Councils, in accordance with the mileage scheme adopted for the area and in respect of patients living more than two miles from the practitioner's surgery or residence. Each mile is regarded as a unit for this purpose, and distribution is in proportion to the number of units claimed by each practitioner in respect of patients on his list. Although indirectly they may do so, mileage payments should not be thought of as an attempt to compensate the practitioner for the expense of running his car to visit the patient at a distance (except in the case of mileage payments for Maternity Medical Services, which are a first charge on this fund), but rather as a compensation for sparsity of population and the greater difficulties of visiting patients in a rural area, occasioned by time and distance. The payment in respect of any one patient is the same whether he is visited many times in a year or not at all.

Special Payments

Provision may be made in any area for payments for emergency calls to patients not on the practitioner's list, and for visits which present special difficulties of access and necessitate unusual expenditure of time and sometimes, as for example where ferries have to be used, of money. Full particulars of local schemes may be obtained by reference to the Clerk to the Executive Council.

Other payments which are made in certain instances are for anaesthetics, special hardship payments to certain doctors who suffered financial loss as a result of the new methods of remuneration introduced in April, 1953, for emergency treatment, for temporary residents, inducement payments and Initial Practice Allowances. Fees for the supervision of trainee general practitioners and payments for maternity medical services and for the provision of drugs and appliances are not drawn from the Central Pool. In Scotland there are special arrangements, subject to the approval of the Secretary of State in each case, for remuneration of practitioners providing medical services to workmen residing in camps.

Inducement Payments

These payments are made in certain circumstances in order to encourage doctors to practise in areas which are sparsely populated, or are otherwise unattractive to doctors and in which the ordinary remuneration is too little to ensure the maintenance of an adequate service. Applications for inducement payments are considered by the Executive Council in consultation with the Local Medical Committee and are subject to approval by the Minister or Secretary of State. The amount awarded is subject to annual review. The doctor is required to supply, with his application, information regarding his professional income from all sources and the general circumstances of his practice.

Initial Practice Allowance

This allowance is given to assist a doctor setting up in a new single-handed practice, where a new practice is necessary to ensure an adequate service and sometimes for the same reason to a doctor filling a small practice vacancy. The allowance is payable for a maximum of three years and is on a sliding scale related to the earnings of the practice. The object of the allowance is to enable the doctor to receive a competence during the time he is establishing a satisfactory practice.

Group Practice Loans

A sum of money from the general practitioners' Pool is set aside annually to assist practitioners in the National Health Service in building up a group practice. In general, the money is provided in the form of an interest free loan for the acquisition of land and the erection of group practice surgeries, and for developing and converting existing premises for the same purpose.

The full definition of group practice for this purpose is set out in the *Handbook for General Medical Practitioners*. Usually at least three doctors (possibly two in some rural areas) are required to form the proposed group practice. Application for a group practice loan is made to the Executive Council, which will consult the Local Medical Committee. The final decision rests with a special Committee known as the Group Practices Loan Committee, on which the General Medical Services Committee is strongly represented.

In Scotland the exact definition of group practice is sometimes departed from, and practitioners are advised not to be deterred from applying for a loan should their group practice arrangements differ from the definition.

33

OTHER SERVICES IN THE NATIONAL HEALTH SERVICE

In his general practice work the doctor is constantly finding himself in close relationship, in the interest of his patients, with other services, in particular the Ophthalmic, Pharmaceutical and Dental Services. It is helpful to the doctor to know something of these services so that he may use them in the best interests of his patients.

Domiciliary Consultations

A general practitioner requiring a specialist opinion on a patient who is, by reason of his medical condition, unfit to be sent to hospital for the purpose may request a domiciliary visit from the specialist. A domiciliary visit is described as a visit to the patient's home, at the request of the general practitioner and normally in his company, to advise on the diagnosis or treatment of a patient who on medical grounds cannot attend hospital.

Specialists who may be called out to domiciliary consultations are those who have agreed to do so in their contract with the Regional Hospital Board or Board of Governors. They are usually Consultants, but in some instances, normally in an area in which an adequate Consultant service for the purpose is not available, Senior Hospital Medical Officers may be authorised to undertake domiciliary consultations. Except that whole-time specialists do not receive a fee for the first eight consultations in each quarter, specialists are entitled to a fee for each consultation, for mileage and in some instances for the use of apparatus. The number of consultations in respect of which a fee is payable to any one specialist is subject to a maximum of 200 in any year.

Arrangements for domiciliary visits when required are made by application either to the hospital or directly to the specialist at his private address. Specifically excluded from the category of domiciliary consultations qualifying for payment are:

(i) visits made at the instance of a hospital or specialist to review the urgency of a proposed admission to hospital or to continue or supervise treatment initiated or prescribed at a hospital or clinic;
(ii) visits made by a chest physician to a case of tuberculosis under active treatment;
(iii) visits undertaken as part of the work done for a Local Health Authority.

A domiciliary consultation may take place in the patient's home, which means the place where the patient is for the time being resident and may include a hotel, residential school or old people's home, but it does not include a private nursing home except in the instance of bona fide residents who live permanently in nursing homes.

Visits by obstetricians or paediatricians accompanied by anaesthetists, where required, may be made available in an emergency for a patient who has been admitted for her confinement to a private maternity home or for her baby during her stay in the maternity home when it is not feasible on medical grounds for the patient to be removed to hospital.

The general practitioner will be called upon to sign a form stating that the consultation at the home of the patient was necessary on medical grounds.

The Regional Psychiatrist

Local Health Authorities under Sections 28 and 51 of the National Health Service Act and under the Lunacy and Mental Treatments Acts and Mental Deficiency Acts, are required to secure that patients who are mentally ill or mentally defective are brought under care by arrangements with the Regional Hospital Board. A regional psychiatrist or other practitioner experienced in mental health is made available for consultation in this particular context.

Ophthalmic Services

Section 41 of the National Health Service Act and Section 42 of the Scottish Act provide for Ophthalmic Services. It is intended that eventually all ophthalmic services shall be provided solely through the Hospital and Specialist Services. When the Minister and the Secretary of State are satisfied that adequate services exist in an area for the provision of all ophthalmic requirements they will be fulfilled solely from that source. Until that point is reached the Supplementary Ophthalmic Service will continue to operate. This Service is conducted by the Executive Council and is strictly limited in its scope, the only treatment provided being the correction of errors of refraction. The sole supply of optical appliances other than spectacles is under the Hospital Service.

The functions of the Executive Council in this connexion are to be found in the N.H.S. (Executive Council) Regulations.* The Council makes arrangements for and keeps lists of medical practitioners and ophthalmic opticians for sight testing, and ophthalmic and dispensing opticians for the dispensing of glasses.

Ophthalmic Services Committee

It discharges its duties with relation to the Supplementary Ophthalmic Service through an Ophthalmic Services Committee.

The administrative functions include the maintenance of the ophthalmic list, approval of prescriptions and payments and decisions as to carelessness in breakages or loss of glasses in relation to repair or replacement. The Committee includes members appointed by the Executive Council, by ophthalmic medical practitioners and by opticians.

Ophthalmic Medical Practitioners

Medical practitioners having the prescribed qualifications have the right to be included in the ophthalmic list and thus to see and prescribe for patients applying for treatment under the Supplementary Ophthalmic Service. The qualifications have to be approved by 'a central professional Committee

* See Appendix D.

recognized by the Minister'. This Committee, known as the Ophthalmic Qualifications Committee, consists of members nominated equally by the Ophthalmic Group Committee of the British Medical Association and by the Faculty of Ophthalmologists.

In order to obtain approval of the Committee, an applicant must fulfil certain requirements such as having held appointments of a certain status in an ophthalmic department or he should have a diploma in the subject and have held an appointment in an approved ophthalmic hospital or department. The precise requirements are set out on the admission form which is obtained from the Secretary of the Ophthalmic Qualifications Committee, Tavistock House, Tavistock Square, London, W.C.1.

The Terms of Service for Ophthalmic Medical Practitioners require him to give proper care and attention to the testing of sight and to provide adequate premises for the purpose. He must keep proper records which are open to inspection by any officer of the Ministry. He may accept no fee for Supplementary Ophthalmic Services except that paid by the Executive Council, though he is permitted to charge the patient for a broken appointment or for a home visit at the request of the patient. If treatment other than the provision of glasses is indicated the Ophthalmic Medical Practitioner must refer the patient back to the general practitioner who may then refer the patient to the hospital eye service but not to another Ophthalmic Medical Practitioner. The practitioner must also be informed if the patient does not require glasses or if glasses are unlikely to provide satisfactory vision, or if the patient should return for further examination within six months.

The patient may apply to the Ophthalmic Medical Practitioner or optician for further examination, without the need for a further Form O.S.C.1, after an interval of one year.*

Reference of Patients for Eye Testing

The general practitioner wishing to refer a patient to the Service certifies that: 'I have examined you and that, in my opinion you require to have your sight tested.' This may be

* The possibility of requiring Form O.S.C.1 for subsequent examinations is under discussion.

done on the form provided, O.S.C.1, or in similar terms on ordinary notepaper. Any registered medical practitioner, whether or not in the National Health Service, may refer a patient in this manner. The patient has the right to choose any medical practitioner or ophthalmic optician on the list for the examination and to him he presents the completed certificate. The general practitioner has the right to advise the patient as to whom he should consult if he deems such advice to be in the patient's interest. Subsequently, if glasses are prescribed, the patient has free choice of optician for the dispensing, from among those on the list. For this purpose the prescription is written on Form O.S.C.2, which is sent by the examiner to the Clerk of the Council for endorsement. The Clerk sends it to the patient who presents it to the optician of his choice to have his glasses dispensed.

Pharmaceutical Services

The Act places upon Executive Councils the duty of providing for Pharmaceutical Services so that any person receiving General Medical or Dental Services under the Act can obtain proper medicines, drugs and prescribed appliances ordered by practitioners. These arrangements can only be made with registered pharmaceutical chemists or authorised sellers of poisons (within the meaning of the Pharmacy and Poisons Act, 1933) who undertake that dispensing is only undertaken by or under the direct supervision of a registered pharmaceutical chemist, or by a person who for three years before December 16th, 1911, acted as dispenser to a medical practitioner or to a public institution. The Terms of Service for Pharmacists are to be found in the Fourth Schedule to the National Health Service (General Medical and Pharmaceutical) Regulations for England and Wales and for Scotland. Local Health Authorities (in Scotland the Secretary of State) are permitted to employ pharmaceutical chemists at health centres.

The Regulations both for England and Wales, and for Scotland, provide for arrangements for the supply of drugs by the practitioners themselves. There are slight differences as between England and Wales and Scotland, but in general an Executive Council may request or require a practitioner to undertake dispensing and the provision of drugs for patients on his list where, owing to distance or inadequacy of means of communication, the patient would have serious difficulty in obtaining his medicines from a chemist. In the English Regulations distance of more than one mile from a chemist in a rural area is specifically mentioned as a reason for this purpose. A practitioner is not required to dispense if he can satisfy the Executive Council (or on appeal the Minister or Secretary of State) that he is not in the habit of supplying drugs. In any case he is entitled to reasonable notice of the requirement or its discontinuation.

In no circumstances is a practitioner permitted to prescribe or supply drugs, medicines or appliances under these Regulations to a private patient.

Dental Services

Dental Services are provided for under the National Health Service Acts and various Regulations.

The dental services in the hospitals are organized similarly to the medical services in hospitals under Part II of the Acts, the appointment of dental practitioners to the hospitals being under arrangements similar to those for medical practitioners.

General Dental Services are provided for under Part IV of the Acts. The employment of dental practitioners differs from that of medical practitioners in general practice (National Health Service Act, 1946, Section 40, National Health Service (Scotland) Act, 1947, Section 39 and Regulations). As opposed to the guarantee of general medical services for all, general dental services are only provided in so far as there are sufficient dental practitioners to do so.

The Executive Council prepares and maintains a list of general dental practitioners willing to provide general dental services under the Acts. The dentists are paid for the services they provide not, as in the case of doctors, by capitation fees but according to a scale of fees for each service provided, on the authority of the Dental Estimates Board. Certain types of treatment may be undertaken without prior approval; in other cases prior approval must be obtained by the dentist from the Dental Estimates Board.

There is free choice of dentist for patients. They may apply for treatment to any dentist on the Executive Council list. A dentist may agree to treat the patient under the National Health Service arrangements or may decline to do so, as he pleases.

The National Health Service Acts, 1951 and 1952, provide for part payment of the cost of treatment by the patient, except those under twenty-one years and expectant and nursing mothers. If called upon to do so, the patient accepting treatment under the Service must submit to an examination by a dental officer appointed for the purpose of checking the treatment.

Once the dentist has agreed to provide the necessary treatment under the Service, he is required to complete it. The dentist is responsible for the provision of a medical or dental practitioner to administer an anaesthetic for his patient where this is necessary, and the choice of the individual is his. He is also required to visit the patient at home or in a nursing home if within five miles of his surgery and the patient's condition requires it.

The Executive Council may arrange for dentists to work in a health centre by employing them on a whole-time or a part-time salaried basis, on a sessional basis, or under the General Dental Services Scheme (above) by their renting accommodation at the centre.

The Acts lay a duty upon Local Authorities to provide dental services for priority classes which are, for this purpose, expectant and nursing mothers and children in connexion with the Maternity and Child Welfare Service and the School Dental Service. Patients entitled to treatment under these Services may, however, if they so wish, obtain treatment under the General Dental Service or make arrangements for dental treatment under a private practitioner.

Dental practitioners working in the National Health Service are subject to disciplinary procedure similar to those for medical practitioners. There are Dental Service Committees, some members of which are appointed by the Local Dental Committee, and a Tribunal.

Section 79 of the National Health Service Act, 1946 (National Health Service (Scotland) Act, 1947, Section 80) defines a 'dental practitioner' as a person registered in the dentists' register under the Dentists' Acts, 1878 to 1923. Thus although registered medical practitioners are permitted to practise dentistry, they are not eligible to practise dentistry under the National Health Service Acts unless their names are also on the Dentists' Register.

For information regarding ethical relationships between doctors and dentists, see Chapter 10.

Ambulance Services

It is the duty of the Local Health Authority (in Scotland, the Secretary of State) to provide, or to arrange for the provision of, ambulance services. A doctor in practice will make a point of knowing how to request the services of an ambulance in the area of his practice.

Ambulance services are provided free of charge where considered necessary by the doctor who must declare that the patient is unfit to travel by public transport. The service should be used only exceptionally otherwise than for journeys between home and hospital or nursing home. Ambulance journeys are sometimes so arranged as to enable several patients to be carried on the same journey so that there may not always be room for a patient's relative to travel in the ambulance. If the doctor considers it necessary for a relative to travel with the patient, he is advised to inform the ambulance station of this at the time he gives the authority for the use of the ambulance.

When it is necessary for an out-patient to travel to hospital by ambulance the decision as to this rests with the general practitioner for the first attendance. The decision as to the need for an ambulance on subsequent occasions rests with the hospital, where the patient is given a note to that effect. A general practitioner may, however, authorize an ambulance journey on a later occasion when the patient's condition has deteriorated and he has no such note. Arrangements for ambulances returning patients from hospital are made by the hospital.

In some areas the ambulance service includes a car service for patients not able to travel by public transport but who do not require an ambulance. Alternatively, a car service is provided by a voluntary organization but these cars are not usually available for emergency cases.

Local Authority Services

The Public Health Act, 1936

The Public Health Act, 1936, deals with Local Authorities, Port Health Authorities, sanitation, buildings, removal of refuse, verminous persons and premises, nuisances and offensive trades, smoke, water supplies, prevention, notification and treatment of disease, nursing homes, laboratories, ambulances and mortuaries, welfare authorities, maternity and child welfare, notification of births to Local Authorities, foster children, public baths, common lodging houses and canal boats.

Provisions as to Medical Officers of Health are to be found in the First Schedule to the Act.

Local Health Authorities

The health services to be provided by Local Health Authorities are set down in Part III of the National Health Service Act, 1946, and of the National Health Service (Scotland) Act, 1947.

These include care of mothers and young children, midwifery, health visiting, home nursing, vaccination and immunization, prevention of illness, aftercare, domestic help, health centres and ambulance services. In Scotland, duties as to the last two are not charged to the Local Health Authority but are included under Part II of the Act (Services provided by the Secretary of State). Section 51 of each of the Acts requires Local Health Authorities to submit proposals to the Minister or to the Secretary of State as to their duties under the Lunacy and Mental Deficiency Acts.

Under the Fourth Schedule to the Act (Scottish Act, Fifth Schedule) all matters relating to the discharge of the functions of the Local Health Authority stand referred to the Health Committee of the Authority.

Practitioners having any problems relating to or inquiries to make regarding the services mentioned above are advised to approach the Medical Officer of Health of the Authority. A close liaison with the Medical Officer of Health's Department is desirable and often of great value in the day-to-day work of a general practitioner.

The Medical Officer of Health is the adviser to the Local Authority, and his principal field is that of preventive medicine.

Many of the services of his Authority are available for the patients of every general practitioner. There is much that the Medical Officer of Health and his staff can do, and will do, to help the general practitioner if he needs it and asks for it. There are some things that, by statute, the Medical Officer of Health must do in the interests of Public Health and Preventive Medicine. In carrying out his duties, which are laid upon him by Act of Parliament, his activities will from time to time impinge upon those of his colleague in general practice. Unless the general practitioner has acquired some knowledge of what the Medical Officer of Health can do, and what he must do, he may well find himself resenting what he pleases to think, in his ignorance, are acts of interference in his treatment of his patients.

Examples of spheres in which consultation with the Medical Officer of Health may help the general practitioner and the patient are health visiting, home nursing, home helps, welfare foods, the care of unmarried mothers, homes for the disabled and for the elderly, workshops and hostels for tuberculous patients and the welfare of the handicapped, blind, deaf, dumb, epileptics and spastics. Full details of health and welfare services are to be found in the *Health and Welfare Services Handbook* (Moss: Hadden Best and Co. Ltd.).

A doctor having a patient needing care and attention and being unable to obtain admission to hospital in the ordinary way, may inform the Medical Officer of Health and ask him to take action under the National Assistance Act, Section 47. This enables him to apply to the magistrates for an Order for Compulsory Removal of the patient to a suitable hospital or institution.

This Order is used for the aged, infirm and physically handicapped and those suffering from serious chronic disease. Their admission to hospital may be deemed necessary on account of inability to care for themselves or to prevent harm to others or a serious nuisance to others. The procedure may involve a fortnight's delay before admission is obtained, but in certain circumstances more expeditious action may be effected under the National Assistance (Amendment) Act of 1951.

Midwifery

Apart from the arrangements under the National Health Service from maternity medical services (see Chapter 26) a practitioner may be called in by a Local Authority midwife for emergency treatment under the medical aid scheme. The fees for the services given under these circumstances are prescribed in the Medical Practitioners (Fees) Regulations* and apply only when the practitioner has not made any arrangement to provide the patient with maternity medical services or is required to give treatment as a hospital doctor. The fees are payable only to a general practitioner obstetrician unless one was not available when the emergency arises. The practitioner is required to furnish a report to the Medical Officer of Health in the prescribed form which is supplied to him. If treatment is required beyond the fourteenth day after his first attendance he must report in writing to the local supervising authority that further attendance is necessary. No fee is payable for services rendered after four weeks from the birth. The practitioner must not have arranged to receive a fee from the patient or her representative.

Vaccination and Immunization

Section 26 of the National Health Service Acts requires Local Health Authorities to make arrangements with practitioners for vaccination against smallpox and immunization against diphtheria. They may also, with the approval of the Minister, make arrangements for vaccination or immunization against any other diseases. Vaccination is no longer compulsory. Vaccines, sera and other preparations for these purposes are provided free of charge to Local Health Authorities and to medical practitioners providing these services, who may obtain from the Medical Officer of Health information as to where to apply for supplies of prophylactic material. All general practitioners in the National Health Service are entitled to an opportunity to provide these services in their area. The services are given free under the National Health Service but practitioners may receive a fee for notification of vaccinations where these are required by the Medical Officer of Health.

* See Appendix D.

The fee for each notification is payable when the record shows, in a case of smallpox vaccination:

(*a*) that either a first or, if it has failed, a second vaccination has been successful; or
(*b*) that neither first nor second vaccination has been successful.

For diphtheria immunization (either the normal two injections or, where appropriate, one boosting dose) the fee is payable on completion of the procedure.

The Local Health Authority makes arrangements with the doctor for these services as above or may arrange for him to undertake this work in sessions for payment of a sessional fee.

Health Visitors

Under Section 24 of each of the National Health Service Acts Local Health Authorities must provide the services of Health Visitors whose function is to visit homes and advise on the care of individuals suffering from illness, the health of the household and precautions against the spread of infection. The Health Visitor has a part to play in health education. She is expected to work in close co-operation with the family doctor but not to usurp his proper functions or those of the district nurse or sanitary inspector.

Public Health Laboratory Service

To assist general practitioners in the diagnosis, prevention and control of infectious diseases, there are the Public Health Laboratories. The addresses of the laboratories are to be found in the *Handbook for General Medical Practitioners*. In Scotland equivalent services are provided by the Regional Hospital Boards. The main concern of the Service is with epidemiological and bacteriological investigations as opposed to other pathological investigations which are normally referred to a hospital pathology department. Help is given to general practitioners in investigating outbreaks of infectious disease and application should be made to the area laboratory when required.

The Laboratory Service also supplies vaccine lymph and diphtheria prophylactic for doctors taking part in Local Health Authority schemes, and also gamma globulin, typhus vaccine and rabies vaccine. Other vaccines are obtained through chemists or other suppliers.

Sera for treatment of anthrax, botulism, snake bite and rabies are obtainable from some Regional Centres (Appendix X of the *Handbook for General Medical Practitioners for England and Wales*).

34

SUPERANNUATION FOR THE GENERAL PRACTITIONER

GUIDE TO EXAMPLES APPEARING IN THIS CHAPTER.

Introduction

There have been many attempts to explain in simple terms the very complicated Regulations under which the National Health Service Superannuation scheme is administered. All those who attempt this task find themselves in a dilemma; they cannot be both brief and comprehensive. To deal with the main principles of the scheme without taking into account the many exceptions and 'provisos' may mislead and therefore be dangerous; and yet to include all the varied problems arising from differing individual circumstances would make the explanation almost as abstruse as the Regulations themselves.

One is forced to compromise and to present the main features of the scheme as briefly and clearly as possible, relying on those who feel that their cases are not covered by basic rules, to seek advice from the experts who administer the scheme or from their professional association.

Nevertheless, it should be possible for most general practitioners to glean from the following paragraphs sufficient information to enable them to assess, with reasonable accuracy, the pensions and other benefits to which they will be entitled.

The National Health Service Act, 1946, gives to the Minister of Health the right to determine any question arising under the Superannuation Regulations 'as to the rights or liabilities' of any person or employing authority connected with the scheme. It is usually possible in advance of final determination, against which there is no appeal, to obtain a ruling or an opinion on any point in doubt by writing to the appropriate Government Department. Letters should be addressed:

(1) in England and Wales, to:

The Secretary, Ministry of Health, Health Services Superannuation Division, Government Buildings, Honeypot Lane, Stanmore, Middlesex.

(2) in Scotland, to:

The Department of Health for Scotland, Health Services Superannuation Branch, Broonhouse Drive, Saughton, Edinburgh 11.

(3) in Northern Ireland, to:

Ministry of Health and Local Government, Stormont, Belfast.

The N.H.S. Superannuation Regulations were first issued in August 1947. They were revised and re-issued in 1950 and again in 1955. The 1955 Regulations which came into operation in October 1955 consolidate and supersede earlier regulations and contain some important amendments affecting the position of practitioners, mainly to their advantage.

In general they may be said to implement the Minister's expressed intention to design a flexible scheme which will 'serve the best interests of all those working in the Health Service as well as the interests of the Service itself'.

The Scheme in Outline

Like many other pension schemes *the National Health Service Superannuation Scheme is Contributory.* The fund from which benefits are payable at retirement on or after attaining a minimum pensionable age, is built up and maintained by contributions both from those who work in the Service and from the appropriate Employing Authority, be it a Regional Hospital Board or Executive Council. In order to maintain the pension fund on a sound actuarial basis a certain number of contributions must be paid before benefits accrue; in other words, there is a qualifying period. In the N.H.S. scheme this is ten years, though certain limited benefits are payable on retirement after five years' service.

The general principle on which the scheme is based, and which is common to most contributory pension schemes, is that contributions are a fixed percentage of remuneration and pensions are proportional to income at retirement, depending on the number of years during which contributions have been paid.

In addition to pension other benefits include a lump sum retiring allowance, a widow's pension, a death gratuity and provision for enforced retirement due to incapacity. These are described in detail later.

Contribution to the scheme is compulsory for all who work in the Health Service. For a limited time after the inception of the Service in July 1948, practitioners had an option to contract out provided they held endowment assurance or annuity policies sufficient to provide for their retirement. The Minister agreed to pay the employer's contribution to those who exercised this option, to help maintain their policies on condition that these were to be regarded as in lieu of pensions and, therefore, not assigned or pledged in any way. The decision to contract out is irrevocable, the Minister being bound by regulation to pay the employer's contribution for as long as the person concerned remains a practitioner or until his policies mature.

Special Assessment

As already mentioned, pension is usually calculated as a fraction—one-eightieth—of salary at retirement multiplied by the number of years of contributing service. Thus in the case of an Officer who had completed forty years' service, his pension would be half his salary on retirement which by then would have reached its maximum rate.

When the scheme was being drafted, however, it soon became apparent that this method of assessing pensions could not be applied to general practitioners. Very many general practitioners are not earning their maximum income when they retire; some may have deliberately reduced their commitments; some may have taken assistants or partners or adjusted their partnership shares. It was finally agreed that the equivalent of one-eightieth of salary at retirement for each year of service was $1\frac{1}{2}\%$ of the total superannuable income earned during the whole period. It was also accepted that this method of assessing pensions and other benefits was the only satisfactory alternative where 'peak' earnings might occur many years before retirement.

Thus, as far as the medical profession is concerned, there are two classes of contributors. Firstly Officers, comprising all those in whole-time salaried appointments, including specialists and all resident hospital officers. Secondly, Practitioners including not only general practitioners but also part-time specialists who work on a sessional basis. There are two exceptions:

(1) An assistant in general practice, though paid by salary, is classed as a Practitioner.

(2) Part-time specialists on maximum sessions, though normally classed as practitioners, may, by application to the Ministry of Health, be designated as Officers for superannuation purposes.

Medical Officers of Health and other Medical Officers in Local Government Service contribute to superannuation schemes administered by local Health Authorities. These schemes have recently been unified by the Local Government Superannuation Act, 1953, which introduced benefits similar in essentials to those in the Health Service Scheme.

Mixed Service

Under the Medical Act, 1950, every doctor on qualification has to spend a year in resident hospital appointments. This means that all pay superannuation contributions as Officers to begin with. They may remain in salaried appointments for some years. However, once established as Practitioners, all the pay received as salary counts towards 'total remuneration' in assessing benefits. Only if the period of salaried service as an Officer (excluding of course assistantships) exceeds ten years are the benefits calculated separately in respect of each period, and then added together.

Example I

Entered Hospital Service on qualification at 26.
After 4 years became Practitioner—retired at 65.

Total of Hospital remuneration say	£2,800
Total of Practitioner remuneration say ..	£54,000
	£56,800

Pension $1\frac{1}{2}$% of £56,800 = £852.

Example II

Entered Hospital Service on qualification at 26.

After twelve years and when average salary for last three years was, say, £1,200 p.a. became assistant with view to partnership and retired as senior partner at 65.

Value of pension based on Officer Service: $\frac{1}{80}$ of £1,200 × 12 (years service) = £180.

Total net remuneration as Practitioner, say, £46,000.

$1\frac{1}{2}$% of £46,000 = £690

Pension = £870

The distinction between Officer and Practitioner has led to a good deal of confusion particularly since all start their careers as Officers, but once the principles on which contributions and benefits are based are understood there should be no need for temporary status as an Officer to complicate the picture.

The following paragraphs deal only with the position of Practitioners.

Contributions

Every practitioner contributes 6% of his remuneration. This is deducted at source by the Executive Council or other Employing Authority which itself contributes 8%. No income tax is payable on superannuation contributions.

Remuneration

In the case of a principal in general practice Remuneration is defined as: 'All payments made by the Executive Council . . .

in respect of general medical services . . . provided by him . . . less such sum on account of practice expenses as may be appropriate in accordance with a formula laid down by the Minister for the purpose and less the remuneration approved by the Minister of any assistant practitioner in his employment.'

The sum deducted on account of practice expenses is 30%, but where payments are made for mileage or dispensing 50% of these payments is deducted.

Gross remuneration includes maternity fees, initial practice allowance, supplementary annual payments, payments for temporary resident and emergency and anaesthetic fees if these are payable under the local distribution scheme.

In general, therefore, and for the purpose of rough calculation, NET superannuable income may be regarded as approximately 70% of payments made by the Executive Council.

Payments for Supplementary Ophthalmic Services do not count as remuneration for superannuation purposes.

The grant of £150 payable to a principal employing a trainee practitioner is superannuable income, but as it does not constitute payment for general medical services 'provided by him', there is no deduction for expenses.

The salary (but not car allowance) of any assistant employed whole time or of a trainee practitioner must be deducted to arrive at NET remuneration.

To sum up:

Remuneration as defined for superannuation purposes (i.e. net superannuable income) consists of:

(1) 100% of the grant of £150 payable where a trainee practitioner is employed.

(2) 70% of:—Capitation fees
Payments for Temporary Residents
Fees for Maternity Services
Emergency fees
Anaesthetic fees
Initial Practice Allowance
Supplementary Annual Payments.

(3) 50% of:—Mileage payments
Payments in respect of drugs and appliances.

From the total of these items must be deducted the salary

(excluding car allowance) of an Assistant or Trainee Practitioner.

Payments made under the Supplementary Ophthalmic Service do not count as remuneration for superannuation purposes.

Assistants, Trainee Practitioners and Locums

An assistant practitioner is defined as an employee of a medical practitioner on the list of an Executive Council *wholly or mainly* engaged in the actual discharge of his duty as such practitioner other than an employee of a medical practitioner *for whose employment the consent of the Executive Council is not required.*

Two points of importance arise here. For an assistant to be 'mainly' employed he must spend more than half his time in assisting in N.H.S. practice. This excludes many part-time assistants who contract to do three or four surgeries a week or to be on call at odd times. Again, if an assistant is employed temporarily for less than three months the consent of the Executive Council is not required and for superannuation purposes he ranks as a locum.

Locums in general practice do not pay superannuation contributions, they are deputies and have no contract with the Executive Council. Curiously enough locums in hospitals are regarded as in contractual relationship and superannuation contributions are deducted from their pay. The position of part-time or temporary assistants and locums is important when there have been breaks in continuity of service and there have been many cases of loss of superannuation rights because of failure to realize the position. Difficulties frequently arise because the terms assistant and locum are used loosely and are sometimes interchangeable. In cases of doubt and especially where there is any question of a disqualifying break in service practitioners are advised to consult the Clerk to the Executive Council or their professional association.

The remuneration of assistants and trainee practitioners consists of salary together with any residential emoluments, such as a boarding out allowance, payable. It does not include the usual car allowance payable where the assistant is required to provide a car. Six per cent. of the assistant's remuneration is deducted from the quarterly payments made to the principal and he in turn recovers the amount by adjustment of the payments made to the assistant. The employer's contribution of 8% of the assistant's remuneration is paid by the Executive Council.

Partnerships

The definition of remuneration quoted above justifies the assumption that the income of a practitioner in single-handed practice will be roughly proportional to the number of patients on his list, since capitation fees form the bulk of his remuneration. Clearly to relate the contributions of partners and by implication, their pensions, to the numbers on their individual lists, would be inequitable since the capitation fees payable to a partner need bear no relation to his income as represented by his share in the net profits of the firm. Accordingly, a proviso was added to the definition of remuneration in the 1947 Regulations, to the effect that if the partners notified the Executive Council that they wished their remuneration to be proportional to their shares, their contributions could be assessed in this way. It was not long before difficulties and anomalies arose. Firstly, the proviso required that all the partners must agree to work on the share, as distinct from the list, method and sometimes partners could not agree. Secondly, it frequently happened that one or more partners held hospital appointments and though the income from these could be shared, there was no provision in the Regulations whereby the superannuation contributions relating to an individual contract with a Regional Hospital Board could be apportioned between partners. The representatives of the profession and the Superannuation Division of the Ministry of Health were at one in desiring to find a way of applying by regulation the important principle that contributions should be related to income, and at long last a solution to both these anomalies has been found and embodied in the 1956 Regulations.

These provide that from April 1st, 1956, medical practitioners in partnership will have the partnership 'remuneration' (on which contributions and benefits are calculated) divided equally between them for superannuation purposes unless they choose one of the following alternatives:

(*a*) They may elect that their total superannuable remuneration from Executive Councils shall be allocated between them on the basis of their individual shares in the partnership profits; or

(*b*) They may elect that their total superannuable remuneration from Executive Councils shall be allocated between them on the basis of their shares in the partnership profits, but adjusted to take account of superannuable remuneration received by any of the partners from any superannuable Health Service employment other than as a practitioner on the list of an Executive Council.

Example III

Partnership of 3: A, B and C. Profits shared in proportion of 2 : 2 : 1 respectively. A has also a hospital appointment with a salary of £250. Total superannuable remuneration from Executive Council £5,000 will be allocated as follows:

$$\begin{aligned} &\text{A } (£5{,}000 \times \tfrac{2}{5}) - (250 \times \tfrac{3}{5}) = £1{,}850 \\ &\text{B } (£5{,}000 \times \tfrac{2}{5}) + (250 \times \tfrac{2}{5}) = £2{,}100 \\ &\text{C } (£5{,}000 \times \tfrac{1}{5}) + (250 \times \tfrac{1}{5}) = £1{,}050 \end{aligned}$$

A's superannuation in his hospital appointment continues to be personal to him and his total superannuable remuneration, i.e. £1,850+£250, is therefore the same as B's and twice C's.

Partnerships in existence in October 1955, when the Regulations came into force, had an option until April 1st, 1956, to continue to contribute on the basis of individual remuneration (i.e. lists). This safeguarded the position of senior partners who with the concurrence of their partners were anxious to secure maximum benefits in the relatively short period available to them.

Pensionable Age

There is an important distinction between the terms *Pensionable Age* and *Retiring Age*.

There is no compulsory retirement age for general practitioners, they may continue to give general medical services in contract with the Executive Council for as long as they wish unless obviously incapable of carrying on. There is, however, an age limit beyond which they cannot normally continue to contribute to the superannuation scheme. *This is known as Pensionable Age and is* 65 *years.*

A practitioner may, however, elect to retire and receive all the benefits to which he is entitled at or after age 60 provided, of course, that he has completed the qualifying period. The age of 60 is sometimes referred to as *Minimum Pensionable Age.*

Extension of Pensionable Age

At 65 a practitioner normally ceases to pay contributions and his benefits are held in cold storage until he retires. He may, however, apply at any time after reaching age 60, and before he is 65, for extension of pensionable age up to age 70. This provision leads to increase of benefits and also enables many who could not otherwise complete the ten-year qualifying period to obtain a pension. Border line cases who would otherwise miss qualification by a few months may be granted extension up to the end of their seventy-first year.

Application for extension of pensionable age is made to the Minister, which means to the appropriate Superannuation Division or Branch (see p. 298). Before granting the extension the department will consult the Executive Council, which in turn may seek evidence from the Local Medical Committee about the health of the practitioner.

Once extension is allowed to any specified age short of 70, it cannot be further extended, though the practitioner is at liberty to retire earlier if he wishes to do so.

Re-employment after Retirement

A practitioner who retires at 65 but subsequently re-enters superannuable employment in the Health Service—for instance, as a principal in another area or as an assistant—may continue to earn and to receive his pension until he is 70. On reaching that age his pension will be either reduced or suspended so that his remuneration and pension together do not exceed the annual or average remuneration, whichever is the greater, of the employment in relation to which he became entitled to the pension. This sounds very complicated; curiously enough the actual Regulation which covers this provision is both brief and to the point. 'Further employment *as a practitioner* between the ages of 65 and 70 years, in the case of a person who became entitled to a pension as a practitioner, on or after attaining the age of 65, shall be disregarded.' This provision applies only to 'Practitioners'.

Benefits

To qualify for full benefits under the N.H.S. Superannuation scheme a practitioner must fulfil two conditions:

(*a*) He must have attained minimum pensionable age of 60.
(*b*) He must have completed ten years' service.

Certain benefits are payable to those who retire at or after age 60 having completed five but less than ten years' service.

Injury Allowance

There is one important exception. If a practitioner is forced to retire at any time because of a disease or injury which is 'attributable' to his service; that is to say, permanent incapacity as a result of injury or disease sustained or contracted in the actual discharge of his duty, the Minister may grant a pension up to but not exceeding two-thirds of his average remuneration during his last three years of service. Further, if a practitioner dies as the result of an attributable disease or injury, the Minister may grant a gratuity or annual allowance to the widow. If at the time of his death the practitioner was already receiving an injury pension, his widow is entitled to a widow's pension of one-third of the amount of the injury pension, provided that they were married before the pension was first payable.

Failure to Qualify—Return of Contributions

Those who fail to qualify for benefits, either because they reach pensionable age and retire before completing five years' service, or because they leave the Service voluntarily before reaching the age of 60, receive a return of their own contributions together with compound interest at 2½%. Income tax is payable on the whole amount returned in this way.

Retirement at or over Age 60

1. *With more than Five but less than Ten Years' Service*

A practitioner who, having reached minimum pensionable age, retires with more than five but less than ten years' service receives:

A. *A LUMP SUM RETIRING ALLOWANCE.* This may be either $4\frac{1}{2}\%$ of his total net remuneration or a capital sum equal to the amount of his contributions with interest, whichever is the greater. As the contributions are 6% of net remuneration, the practitioner will normally receive the latter alternative and it should be noted that unlike a return of contributions, a gratuity consisting of *a sum equal to his contributions* is not subject to deduction of tax.

B. *A DEATH GRATUITY.* This is either $4\frac{1}{2}\%$ of total net remuneration, or a sum equal to his contributions with interest, or his average superannuable remuneration whichever is the greatest. Usually, if a practitioner retires after only six or seven years his average remuneration is likely to be the greatest of these three. The amount of the Death Gratuity is reduced by the amount of the lump sum retiring allowance or any other benefit paid at the time of death.

Payment of the Capital Value of the Death Gratuity

When the retiring allowance is less than one year's superannuable income, the practitioner may elect to have it increased by the capital value of the Death Gratuity. Instead of waiting until he dies he can, as it were, draw the surrender value of the gratuity when he retires. The capital value has to be assessed in the individual case but depends on age at retirement varying roughly from 70% at age 60 to 80% at age 70. By receiving the capital value as a subsidy to the retiring allowance, the practitioner surrenders further claim to any death gratuity.

Example IV

Entered Service on July 5th, 1948, aged 58.
Retired at 65 with *seven years'* service.
Died at 68.
Total net remuneration, say £12,000.

Benefits

(*a*) Retiring allowance 6% of £12,000 = £720 with interest, approximately £790.

(*b*) Death Gratuity = average remuneration over last three years, say £1,600 = amount payable at death less retiring allowance already paid: £1,600−£790 % £810.

Capital value of Death Gratuity if taken at retirement, approximately 75% of £810 = £600. If the practitioner had elected to take his benefits in this way he would have received on retirement at 65, £790+£600 = £1,390.

C. *SHORT SERVICE GRATUITY.* If a practitioner having completed five but less than ten years' service has to retire because of permanent ill-health or incapacity, he is entitled to a Gratuity equal to his average net remuneration during his last three years of service. The condition need not, as in the case of the Injury pension, be attributable. As the Short Service and Death Gratuities are the same in amount, no Death Gratuity is payable to those who have received a Short Service Gratuity.

D. *INJURY ALLOWANCE.* As already described (p. 307).

2. *With more than Ten Years' Service—Full Benefits*

A. *PENSION*

A practitioner's pension is $1\frac{1}{2}$% of total net remuneration during his whole period of service up to a maximum of forty-five years.

(1) *Allocation of Pension.* On becoming entitled to a pension a practitioner may elect to surrender part of his pension in favour of his wife or other dependant, after his death. Not more than one-third of the pension may be allocated in this way, but where a widow's pension would be payable in any case the effect of allocation would be to increase its amount.

(2) *Incapacity Pension.* If a practitioner having completed ten but less than twenty years' service is forced, at any time, to retire through permanent incapacity, he may receive a pension which will be calculated as if he had completed twenty years' service. It is assumed for purposes of calculation that he would for the remainder of the twenty years have continued to earn the same average remuneration. If the practitioner

could not have completed twenty years' service before reaching the age of 65 his pension is calculated as if he had served up to that age and continued to earn at the same average rate.

Example V

Entered service at 40.

Retired because of permanent incapacity at 54—fourteen years' service.

Total net remuneration, £21,000 (average £1,500).

Incapacity pension = $1\frac{1}{2}\% \times £1{,}500 \times 20 = £450$.

but for this 'weighting' the pension would have been $1\frac{1}{2}\% \times £21{,}000 = £315$.

Example VI

Entered service at 50.

Retired because of permanent incapacity at 62—twelve years' service.

Total net remuneration, £18,000 (average £1,500).

Incapacity pension $1\frac{1}{2}\% \times £1{,}500 \times 15 = £337$ 10*s*.

but for the weighting the pension would have been $1\frac{1}{2}\% \times £1{,}800 = £270$.

(3) *Widow's Pension.* The widow of a practitioner who dies after having served for ten years, or who dies while drawing a pension under the scheme, receives an annual payment for life of one-third of her husband's pension.

If her husband dies while in the service her entitlement is based on the same calculations used for assessing the incapacity pension described above. Her husband is assumed to have completed twenty years' service or to have served until 65 whichever is the shorter, and she receives one-third of the amount which would have been due to him under these circumstances. In the Examples above the widow's pension would therefore be:

Example V: $\frac{1}{3}$ of £450 = £150.
Example VI: $\frac{1}{3}$ of £337 10*s*. = £112 10*s*.

If the practitioner's service had exceeded twenty years but he died before receiving a pension, his widow is entitled to one-third of the pension he would have received had he retired on pension the day before his death.

Example VII

Entered service at 35.
Died at 58 (twenty-three years' service).
Total net remuneration, say £40,000.
Assessment of practitioner's entitlement at date of death $1\frac{1}{2}\%$ of £40,000 = £600.
Widow's pension, £200 per annum.

A pension is payable to the widow of a practitioner who dies within twelve months of resigning from the Health Service, provided he had not received a return of contributions or become subject to any other superannuation scheme. The assessment is the same as if he had died on the date he left the service.

Ordinarily a widow cannot receive a pension as part of her husband's benefit if she is entitled to a Health Service pension in her own right. In the case of a woman practitioner, however, there is no disqualification. She is entitled to both the widow's pension and the pension she herself earns.

A widow's pension is not payable if the marriage took place after the husband became entitled to a pension. If a widow in receipt of a pension marries again the pension ceases.

The widow's pension is not affected by any pension she may be receiving or be entitled to under the National Insurance Acts (see p. 317).

B. *RETIRING ALLOWANCE*

A gratuity or lump sum retiring allowance is payable on retirement and is a capital sum equal to three times the annual pension, i.e. $4\frac{1}{2}\%$ of total net remuneration.

If, however, the practitioner is married and entitled to the widow's pension as part of his benefits the retiring allowance is $1\frac{1}{2}\%$ of total net remuneration, or the same as the pension itself.

If during his service the practitioner ceases to qualify for the widow's pension, through the death of his wife or other cause, he gains the benefit of the higher rate of assessment for the remainder of his contributory service.

Example VIII

Entered service in 1948—aged 35 (married).
Wife died in 1965 (seventeen years' service).
Retired in 1975 aged 62 (twenty-seven years' service).

Remarried 1976.
Died 1980.
Total net remuneration:
1st period seventeen years, say £32,000
2nd period ten years, say £18,000

£50,000

Pension $1\frac{1}{2}$% of £50,000 = £750 per annum.
Retiring Allowance:

$1\frac{1}{2}$% of £32,000 = £480
$4\frac{1}{2}$% of £18,000 = £810

£1,290

No pension payable to widow of second marriage as this took place after retirement and receipt of the above benefits.

C. *DEATH GRATUITY*

As already mentioned a gratuity equal to one year's superannuable income is payable at death but is reduced by the amount of any pension or other benefits already received. There is one exception to the general rule: If a widow's pension is payable, the death gratuity is limited to $1\frac{1}{2}$% of total net remuneration.

D. *INJURY ALLOWANCE*

A pension is payable under the conditions already described (p. 307), but if the practitioner is also entitled to a pension or other benefit when the attributable injury or disease occurred, the amount of this may be taken into account when assessing the injury pension.

Summary

To sum up:

1. A practitioner is entitled on retirement to receive *a pension* together with benefit of widow's pension, if:

(*a*) he has completed ten years' service and has attained the age of 60 years.

(*b*) he has completed ten years' service and is incapable of discharging the duties of his employment because of permanent ill-health or infirmity.

2. In addition, a practitioner is entitled to a *Lump Sum Retiring Allowance* if:

(*a*) he has completed five years' service and has attained the age of 60 years.
(*b*) he has completed five years' service but is forced to retire owing to permanent incapacity (*Short Service Gratuity*).

3. *A Death Gratuity* is payable after five years' service.
4. There is no qualifying period for an *Injury Allowance*.

Interrupted Service

Usually a general practitioner will have served as an Officer in Resident Hospital appointments or as an Assistant, for some years before he is established in practice. It is of some importance, therefore, that his income from salaried appointments should count towards the Total Net Remuneration on which his pension will eventually be assessed. There may well be periods, however, when he will not be in Health Service employment; during National Service, for instance, or during a period of post-graduate study for a higher degree or diploma. With a little forethought most contingencies of this kind can be provided for and superannuation rights maintained or at least kept in cold storage pending resumption of Health Service practice. Unfortunately it frequently happens that doctors take things for granted, and later find they have forfeited benefits because of technical breaches of Regulations that could have been avoided or at least realized and accepted beforehand. A break in continuity of service of *more than twelve months is a disqualifying break*.

A doctor who has a disqualifying break in his service is entitled to a return of contributions previously paid from which tax is deducted at the standard rate. He cannot count his previous service when he subsequently resumes payment of contributions. He starts again from scratch unless he elects to buy back the lost period by making *additional contributory payments*. These vary according to age and may be paid either by a lump sum or in part by instalments.

There are certain appointments or forms of employment which need not count towards a break in service provided the approval of the Minister is obtained or where there is special statutory provision. A hospital appointment overseas or a course of training for a diploma come into the first category; service with the armed forces or Her Majesty's overseas civil service, in the second.

Study Leave

The Regulations provide that where a person leaves Health Service employment in order to enter an *approved* course of study or training, no account shall be taken of any period spent by him on that course of study or training. The rule applies whether or not the course was taken immediately before or following a period of National Service, the essential point being that it should be 'approved'.

Application for approval should be made to the appropriate department (see p. 298) and if granted any superannuation rights which have already accrued are kept in cold storage. A doctor who is not in Health Service employment, even if his appointment or post-graduate course is approved, cannot increase his superannuation benefits by making voluntary contributions.

National Service

A doctor, whether an Officer or a Practitioner, who leaves Health Service employment to undertake a period of National Service may elect to continue to pay contributions at the rate that would have obtained had he continued in his last superannuable appointment (see note on locums, p. 303). There is provision for the employer's contribution to continue during this period.

Alternatively he may apply for a return of his contributions, in which case he loses the benefit of all previous service.

Between these two extremes there is a compromise. If he re-enters Health Service employment within six months of completing National Service, he may elect to pay back any contributions returned to him. His previous service but not his National Service will then count as contributory service.

Short Service Commissions

A doctor who takes a short service commission in the armed forces may if he wishes to do so, continue to pay superannuation contributions, but in this case he must pay both the employee's and employers' contributions, amounting to 14% of his net remuneration. His pension rights are maintained and he continues to add to his benefits, but if on leaving the services he does not re-enter Health Service employment—if for instance he goes abroad—the employee's contribution of 6% only is returned to him and he loses the 8% which he has paid.

It is usual, with the Officer's consent, for the contributions to be deducted from the gratuity, payable on relinquishing a short service commission; indeed the gratuity has been described as a return of payments which would have been credited towards a non-contributory service pension.

Relief of income tax may be claimed on the total contribution of 14% but it is advisable to make a claim each year although each annual claim may be for relief to be given in due course on the total amount deducted from the gratuity.

The choice open to a doctor when he takes up a short service commission is not an easy one to make. He is apt to regard the gratuity as savings which can be applied to the initial expenses of establishing himself in practice—purchase of a car, equipment, etc. Fourteen per cent. of his pay over a period of years makes a significant difference and the question arises, '*Is it worth it?*' In the case of a doctor who intends to enter whole-time salaried service it is generally 'well worth it' because pension is related directly to years of service. Where pension is related to total remuneration the number of years is not quite so important, but since all previous contributions will cease to count towards benefits a doctor intending to enter general practice should think carefully before refusing to 'exercise the option' for the sake of short-term advantages.

Changes in Employment—Transfer of Superannuation Rights

Superannuation rights may be maintained and continuity secured when transferring to or from a number of employments or appointments not covered by the N.H.S. scheme. A practitioner who enters general practice after holding a superannuable teaching post in a university, or a practitioner who transfers to a whole-time appointment in the Local Government or Civil Service, are cases of this kind. Advice as to the effect on superannuation should always be sought when such a change is contemplated and *before* it actually takes place. Information can always be obtained from the appropriate Government Department (see p. 298).

Concurrent Employment

Until recently concurrent appointments under different Employing Authorities in the Health Service were treated separately for superannuation purposes. Even contracts with two or more Executive Councils were regarded as separate entities. For instance, if a practitioner undertaking hospital sessions in addition to general practice decided to devote himself entirely to hospital work and resigned from the list of the Executive Council before he was 60, he would have had to accept a return of contributions in respect of his service as a general practitioner and it could not count towards his pension. Now this has been changed and in general the 1955 Regulations provide for all accrued superannuation rights to count towards ultimate benefits. The position is quite straightforward where two or more Executive Councils are concerned, but is a little more complicated where both Executive Council and Regional Hospital Board come into the picture. Here again advice should be sought before making a decision to resign a superannuable appointment.

Where a change takes place after minimum pensionable age is reached (with of course ten years' qualifying service) benefits may be assessed and paid separately, but this has no significance and may be to the advantage of the practitioner.

Example IX

A. Service as a practitioner on the list of an Executive Council.

B, C } Part-time hospital appointments.

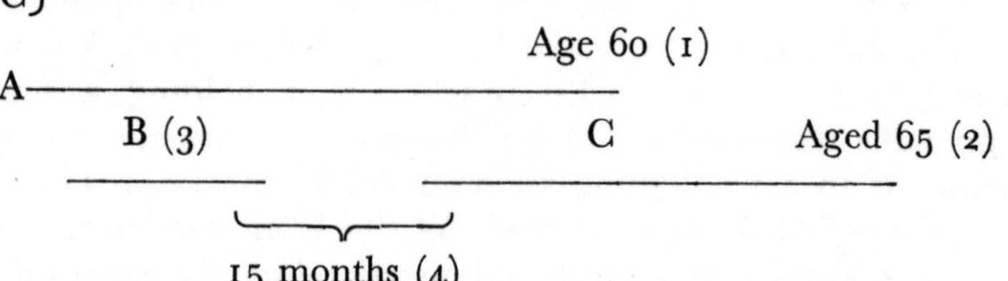

(1) On retirement from A benefits will be payable on A and B.
(2) On retirement from C further benefits payable in respect of C only.
(3) Contributions in respect of B not returnable because a concurrent superannuable appointment (A) held.
(4) No disqualifying break because of concurrent Health Service employment (A).

Adjustment in Respect of National Insurance Pension

Except in the case of those who were in the Health Service at its inception in July 1948, and except for those who by reason of age cannot qualify for a National Insurance Pension, all contributions and pensions *but not the widow's pension* are subject to modification to take into account the National Insurance Pension payable at 65.

The employees' contributions are reduced by 1*s.* 2*d.* per week (1*s.* 3*d.* for women). The employers' contributions are reduced by the same amounts. Retirement pensions are reduced by £1 14*s.* a year for each year of service during which reduced contributions have been paid.

Example X

Entered Health Service after July 1948, age 32.
Retired at 62 after thirty years' service.
Total net remuneration, say £45,000.
Contributions, assuming a steady average remuneration of £1,500 net per annum:

6% of £1,500	=	£90 per annum
Less 1*s.* 2*d.* per week	=	£3 0*s.* 8*d.*
		£86 19*s.* 4*d.*

Benefits:

Pension: (*a*) from 62–65, $1\frac{1}{2}$% of £45,000 = £675 p.a.
(*b*) from 65 (when eligible for N.I. pension) $1\frac{1}{2}$% of £45,000 less £1 14*s.* × 30 = £624 p.a.

Lump Sum Retiring Allowance:
$1\frac{1}{2}$% of £45,000 = £675 (unaffected).

Widow's Pension whether he dies before or after 65:
$\frac{1}{3}$ of £675 = £225 p.a. (unaffected).

35

INCOME TAX FOR THE DOCTOR

Introduction

The income of a doctor may be taxed in one of two ways:

(1) By deduction at the source.
(2) By direct assessment.

Wherever possible the Inland Revenue prefer the former method as it is a sure, quick method of gathering in the tax. It is economical in operation and reduces tax evasion to a minimum.

Deduction of tax at source. With a few exceptions, interest, dividends and annuities are normally received less a deduction for income tax, and from April 6th, 1944, when the 'Pay As You Earn' system commenced, salaries and wages were brought into this category also. It is worth noting that, where the tax should have been deducted but has not been deducted, the person receiving the interest may be assessed under Case III of Schedule D (*Glamorgan Quarter Sessions* v. *Wilson* (1910), 1 K.B. 725).

Direct assessment. On the other hand, a practitioner is taxed by direct assessment on the profits he earns from his practice, as well as any untaxed interest he may receive from War Loan, interest in excess of £15 in any year from Post Office Savings Bank and Trustee Savings Bank deposits, Deposit Account interest and Discount on Treasury Bills.

Statutory Income. In assessing income, the Board of Inland Revenue do not in every case take the actual income of the fiscal year ending April 5th. In certain circumstances the income of the preceding year may be used. A practitioner's

Statutory Income is therefore arrived at by taking the actual income arising in the tax year from certain sources and the income arising in the year preceding the year of assessment from other sources, according to the nature of the income, and then deducting annual charges such as mortgage interest, ground rents, etc.

Allowances and Relief

No matter under which of these two headings he makes his contribution to the Exchequer, the practitioner, like all taxpayers, is entitled by right to certain allowances and relief. These allowances, with the exception of Earned Income Relief, are not granted automatically. They must be claimed, and it rests with the practitioner to fill in the appropriate claim sections in his Income Tax Return form. These allowances are set out briefly as follows:

(*a*) *Earned Income Relief*

A practitioner is allowed as a deduction from his statutory total income a sum equivalent to two-ninths of his earned income up to a maximum earned income of £4,005. In addition there is an allowance of one-ninth of earned income in excess of the income over £4,005 on a further £5,940. This means that the limit at which earned income relief ceases is £9,945. The maximum amount of earned income relief will be £890 at the full rate and £660 at the half rate, making a total of £1,550.

If his total income includes any earned income of his wife additional relief will be given amounting to seven-ninths of the wife's personal earnings up to a maximum of seven-ninths of £180. Earned income includes:

(1) Remuneration from employment, including the wages received by a married woman who acts as her husband's receptionist, secretary, etc.

(2) Pensions, including old age and widows' pensions granted to survivors of a deceased person in respect of past services of the deceased.

(3) Directors' remuneration.

(4) Income from property taxable under Schedule A

where the right to occupy the property forms part of the emoluments of the office or employment.

(5) Profits from a practice.

Notes regarding earned income. The following points should be noted with regard to earned income relief:

(*a*) The share of profits due to a sleeping partner is unearned income, but very slight action on his part will be sufficient to entitle him to relief.

(*b*) Each member of a partnership receives relief up to the limit of £1,550. This means that the aggregate earned income relief in the firm's assessment may exceed £1,550.

(*c*) Limited companies do not receive relief.

(*d*) It has been decided in the case of *Frame* v. *Farrand* (1928), 13 T.C. 861, that, where expenses are properly deductible from remuneration, the earned income relief must be calculated on the net amount of the remuneration after deducting allowable expenses.

(*b*) *Age Relief*

In substitution for earned income relief, where the practitioner or his wife, who must be living with him and maintained by him is 65 years of age or over at any time during the year of assessment, he may deduct from his statutory total income an amount equal to two-ninths of his total income, whether earned or not, provided the total income from all sources does not exceed £700. Marginal relief is given where the income slightly exceeds £700 per annum, in which case he can elect to pay:

(1) The amount of tax payable assuming his income is £700, plus

(2) Three-fifths of the amount by which his income exceeds £700.

If a practitioner is unmarried and has at any time during the year reached the age of 65 years, total exemption from income tax is given if his income does not exceed £250. Where the practitioner is married, and his wife is living with him, total exemption is given if the income does not exceed £400, and the allowance should be claimed if either husband or wife is aged 65. There is marginal relief if the income slightly exceeds these figures. The tax payable will be limited to one-half of the amount by which the income exceeds £250 and £400 respectively.

(*c*) *Relief for Small Incomes*

Where the total income of a practitioner, not entitled to Age Relief, does not exceed £300, an allowance of two-ninths of the income will be made, whether or not the income is earned. In cases where the income exceeds £300 but is less than £397 the tax payable may not exceed the amount which could have been payable if the income had been £300, plus nine-twentieths of the income in excess of £300.

(*d*) *Personal Relief*

The allowance given to an unmarried practitioner or a separated or divorced person or a widower is now £140. The allowance for a married man is £240 provided his wife is living with him or is wholly maintained by him during the year of assessment.

(*e*) *Child Relief*

The practitioner is given an allowance in respect of each child born during the tax year, each child under sixteen at the beginning of the tax year or for each child over sixteen who is receiving full-time instruction at a school, college or university, or undergoing whole-time training for a trade, profession or vocation for a period of not less than two years. This relief is given on the following scale:

(1) Child not over the age of 11 .. .. £100
(2) Child over the age of 11 but not over 16 .. £125
(3) Child over 16 years of age £150

If the child's income in his own right, excluding income from any scholarship, bursary or other educational endowment, exceeds £100 per annum, the parent is not entitled to a child allowance for him. Children include step-children. In the case of an adopted child, the allowance applies only if he is maintained by and in the custody of the taxpayer, and provided it is not claimed by the child's own parents.

Incapacitated children who are over sixteen years of age and not receiving full-time instruction are treated as dependents for whom an allowance of £60 may be claimed (see below).

(*f*) *Relief for Dependent Relatives*

If the practitioner maintains at his own expense a relative of his own or of his wife, and if the relative is incapacitated by old age or other infirmity from maintaining himself or herself, he is entitled to an allowance of £60 for each such relative. In addition, if his widowed mother or mother-in-law, whether incapacitated or not, is maintained by him, a similar allowance is granted. For this relief to be granted in full the relative's income must not exceed £165 per annum, but it will be partially granted if the income is between £105 and £165 per annum.

(*g*) *Relief for Daughter's Services*

Should the practitioner maintain a daughter who lives with him because he is old or infirm he may claim an allowance of £40.

(*h*) *Relief for Housekeeper*

A widower (or a widow) may claim relief of £60 in respect of a female relative of his or of his deceased wife, if that relative resides with him as housekeeper or looks after children, for whom the child allowance is given. If it is a stranger who acts as housekeeper or looks after children, it was held in the case of *MacFarlane* v. *Hubert*, 19 T.C. 660 that there must be a bona fide relationship of employer and employee. It should be noted that, in accordance with *Kliman* v. *Winckworth*, 17 T.C. 569, a separated or divorced person cannot obtain the allowance.

Relief of £60 may also be claimed where the claimant is unmarried and has a female relative living with him to care for his brothers and sisters, for whom the child allowance is obtainable.

An allowance of £60 will be given to a man who is in receipt of the lower personal allowance of £140 for a female person resident with him and maintained or employed by him to look after a child for whom he receives the child allowance. A married man may claim this relief of £60 if his wife is totally incapacitated throughout the year of assessment. Similarly a claim may be made by a woman who is incapacitated throughout the year or is in full-time employment.

(*i*) *Reduced Rate Relief*

The first £360 of taxable income is liable to tax at rates less than the standard rate, as follows:

On the first £60 of taxable income 2*s*. 3*d*. in the £.
On the next £150 of taxable income 4*s*. 9*d*. in the £.
On the next £150 of taxable income 6*s*. 9*d*. in the £.

Thereafter tax at the full standard rate of 8*s*. 6*d*. in the £ is payable.

In addition, similar relief is given against a wife's earned income after deducting the total earned income relief due on her earned income and any unabsorbed balance of her husband's allowances, other than reduced rate relief.

Thus the following figures show that a married woman may earn up to £643 per annum before tax is payable at the full standard rate:

	£ *s*. *d*.	£ *s*. *d*.
Earned Income		643 0 0
Deduct:		
(*a*) Earned Income Relief $\frac{2}{9}$ths of £643 =	143 0 0	
(*b*) Wife's Earned Income Relief (maximum) $\frac{7}{9}$ths of £180 =	140 0 0	
		283 0 0
		£360 0 0

Tax payable:	£ *s*. *d*.
£60 at 2*s*. 3*d*. in the £	6 15 0
£150 at 4*s*. 9*d*. in the £	35 12 6
£150 at 6*s*. 9*d*. in the £	50 12 6
£360	£93 0 0

(*j*) *Life Assurance Relief*

If a practitioner has life assurance policies on his own life or on that of his wife, or pays premiums for a deferred annuity, there is relief due on the premium subject to certain restrictions.

(1) The premium on any policy must not exceed 7 per cent. of the capital sum assured.

(2) The allowable premiums must not exceed one-sixth of the total income.

(3) If the policy was taken out before June 22nd, 1916, the relief is a deduction of tax at the following rates on the total of allowable premiums:

Where total income does not exceed £1,000, 3*s*. 6*d*. per £.
Where total income does not exceed £2,000, 5*s*. 3*d*. per £.
Where total income exceeds £2,000, 7*s*. per £.

(4) For policies made after June 22nd, 1916, the allowance is as follows:

(*a*) If the total allowable premiums do not exceed £25, £10 or the amount of the premiums, whichever is less.
(*b*) If the total allowable premiums exceed £25, two-fifths of the amount of the premiums.

Receipts for the premiums should be kept in readiness to support the claims if required by the tax office.

The Tax Schedules

If a practitioner is taxed by direct assessment, his income is classified according to Schedules. A very brief account of these schedules is given below and Schedules A, D and E are considered in greater detail on pp. 326–343.

(*a*) Schedule A relates to the income from the *ownership* of land and buildings.
(*b*) Schedule B deals with the profits from the *occupation* of lands.
(*c*) Schedule C relates to income from Government Stocks taxed at the source where payment is entrusted to an agent.
(*d*) Schedule D takes charge of profits from trade or business including medical practices and any other annual

profits or gains which do not come under any other schedule.

(*e*) Schedule E covers income of all employed persons accruing as salary, fees or commission.

Before an assessment is made the practitioner generally receives an Income Tax Return form. This form should be completed with every care and with reasonable expedition. Heavy penalties can be enforced if it is ignored.

If a person has income liable to tax, he must by law give notice to the Inspector of Taxes even if no Return Form has been received. In the case of a practice the Inspector invariably asks for a copy of the Balance Sheet and Accounts to assist him in making the correct assessment. While an Inspector of Taxes has no legal right to demand the production of accounts it is usually to the taxpayer's own benefit that these should be supplied. If accounts are not produced to substantiate the figures returned to the Inspector, an estimated assessment will in all probability be made, and the Inspector of Taxes seldom errs on the lenient side.

After the return form has been submitted, an assessment notice is issued to the taxpayer showing the tax due to be paid. The person assessed has the right of appeal if the assessment is not, in his opinion, correct. It is most important that as soon as the notice is received its accuracy should be checked with the details already supplied on the return form and any agreed computations based on the accounts and balance sheet. All allowances should be verified likewise. If the practitioner decides to appeal against his assessment, he must give notice of his intention within twenty-one days from the date of his assessment notice. At the same time he must state the grounds for the appeal, which may be that the assessment is an estimate and not in accordance with the facts or that there is an overcharge. It is not sufficient for the practitioner to state that he does not agree with the assessment; he must give his reasons.

On the other hand, if an Inspector finds that a taxpayer has been undercharged or that he has obtained allowances to which he is not entitled, he may make an additional assessment at any time not later than six years after the end of the year to which the assessment relates.

(*a*) *Schedule A*

Under Schedule A, tax is levied on the net annual value of lands, houses, buildings, etc., owned by a practitioner in the United Kingdom. The gross annual value is based on the annual sum for which the property would be let if the landlord carried out all the repairs and the tenant paid the rates. The net annual value on which the tax is charged is arrived at by deducting from the gross annual value the Statutory Allowance for Repairs, viz.:

Lands, one-eighth.
Houses up to £40 annual value, one-fourth.
Houses of annual value £40 to £50, £10.
Houses of annual value £50 to £100, one-fifth.
Houses of annual value over £100, £20 plus one-sixth of the excess over £100.

The tax is due in full on January 1st and is payable in the first instance by the occupier, as the net annual value is regarded as his statutory income. The occupier may then reimburse himself by deducting the tax paid from the next payment of rent. The landlord is bound to allow this deduction against the production of the official receipt. He is not compelled, however, to allow this deduction from any but the next payments of rent (*Hill* v. *Kirshenstein* (1920), 3 K.B. 556).

Where a change of occupier takes place the assessment is made on the occupier for the time being, and he may deduct the tax from the rent paid in the normal way. It should be remembered, however, that an occupier who relinquishes occupation remains liable for the Schedule A tax due for the period of his occupation so far as this tax should be ultimately paid by him.

In the event of a change in the ownership of a property, the usual custom is for the tax payable under Schedule A to be apportioned so that the person who pays the tax, or suffers it by deduction from rent, bears only the tax for his term of ownership.

Building Society interest payable is usually paid in full without tax being deducted, and the Schedule A tax otherwise payable on the property will be reduced by tax on the interest so paid. Should the interest exceed the net annual value, relief on the excess is allowable against other tax payable by the borrower.

Other mortgage interest payable on property should have tax deducted at the standard rate. Any excess of such tax over the Schedule A tax paid on the property can be set against tax paid on other income. If this is impossible, the excess has to be accounted for to the Revenue Authorities who will make an additional assessment to recover it.

Empty houses are exempt from Schedule A tax so long as no rent is being paid and all furniture removed.

If the owner of property finds that the cost of maintenance, repairs, insurance and management of the property according to the average yearly expenditure for the five preceding years exceeds the statutory allowance, he may claim repayment of tax on the excess. The taxpayer must take the initiative and provide the Inspector with vouchers and receipts to support the claim. Outside painting, interior decoration, repairs to burst water pipes and electrical wiring, the replacement of a worn-out fireplace, an accountant's charges for preparing a claim, are all allowable. Expenditure of a capital nature or expenditure made to effect an improvement is not allowed. No repayment of tax will be made in respect of any expenditure which has been otherwise allowed as a deduction in computing income for tax purposes: e.g. if the cost of repairs has been charged against practice income assessed under Schedule D; nor can the tax recoverable exceed that paid under Schedule A in respect of the property in question. *The example on* *p. 328* *will clarify the position.*

Thus if tax has been paid on the net annual value of £130, repayment will be made of £17 (being £40 at 8*s.* 6*d.*). If, however, tax has not been paid the Schedule A assessment will be reduced to tax on £90 for 1956–57.

Where property has been recently acquired, it is the practice to allow the previous owner's figures to be brought into the average. If details of such expenditure are not available or if a maintenance claim is made for an entirely new property, the present owner may be permitted to adopt one of the following concessionary alternatives on the condition that he applies the same basis consistently year by year until a five years' average is obtained.

(1) He may base his claim on a five years' average in the usual way, the excess expenditure for the years prior to ownership being treated as 'nil'; or

(2) He may claim any excess of the actual expenditure over the statutory allowance each year until a five years' average is obtained. This latter method is the preferable one provided the Inspector of Taxes allows the concession.

Where dilapidated property has been purchased and large sums expended on repairs, the Revenue usually insist on the average basis only, the previous owner's expenditure if not known being taken as 'nil'. *The Law Shipping Case* (1923), 12 T.C. 621, is sometimes quoted as an authority for excluding from maintenance claims expenditure on property bought in a dilapidated condition, but this is open to question.

House, Gross annual value	£160
Statutory repairs allowable:	
£20 plus $\frac{1}{6}$th of excess over £100	30
Net annual value 1956–57	£130
Allowable repairs, etc.:	
1951–52	£125
1952–53	63
1953–54	10
1954–55	44
1955–56	108
	5 / 350
	70
Deduct statutory allowance..	30
Maintenance claim, 1956–57	£40

(*b*) *Schedule E*

If a practitioner holds a salaried appointment or receives director's fees, he is taxed under Schedule E. It is under this schedule that assessments are made on all employees in respect of wages, salaries, bonuses, commissions and generally speaking on all remuneration arising from any employment. Pensions and retirement annuities resulting from employment do not escape.

The Finance Act, 1956, brings all offices and employments within the scope of this schedule. For this purpose incomes are classified into the following three cases:

Case I deals with emoluments from offices and employments held by persons ordinarily resident in the United Kingdom and where the duties are not wholly performed abroad. The assessment is based on the actual emoluments of the year.

Case II applies where the holder of an office or employment is not ordinarily resident in the United Kingdom. The assessment is on the emoluments for the year in respect of duties performed in the United Kingdom.

Case III covers all other offices and employments where the holder is resident in the United Kingdom, whether ordinarily resident there or not. Liability is based on the emoluments received in the United Kingdom in the year of assessment.

The following receipts, however, are not liable to tax:

(1) Wound and disability pensions.

(2) Pensions granted to war widows in respect of their children.

(3) War gratuities.

(4) Post-war credits.

(5) Sick pay, strike pay, unemployment pay, etc., received from a trade union or friendly society.

(6) Certain payments under the National Health Service (Superannuation) Regulations, 1950.

(*a*) Lump sum retiring allowance (Regulation 7b).
(*b*) Injury allowance (Regulation 9 (1)).
(*c*) Short service gratuity (Regulation 10).
(*d*) Death gratuity (Regulation 12).
(*e*) Gratuity payable to a widow of an officer (Regulation 9 (3)). (The annual allowance paid to a widow under Regulation 9 (3) is, however, subject to tax.)

Where a practitioner, assessable under Schedule E, is obliged to incur expenses which are *wholly, exclusively and necessarily* disbursed in the performance of the duties of his office, he is permitted to deduct such expenses from the emoluments received from that office. A definite distinction is drawn between those expenses incurred *in* the performance of the duties and those incurred *in order* to perform them. From this it will be understood why no deduction is permissible for travelling expenses of employees from their residences to the premises of the employer. Should an employee hold an office in one town and a separate employment in another town, the costs of journeying between the two offices are not allowed. Each employment commences when the employee arrives at the place of employment (*Ricketts* v. *Colquhoun* (1926), A.C. 1).

In the case of *Andrews* v. *Astley* (1924), 8 T.C. 859, it was held that even where, owing to a shortage of houses, an employee finds it necessary to live at a considerable distance from his place of employment, his travelling expenses are not allowed as a deduction.

The following are typical expenses which might be claimed:

(*a*) Compulsory superannuation fund contributions.

(*b*) National Insurance contributions payable under the National Insurance Act, other than that portion of the contributions attributable to unemployment, sickness and maternity benefits.

(*c*) Payments to a locum tenens in the case of illness and ordinary holidays.

(*d*) Renewal of professional books, periodicals, etc., which are necessary to the proper performance of the duties. (But not the cost of the original books which is a capital expense.)

(*e*) Subscriptions to professional societies, but only where the employee is compelled by the terms of his employment to maintain his membership at his own expense, and can produce documentary evidence to this effect.

In the case of *Simpson* v. *Tate* (1925), 9 T.C. 314, it was stated 'that all subscriptions to professional societies and all taking in of professional literature and all that sort of expense which enables a man to keep himself fit for what he is doing are things which can none of them be allowed'.

The case of *Wales* v. *Graham* (1941), 24 T.C. 75, is also of interest. A deduction was disallowed for a subscription paid by a county divisional engineer to the Institution of Civil Engineers; it was held that while he had to be a member of the Institution when appointed he was not specifically required to remain a member.

Another case of particular importance is that of *Hamerton* v. *Overy* (1954), 35 T.C. 73. In this case a doctor was employed full time by a Regional Hospital Board. He claimed before the General Commissioners part of the cost of a telephone in his private house, part of the wages and keep of a maid who answered the telephone at his home and his subscription to the Medical Defence Union. This subscription was paid as a condition of his contract of service. He also claimed the initial and annual allowances for the depreciation of his car. The Commissioners' finding was that 'the appellant was not obliged to incur and defray the expenses claimed' and they confirmed the assessment without allowing the sums claimed on the grounds that this case was covered by the *Simpson* v. *Tate* decision mentioned above. In dismissing the appeal, the learned Judge referred especially to the use of the car. He said that the appellant in order to succeed would have to bring himself within the provisos to the Finance Act, 1949, Schedule 6, Part II, Paragraphs 2 and 4. These sections provide that no initial or annual allowance should be due when sums are received which take into account wear and tear from 'any Government or public or local authority' unless it can be shown that only part of the wear and tear is covered.

As a general principle it will be seen that the majority of expenses incurred by an employed person are inadmissible on the grounds that they were expended antecedent to, or ancillary to, the actual earning of the income.

As from April 6th, 1944, the 'Pay As You Earn' system came into operation, and applied to all emoluments assessable to income tax under Schedule E. This was extended to members of H.M. Forces for 1947-48 onwards.

All employers who make payments to their employees, including practitioners employing assistants, receptionists, domestic staff, chauffeurs, gardeners, etc., are required to deduct the appropriate amount of tax from each payment by reference to Official Tax Tables. These are constructed to ensure that the tax deducted from payments to date from the previous April 5th corresponds with the proportion to date of the year's tax liability of the recipient, after taking into account all allowances and reliefs due.

The employer is notified by the Inspector of Taxes of the Code Number applicable to each of his employees, and, by linking up each code number with the Official Tax Tables, he knows what tax must be deducted each week or month, as the case may be, from each of his employees. Where the employee has no other employment and his rate of payment is less than £3 15*s*. per week (£15 10*s*. per month) no tax is deductible. If the employee has other employment this limit is reduced to £1 per week (£4 per month).

The employer must keep a tax deduction card for each employee. These cards when completed are sent to the Collector of Taxes within fourteen days after the end of the fiscal year (April 5th).

The employer is required also to give each employee a certificate (Form P.60) showing the total remuneration paid and the total tax deducted therefrom during the year. For further information regarding the duties of the employer or special circumstances reference should be made to *The Employer's Guide to Pay as you Earn* which is available from the local Inspector of Taxes.

The employee, on the other hand, has certain responsibilities also. A Notice of Coding is received each year from the Inspector of Taxes. As this has to be prepared in advance of the year of assessment it is essential that the employee should notify the Inspector immediately his circumstances change, so that his code number may be rectified. The employer cannot alter the tax deduction until he is so authorized by the Inspector. When the notice of coding is received the employee should make sure that all the allowances and reliefs to which he is entitled are shown on the notice. If there are figures he does not understand he should call on or write to the Inspector about his difficulties. Once each year the employee receives a notice from the Inspector showing how his total tax liability has been calculated, and the total tax which has been deducted during the year. This statement should be compared with the Form P.60 received from the employer and mentioned above.

(*c*) *Schedule D*

The sources of income assessed under Schedule D are classified into six cases as follows:

Case I extends to all trades.

Case II extends to all professions or vocations.

Case III applies to profits of an uncertain annual value.

Case IV applies to interest arising from securities outside the United Kingdom.

Case V applies to income arising from stocks, shares or rents or other possessions outside the United Kingdom.

Case VI applies to annual profits or gains not falling under the other Cases of Schedule D.

Professional profits are assessed under Case II of Schedule D and (subject to special provisions regarding new and discontinued practices) the basis of assessment is the profit of the year preceding the year of assessment. Normally the profits of the practice year ending within the preceding fiscal year are taken as being the profits of the preceding year. For example, if accounts are made up annually to June 30th, the assessment for 1956–57 will be based on the profits for the year ending June 30th, 1955. If, however, the accounts are for the year ended March 31st, the 1956–57 assessment is on the profits for the year to March 31st, 1956. If there is no account available for exactly twelve months, or if there is more than one account during the previous year, the Board of Inland Revenue may at their discretion decide which twelve months will be taken and they may adjust the preceding year's assessment.

The following are the special rules to be observed where a new practice is commenced:

(*a*) The assessment for the first tax year will be on the proportion, for the period from the start of the practice to the following April 5th, of the profits shown by the first accounts.

(*b*) In the case of the second tax year:

(1) Where the first accounts are for a period of twelve months the profit shown by these accounts will be the normal basis for the second year's assessment.

(2) When the first accounts are for a period of less or more than twelve months, the second year's assessment will be such a proportion of the profits or losses shown by the accounts as refers to the first twelve months of the practice.

Thus, if a practice commenced on June 1st, and the first accounts were for ten months to March 31st, the assessment for the second year would be on the profits for these ten months plus two-twelfths of the following year's profits.

(*c*) The basis of assessment for the third and subsequent years will be on the profits shown by the accounts for the year ended within the preceding tax year.

Illustration

A practice was commenced on June 1st, 1954. The accounts for the year to May 31st, 1955, showed a taxable profit of £600.

Assessments:

1954–55. Actual profits from June 1st, 1954 to April 5th, 1955, say ten months—(see note below) ten-twelfths of £600 = £500.

1955–56. Profits for one complete year from June 1st, 1954 = £600.

1956–57. Profits of accounting year ended in the preceding fiscal year, i.e. year to May 31st, 1955 = £600.

Note. Where it is necessary to apportion the profits of a practice for income tax purposes, it has been laid down that the apportionment shall be made by reference to the number of months or parts of a month. Thus, the proportion of ten-twelfths used above to be strictly accurate should be $\frac{9\frac{25}{30}}{12}$

The practitioner may claim that the assessments for the second and third years shall be adjusted to the actual profits of those fiscal years. He must, however, claim for both years or not at all. The claim must be made in writing to the Inspector of Taxes within two years after the end of the second year of assessment and can be revoked within one year after the end of the third year of assessment.

As for new practices, there are also special provisions which apply where a practice is permanently discontinued. The assessment for the last tax year is adjustable to the actual profits from April 6th to the date of cessation, whether this is more or less than an assessment based on the previous year's profits. If the assessment for the tax year preceding the year of discontinuance (i.e. the penultimate year) is less than the actual apportioned profits for that tax year, an additional assessment will be made by the Inspector for the difference. No adjustment, however, is made in favour of the practitioner if the assessment exceeds the actual profits.

It will be readily appreciated that the profit and loss account of a practice, normally prepared on a commercial basis, will not usually show a profits figure which will satisfy the tax authorities. The preparation of accounts is to some extent a matter of temperament and is largely influenced by individual circumstances. For example, one practitioner may decide to depreciate his equipment or furniture and fittings by writing off an unduly large amount, while another may aim at making the provision for depreciation as small as possible. Again, a single-handed practitioner may charge against his practice expenses which another would regard as personal. In order to distribute the tax burden as equitably as possible, definite rules have been made as to the calculation of profits for Income Tax purposes. Some of these rules appear to be of an arbitrary nature. There is no doubt, however, that a serious endeavour has been made to treat every taxpayer on the same basis. To appreciate this fact will be of great assistance in obtaining a proper understanding of the principles upon which these rules are founded. Very briefly, it is only revenue (as distinct from capital) profits which are assessable, while only those expenses 'wholly and exclusively laid out or expended for the purposes of the trade or profession' may be allowed.

Seldom has a phrase given the Courts as much difficulty as this quotation from the Income Tax Acts. The operative words are 'for the purposes of the trade or profession' qualified, of course, by the expression 'wholly and exclusively'. Lord Davey in *Strong and Co. of Romsey Ltd.* v. *Woodifield* (1906) A.C. 448, said, 'It is not enough that the disbursement is made in the course of, or arises out of or is connected with the trade, or is made out of the profits of the trade. It must be made for the purposes of earning the profits.' The issue in the case of *Strong and Co.* was whether damages and costs recovered by a guest, who was injured as a result of a chimney falling in while he was sleeping at one of the company's tied houses, could be deducted in the computation of the company's profits. The House of Lords unanimously refused to allow the deduction. Lord Davey's words were criticized in the final report of the Royal Commission on the Taxation of Profits and Income, published in June 1955. The Commission did not think that the phrase 'for the purpose of earning profits' was a good interpretation of 'for the purposes of the trade' since it suggested some limiting condition for the expenditure to which it was extremely difficult to give any concrete meaning. The Commission felt that the position might be clarified by an appropriate section in the Finance Act.

The following are a few decisions where expenditure was not allowed:

(*a*) *Copeman* v. *Wm. Flood and Sons* (1940), T.R. 491—Extravagant salaries paid, particularly to members of a family.
(*b*) *Allen* v. *Farquharson Bros. and Co.* (1932), 17 T.C. 59—Legal costs incurred in connexion with a tax appeal to the Commissioners.
(*c*) *Spofforth and Prince* v. *Golder* (1945), 26 T.C. 310—Costs of a successful defence in connexion with a criminal charge.
(*d*) *Curtis* v. *Oldfield* (1925), 9 T.C. 319—Loss arising where the director of a company died and it was found that private payments on his behalf had been made by the company.

As has been stressed already, expenditure charged must have been incurred for the purposes of the practice. The adjustments necessary to bring a practitioner's accounts into line for tax purposes fall into three main categories.

(1) Items which may have been charged against profits

but which are not allowed as deductions for Income Tax purposes, e.g.:

(*a*) Private domestic expenses.
(*b*) Expenses not connected with the practice.
(*c*) Capital expenditure.
(*d*) Appropriations of profit.
(*e*) Interest paid from which tax is deducted at the time of payment.
(*f*) Interest on capital.
(*g*) Legal expenses incurred in acquiring a long lease, or in connexion with a partnership agreement.
(*h*) Any other expenses not wholly and exclusively laid out for the purpose of earning the profits.

(2) Items which may have been credited to the profit and loss account, but are to be eliminated for Income Tax purposes, e.g.:

(*a*) Capital profits.
(*b*) Interest received from which tax has been deducted at the source.
(*c*) Profits not arising out of the practice.

(3) Deductions allowed for Income Tax purposes, but which have not been charged in the Profit and Loss Account, e.g.:

(*a*) Net Schedule A assessment of practice premises owned by the practitioner.

Expenses allowed naturally vary from practice to practice, but as already stated all expenditure which can be proved to have been 'wholly and exclusively laid out for the purposes of the profession' will be allowed as a deduction from practice income. It is probably an appropriate time to mention here that a practitioner who is on a salary basis and therefore assessed under Schedule E must prove that his expenses are 'wholly, exclusively and necessarily' disbursed. The word 'necessarily' has been excluded from the Acts for Schedule D purposes, and this certainly eases the burden considerably for the doctor in practice as compared with his colleague who receives a salary.

The following is a list of expenses which may be charged in

the accounts with a view to ascertaining the net profit for tax purposes under Schedule D:

(1) Salaries, wages or payments to assistants, locum tenens, receptionists, dispensers, secretaries and book-keepers. Wife's salary commensurate with duties involved.

Because husband and wife are assessed jointly the claiming of salary paid to wife above £180, generally speaking, presents no practical advantage.

(2) Salaries, wages or payments to chauffeurs, domestic staff and cleaners in the proportion that they relate to duties in connexion with professional purposes.

(3) Purchase of medicines, drugs, dressings, bottles, etc.

(4) Postages, stationery and printing.

(5) Telephone and telegrams less cost of private calls.

(6) Laundry, cleaning and cleaning materials so far as the cost is attributable to professional use.

(7) The cost of renewal of special garments, such as white surgery coats and operating gowns, may be claimed, but not the cost of ordinary clothing.

(8) Rent, rates and repairs of surgeries and waiting rooms. If the property is owned the net annual value is allowed instead of rent. When premises are partly used for residence a reasonable proportion of the charges is allowable, but not exceeding two thirds of the total applicable to the whole premises.

(9) National Insurance Contributions, insurances for fire, burglary (in the proportion relating to professional purposes), professional risks and for loss of profits.

(10) Superannuation Contributions under the National Health Service rank for an allowance at the full rate of tax and either may be charged as an expense in the accounts or as a deduction from the assessment. As from 1956–57 in certain circumstances and subject to a number of restrictions a practitioner may deduct from his 'relevant earnings' any premium paid by him in that year under an annuity contract, the main object of which is to provide him with a life annuity in old age. For this purpose 'relevant earnings' means any income arising from an office or employment other than a pensionable office or employment.

(11) Periodicals, flowers and journals for waiting rooms.

(12) Renewal of professional books of reference (but not the original cost of such books).

(13) Renewal, replacement and repairs of appliances and instruments. (The initial cost of additional appliances and instruments is a capital expense and not allowable.)

(14) Depreciation of furniture and fittings and equipment at rates approved by the revenue authorities.

(15) Repairs and renewals of furniture, curtains, carpets, etc., used in professional rooms. Entirely new furniture which does not replace old furniture is capital expenditure and not allowable.

(16) Bad and doubtful debts (but the Inspector may ask for details of the larger amounts).

(17) Legal expenses of a revenue nature, as on debt recovery or renewal of a partnership agreement or a lease (but not on the initial agreements).

(18) Defalcations or embezzlement by employees.

(19) Bank charges and commissions.

(20) Bank overdraft interest.

(21) Removal expenses for professional purposes.

(22) Audit and accountancy fees.

(23) Dilapidations are allowed on the termination of a lease of practice premises.

(24) Subscriptions to trade and professional organizations are allowed if the organization has entered into an agreement with the Revenue Authorities to pay tax on the excess of its receipts over its allowable expenses. Payments to the following bodies are normally allowed:

British Medical Association.
College of General Practitioners.
Medical Practitioners Union.
Scientific Societies such as the Royal Society of Medicine and Local Medical Societies.
Defence Societies.

(25) Travelling expenses incurred in visiting patients.

(26) The cost of running and maintaining a car, including licence, tax, insurance, petrol, oil, cleaning, garaging, repairs, renewals of parts, tyres, etc. A claim may also be made for depreciation. This is calculated in two parts as follows:

(*a*) An initial allowance of one-fifth of the cost of a new or second-hand car is given only for the year in which the expenditure was incurred.

(*b*) An annual allowance of 25 per cent. calculated each year on the written-down value of the car.

Where the car is partially used for pleasure or for private affairs, these allowances are restricted to the proportion used for professional purposes as relevant circumstances render just and reasonable. If a second car is held as a reserve, the running costs and depreciation may be claimed on both, only in so far as they are used for professional purposes.

(27) When accommodation and board are provided in kind by a principal for a locum tenens the cost may be claimed as a professional expense. If it is necessary for the locum tenens to be paid in cash in lieu of accommodation and board, the sum is regarded as part of his total remuneration and is subject to tax.

(28) Expenditure incurred in the upkeep of a garden and the approach to a surgery will be allowed only in so far as such expenses are reasonable and necessary to maintain access to professional premises.

(29) In certain cases the cost of providing hospitality for specialists called out for consultation may be allowed as an expense for Income Tax purposes. Individual cases would no doubt have to be argued with the Inspector. It would be necessary to show that the expenditure for this purpose was wholly and exclusively incurred for the purpose of the practice and was reasonably necessary and appropriate. Thus a distinction has to be made between the cost of a dinner party and the provision of necessary hospitality to a consultant who had travelled a considerable distance.

(30) No objection is normally raised by the Inland Revenue Authorities to an allowance for the cost of attending refresher courses to keep one's knowledge up to date as opposed to expenditure in connexion with post-graduate study for a higher degree or professional qualification. This latter expenditure is regarded as being a capital outlay and as such is disallowable.

Mention has already been made of a practitioner who may

decide to depreciate his equipment or furniture and fittings by writing off each year an unduly large amount, compared with his colleague who might make no provision whatsoever. This situation is counteracted by the Revenue Authorities having published fixed rates of depreciation for all the main classes of trade and items of equipment. No rates have been officially fixed for the medical profession, and the normal procedure is for agreement to be reached with the local Inspector of Taxes. Generally speaking the following rates of depreciation apply:

Electrical equipment	$12\frac{1}{2}\%$
Non-electrical equipment	$6\frac{1}{4}\%$
Fixtures and fittings	$6\frac{1}{4}\%$
Typewriters and other office equipment ..	$12\frac{1}{2}\%$

When the equipment is sold, scrapped or destroyed a balancing allowance or charge will be made to ensure that the practitioner is given allowances amounting in total to the difference between his capital expenditure on the equipment and what he obtains when it is sold, scrapped or destroyed.

As an alternative there is the 'renewals basis' under which the normal allowances are not given, but when equipment requires to be replaced the cost of the new equipment less the proceeds from the sale of the old equipment is allowed as a deduction. Any element of improvement, of course, requires to be excluded.

One of the advantages of this type of claim is in cases where it is difficult to keep records of very small assets or if assets are likely to be rapidly renewed as in the case of a practitioner having a new motor-car each year. On the other hand, in a year where there is no renewal there will be no allowance at all for depreciation, whereas capital allowances operate right from the beginning of the life of the asset.

For example, when a consulting-room chair is discarded and replaced by a new chair of similar quality, the cost of the new chair may reasonably be claimed as a replacement. A decision to discard all furniture and to refurnish the consulting room with furnishings of a superior quality is unlikely to result in a successful claim. Increased cost will not preclude a claim for renewals, but a substantial improvement may do so. A practitioner deciding to improve his surgery accommodation by structural alterations is unlikely to be allowed the total cost as a charge on his income. If he can prove that redecoration and repairs to the premises were needed, he may well succeed in achieving a partial allowance. This might amount to the estimated cost of such redecoration and repairs if the structural alterations had not been carried out.

Similarly a renewal allowance would be given for a replacement engine in a practitioner's car if it were similar to the existing engine. If a superior and more costly engine had been fitted the excess cost would be regarded as an improvement, and only the cost of one similar to the original would be allowed.

The point at issue is whether the replacement restores the equipment to its original condition or improves it beyond that limit. If the former, it would be allowable for relief; if the latter the excess over the amount needed for repair would be regarded as capital expenditure.

As already mentioned, professional profits are assessed under Case II of Schedule D, but difficult questions frequently arise where a practitioner in addition holds an appointment with a hospital. While remuneration from a full-time appointment would clearly be assessable under Schedule E (subject to the stringent rules governing expenses) it can be argued that a part-time appointment is merely incidental to normal professional activities, the whole of which are in the scope of Schedule D. Inspectors of Taxes have been reluctant to accept this argument, generally insisting that income from a part-time hospital appointment be assessed under Schedule E. It is interesting to note, however, that the Special Commissioners have recently considered appeals from five part-time consultants and decided that they should not have been assessed under Schedule E but under Schedule D both on the remuneration of their hospital appointments and on fees paid for domiciliary consultations. In the opinion of the Special Commissioners, the consultants' part-time hospital appointments were a necessary part of their profession and not merely incidental thereto. It has been reported that the Crown has appealed against the decision of the Special Commissioners, but no forecast can be given at this stage what the result of the appeal will be.

It is under Case III of Schedule D that interest received without deduction of tax is assessed. This includes untaxed interest from War Loan, Post Office Savings Bank and Trustees Savings Bank deposits, Deposit Account interest and Discount on Treasury Bills.

Subject to special provisions where a new source of income arises or where a source of income ceases, tax under Case III is calculated in respect of the year of assessment in which the income first arises on the full amount arising within that year, and in respect of subsequent years on the full amount arising within the year preceding the year of assessment.

For 1956–57 onwards the first £15 of the total interest received in any tax year from deposits with the Post Office Savings Bank or ordinary deposits with a Trustee Savings Bank is exempt from income tax. While this exemption applies to husband and wife separately, the total interest must be entered in the income tax return form. This concession does not apply for surtax purposes when the exempt amount must be grossed up.

While interest from National Savings Certificates is entirely exempt from tax, certain other annual payments are assessed under Case III. In this connexion the case of *Hawkins* (*Inspector of Taxes*) v. *Leahy* (*et contra*) (1952), 2 All E.R. 759, is of special interest to members of the medical profession. A medical practitioner had entered the National Health Service scheme and exercised the option given to him by the National Health Service (Superannuation) Regulations, 1947, under which he received eight per cent. of his remuneration as a contribution towards the maintenance of a policy of assurance which he held. The doctor was assessed under Case II on the assumption that the payments were profits of his profession, or alternatively under Case III on the grounds that they were annual payments. It was held that:

(1) the receipts did not represent profits of the doctor's profession and were not assessable under Case II.

(2) the receipts represented annual payments in the nature of income and were assessable under Case III.

Partnership Assessments

On the principle that wherever possible tax is collected at the source, the tax levied on a partnership is computed and stated jointly and a joint assessment is made in the partnership name.

If the firm defaults in paying, the Crown has the legal right to demand the whole tax from any partner. Each partner's share of the practice income must be calculated first in order to arrive at the allowances to which he is entitled. The total allowances of both or all the partners are then deducted so that the amount of the tax payable by the partnership may be calculated. Profit-sharing on the basis agreed upon by the partners remains the same for tax purposes. If partners receive salaries or if interest on capital is credited to them, these amounts will be allocated to the individual partners before sharing the balance of profits for Income Tax purposes. For any year of assessment the partnership assessment must be divided between the partners in the same ratio as the profits *for that year* are divided. This ratio could quite easily be different from the one used for dividing the profits of the accounting year used as the basis of the assessment. In other words, it is the *arithmetical proportion* of the profits to which a partner is entitled for the year of assessment that is applied in calculating his share of the assessment.

An example will make this clearer.

A and B are in practice as partners and the following figures apply:

Year ended December 31st, 1953
Profits (shared $\frac{2}{3}$ to A and $\frac{1}{3}$ to B) £3,000
Year ended December 31st, 1954
Profits (shared $\frac{2}{3}$ to A and $\frac{1}{3}$ to B) £2,000
Year ended December 31st, 1955
Profits (shared equally from January 1st, 1955, onwards) £2,500

Assessments on firm (based on previous year's profits).

1954–55 based on £3,000, being the profits earned in the year to December 31st, 1953.

Partners' allocation:	A	B
Proportion from 6/4/54 to 31/12/54 of £3,000 equals £2,250 ..	£1,500 (⅔)	£750 (⅓)
Proportion from 1/1/55 to 5/4/55 of £3,000 equals £750	375 (½)	375 (½)
	£1,875	£1,125

Total £3,000

1955–56 based on £2,000, being the profits earned in the year to December 31st, 1954.

Partners' allocation:	A	B
Proportion from 6/4/55 to 31/12/55 of £2,000 equals £1,500 ..	£750 (½)	£750 (½)
Proportion from 1/1/56 to 5/4/56 of £2,000 equals £500	250 (½)	250 (½)
	£1,000	£1,000

Total £2,000

If any taxed charges, such as mortgage interest or an annuity to a deceased partner's widow, are paid out of the practice income, these should be added back in the Income Tax computation. Tax must be paid on these charges at the full standard rate and no deduction for earned income relief is allowed. If the practice has any taxed income, however, this can be set off against the taxed charges.

If there is any change in the practitioners comprising a partnership from 1953–54 onwards, the practice is automatically treated for Income Tax purposes as having ceased and a new partnership commenced at the date of the change. The partners engaged in the practice immediately before and immediately after the change have the right to elect within twelve months from the date of the change that the partnership shall not be treated as discontinued. There must, however, be one partner common to both periods and all partners must agree. Where one of the partners has died, his personal representative must act in his stead. If advantage is taken of this option the assessment for the year of change will be apportioned by the groups of partners before and after the change 'as may be just' usually on a time basis.

In *Dickenson* v. *Gross* (1927), 11 T.C. 614, the point was made that, although there might be a partnership agreement expressed in writing, partnership does not in fact exist if the terms of the agreement remain inoperative.

Other cases where it was held that no partnership existed in fact are as follows:

McKie v. *Luck* (1925), 9 T.C. 511.
I.R. v. *Williamson* (1928), 14 T.C. 335.
Taylor v. *Chalklin* (1945) 26 T.C. 463.

On the other hand, a partnership may in fact exist even though there is no written agreement. The point was made in *Ayrshire Pullman Motor Services and Ritchie* v. *I.R.* (1929), 14 T.C. 754 and *Waddington* v. *O'Callaghan* (1931), 16 T.C. 187, that a partnership agreement can have no retroactive effect for Income Tax purposes. Thus, if a partnership deed is subsequently prepared fixing the commencing date of the firm, it is not conclusive evidence that the partnership did in actual fact commence on that earlier date.

Surtax

When a practitioner's statutory total income (as defined on p. 318) exceeds £2,000, he becomes liable to Surtax. This is to all intents and purposes a deferred instalment of Income Tax which becomes payable on January 1st following the end of the year of assessment. The rates of Surtax are normally fixed in arrears, and operate on a graduated scale. The rates for 1956–57 were fixed as follows:

		Rates in £	
		s.	d.
On the first £2,000 of total income	.. ..	nil	
,, next 500 ,, ,,	.. .. ..	2	0
,, ,, 500 ,, ,,	.. .. ..	2	6
,, ,, 1,000 ,, ,,	.. .. ..	3	6
,, ,, 1,000 ,, ,,	.. .. ..	4	6
,, ,, 1,000 ,, ,,	.. .. ..	5	6
,, ,, 2,000 ,, ,,	.. .. ..	6	6
,, ,, 2,000 ,, ,,	.. .. ..	7	6
,, ,, 2,000 ,, ,,	.. .. ..	8	6
,, ,, 3,000 ,, ,,	.. .. ..	9	6
On the remainder of total income	.. ..	10	0

The income assessable to surtax for any year is the income finally agreed for Income Tax purposes for the same year after deducting:

(*a*) Annual charges, including interest on a mortgage paid to a Building Society, interest paid to banks on overdrafts and loans, relief due for business losses, or in respect of a claim for repairs and maintenance of property.

(*b*) The amount by which personal reliefs exceed the allowance of £140 given to a single person. The allowances which will be taken into this calculation are as follows:

(1) Allowance due to a married man.
(2) Child allowance.
(3) Dependent relative allowance.
(4) Relief for daughter's services.
(5) Relief for housekeeper.

While the deductions under (*a*) above have been allowed for many years, those falling into category (*b*) may only be made for 1956–57 and subsequent years.

Surtax is payable in arrears on January 1st following the year of assessment. For example, tax for 1956–57 is payable on January 1st, 1958.

It should be noted that the income from taxed dividends to be assessed to Surtax for 1956–57 must be the actual gross amounts receivable during the year to April 5th, 1957.

Building Society interest was chargeable to Surtax up to

1951–52 on the amount received, but thereafter at the grossed amount thereof.

Surtax payers may find it more convenient to make their Surtax return to the Special Commissioners. This can be done by giving notice on or before May 1st in any year following the year of assessment, and by entering in their Income Tax returns only income which is assessable under Schedules D and E, and particulars of the allowances claimed.

In normal circumstances the income of a married woman living with her husband is deemed to be that of the husband, and the assessment on the combined incomes will be made upon the husband. If applications referring to Surtax are made by either party before July 6th, separate assessments will be made on each, but the total amount of tax payable will not be altered. The procedure is for the total tax due on the combined incomes to be divided between husband and wife in proportion to their respective incomes. The application must be made in writing to the Special Commissioners and, when the arrangement is adopted, it will remain in force for all subsequent years until revoked. It should be noted that a husband cannot be assessed to Surtax in respect of income received by his wife prior to her marriage.

Miscellaneous Matters

(*a*) *Treatment of Losses*

Unfortunately there are occasions when a practitioner suffers a loss, as is sometimes the case in the early years of a new practice. Where a loss is sustained relief may be obtained in one of three ways:

(1) The assessment for the year in which the loss is suffered may be reduced by the amount of the loss if a claim is made within twelve months from the end of the tax year in which the loss is incurred. If there should be any excess loss over that assessment, tax on the excess will be refunded against tax paid on any other income. For 1953–54 onwards, in addition to relief being given against the appropriate income of the year of loss it may be given against the appropriate income of the next following year provided the claimant is still in practice and that any relief so claimed shall be given before any relief for a loss incurred in that

year itself. A loss incurred on a practice in any period is to be set off first against other earned income of the claimant, then against his own unearned income and then, unless a contrary claim is made, against first the earned, and then the unearned income, of the spouse.

(2) A loss on a practice may be set off against the profit on any other distinct business, trade or profession carried on by the practitioner concerned, either by himself or in partnership.

(3) Any balance of the practice loss not used as stated above may be carried forward indefinitely and set off against the first profits of the same practice by the same practitioner.

It is interesting to note that, in the case of a partnership, each partner's proportion of the loss is his own personal responsibility, and may be used as outlined above. Consequently should he die or retire his proportion of any claim for unexhausted losses lapses.

(*b*) *Seven Year Covenants*

It is a common practice for charitable institutions to increase their annual income by persuading as many subscribers as possible to sign seven year covenants. By this means with the standard rate of tax at 8*s*. 6*d*. in the £, for every 11*s*. 6*d*. received from covenanters, 8*s*. 6*d*. will be recovered by the institution from the Revenue Authorities and consequently the annual income of the charity is substantially increased. In other words, a taxpayer by signing a deed binding himself to pay an annual net subscription to the charity for seven years or until previous death, enables the charity to benefit by the subscription being treated as though it were the net amount after deduction of tax, and a refund of that tax is claimed by the charity. This is an ideal method for a charity to raise funds, and for a subscriber to enhance very considerably his financial support of the organization in which he is interested.

To be effective the covenant must be in proper deed form, and it is important to remember that a new deed must be executed immediately the old one expires if it is the intention to continue the arrangement. There are in addition the following most important aspects to be kept in mind:

(1) When a taxpayer signs a seven year covenant say for £50 per annum less income tax, he is in actual fact alienating that part of his income. He will find that this will in the first place be set against his unearned income. Any balance will be offset against earned income, and, of course, his earned income relief will be correspondingly restricted.

(2) Payments made under deeds of covenant dated after April 10th, 1946, are not allowed as deductions for Surtax purposes.

(3) A taxpayer not subject to Income Tax at the full standard rate should not adopt this system. If he does, he will find that the Inspector of Taxes will keep him to the terms of the covenant under which he binds himself to pay the net amount to the charity and account for the tax to the Revenue Authorities at the full standard rate. Even if the taxpayer has no income and makes the payment out of capital, he is still liable to pay this tax. The Revenue Authorities will recover the tax in the normal way or, if that is not possible, by raising a special assessment.

(*c*) *Form of Accounts*

Practitioners frequently prepare their accounts on a cash basis. This means that they calculate their net profit on the cash actually received less cash actually spent during the year, and no credit has been taken for work carried out and fees earned during that period when payment therefor has not yet been received. It is contended in some quarters that this basis is equitable, because amounts owing at the end of the financial year for work done but not paid for may never be received; even if they are received later they are automatically brought into account the following year. The same principle, it is held, applies to expenses incurred in one year and paid in the following one.

The Inland Revenue, however, maintain that accounts based on a cash basis do not show the true income of the practice. This attitude was supported in the case of *E. Collins and Sons Ltd.* v. *Commissioners of Inland Revenue* (1925), 12 T.C. 773, when the point was made: 'It is elementary that a profit and loss account is not an account of receipts and expenditure in cash only.' Again, Lord Morison in *Commissioners of Inland Revenue*

v. *Morrison* (1932), 17 T.C. 325, said that 'The word "profit" for Income Tax purposes is in general to be understood in its natural and proper meaning, and that the assessable profits are to be ascertained on the ordinary principles of commercial accounting.' No professional accountant looks with favour on accounts prepared on a cash basis only.

Again the Revenue Authorities contend that, if the practice is sold or disposed of and the outgoing practitioner retains his personal book debts and fees owing, the amounts collected cannot be assessed. In *Bennett* v. *Ogston* (1930), 15 T.C. 374, the learned Judge said 'that there is no question of assessing these receipts to Income Tax'. Two main reasons are held by the Board of Inland Revenue to support their contention. Firstly, the liability of the outgoing practitioner ceases on the date on which the transfer of the practice takes place, and, secondly, that the collection of book debts is merely the realization of capital assets.

It will consequently be found that the Inland Revenue will accept accounts prepared on a cash basis, if this has been the custom in past years. They will not usually countenance the adoption of a cash basis in the case of new practices, and will insist on the submission of a proper Income and Expenditure Account. It is, however, a matter for the Commissioners ultimately to decide.

(*d*) *Penalties*

Where a person makes incorrect or false returns or refuses or neglects to make a return, he renders himself liable to heavy penalties. As these are not as widely known as they should be, a brief outline of the principal ones is given below:

(1) If any person without reasonable excuse fails to give notice to the Inspector of Taxes that he is chargeable to Income Tax in any particular year, or neglects to make returns, if proceeded against by Court action, he will forfeit the sum of £20 and treble the tax due. If proceeded against by the General Commissioners the penalty will be a sum not exceeding £20 plus treble the tax due.

(2) The penalty for making fraudulent claims for any allowance or deduction is £20 and treble the tax chargeable

in respect of all the sources of income as if such a claim had not been allowed. For aiding and abetting the fine is £500.

(3) Where it is proved that a person who ought to be charged with tax has fraudulently changed his place of residence or made any false statement regarding his properties he will be charged treble the amount of the excess tax chargeable. For aiding and abetting the penalty is £500.

(4) If any person liable to Surtax fails, without reasonable excuse, to make a return, he will be liable to a penalty not exceeding £50, and after judgment has been given for that penalty, to a further penalty of £50 for every day during which the default continues.

(5) Should a person knowingly make any false statement to obtain any allowance or reduction or repayment of Income Tax he will be liable on summary conviction to imprisonment for a term not exceeding six months. If, however, the proceedings are taken under the Perjury Act, 1911, the penalties are much more severe.

Conclusion

It will be readily appreciated that this brief chapter on Income Tax deals with a very vast subject in a most limited way. Many matters affecting the taxpayer of necessity have been omitted. The information provided has been given in the light of the Income Tax Act, 1952, and subsequent Finance Acts. Principles have been stated in as simple a manner as possible in an attempt to bring an understanding of certain tax problems to members of the profession.

In these days when the incidence of taxation has such crippling effects, it is suggested that much unnecessary worry and expense can be avoided by approaching a tax expert such as a chartered accountant for advice. It should not be forgotten, however, that the taxpayer can obtain advice and help from the local Inspector of Taxes if he so desires.

APPENDICES

APPENDIX A

QUALIFICATIONS

Granted in the United Kingdom and the Republic of Ireland which are Registrable under the Medical Acts

Licensing Body	*Primary Qualifications*	*Additional Qualifications*
University of Birmingham	M.B., Ch.B.	M.D., Ch.M.
University of Bristol	M.B., Ch.B.	M.D., Ch.M.
University of Cambridge	M.B., B.Chir.	M.D., M.Chir.
University of Durham	M.B., B.S.	M.D., M.S.
University of Leeds	M.B., Ch.B.	M.D., Ch.M.
University of Liverpool	M.B., Ch.B.	M.D., Ch.M., M.Ch.Orth.
University of London	M.B., B.S.	M.D., M.S.
University of Manchester	M.B., Ch.B.	M.D., Ch.M.
University of Oxford	B.M., B.Ch.	D.M., M.Ch.
University of Sheffield	M.B., Ch.B.	M.D., Ch.M.
University of Wales	M.B., B.Ch.	M.D., M.Ch.
University of Aberdeen	M.B., Ch.B.	M.D., Ch.M.
University of Edinburgh	M.B., Ch.B.	M.D., Ch.M.
University of Glasgow	M.B., Ch.B.	M.D., Ch.M.
University of St. Andrews	M.B., Ch.B.	M.D., Ch.M.
Queen's University of Belfast	M.B., B.Ch.	M.D., M.Ch., M.A.O.
University of Dublin	M.B., B.Ch. L.Med., L.Ch.	M.D., M.Ch., M.A.O.
National University of Ireland	M.B., B.Ch.	M.D., M.Ch., M.A.O.
Royal College of Physicians of London	L.R.C.P.Lond.	M.R.C.P., F.R.C.P.
Royal College of Surgeons of England	M.R.C.S.Eng.	F.R.C.S.
Society of Apothecaries of London	L.M.S.S.A., L.S.A.	
Royal College of Physicians of Edinburgh	L.R.C.P.Edin.	M.R.C.P.Edin., F.RC.P.Edin.
Royal College of Surgeons of Edinburgh	L.R.C.S.Edin.	F.R.C.S.Edin.

Licensing Body	*Primary Qualifications*	*Additional Qualifications*
Royal Faculty of Physicians and Surgeons of Glasgow	L.R.F.P.S.Glasg.	F.R.F.P.S. Glasg. (P.) F.R.F.P.S. Glasg. (S.)
Royal College of Physicians of Ireland	L., L.M., R.C.P.Irel.	M.R.C.P.Irel. F.R.C.P.Irel.
Royal College of Surgeons in Ireland	L., L.M., R.C.S.Irel.	F.R.C.S.Irel.
Apothecaries' Hall of Dublin	L.A.H.	

Note: A 'primary qualification' may be registered as a qualification additional to qualifications already registered by a medical practitioner; and an 'additional qualification' may in certain circumstances be registered as a 'primary qualification'.

APPENDIX B

GENERAL MEDICAL COUNCIL

DISCIPLINARY COMMITTEE

WARNING NOTICE

For the Guidance of Registered and Provisionally Registered Medical Practitioners

Section 33 of the Medical Act, 1956, provides that if any fully or provisionally registered practitioner

(*a*) is convicted by any Court in the United Kingdom or the Republic of Ireland of any felony, misdemeanour, crime or offence, or

(*b*) after due inquiry is judged by the Disciplinary Committee to have been guilty of infamous conduct in any professional respect,

the Disciplinary Committee may if they think fit direct his name to be erased from the Register.

In accordance with the long-established practice of the Council, the Committee issue this Notice for the information and guidance of practitioners with reference to judgments and decisions of the Committee and of the Council in relation to a number of disciplinary cases.

It must, however, be clearly understood that the particulars which are given below do not constitute, and are not intended to constitute, a complete enumeration of the professional offences which may entail erasure from the Register; and that by issuing this Notice the Committee are in no way precluded from considering and dealing with any form of professional misconduct (as, for example, adultery committed in professional relationship) which may be brought before them, although it may not appear to come within the scope or precise wording of any of the categories set forth in this Notice. Circumstances may and do arise from time to time in relation to which there may occur questions of professional conduct which do not come within any of these categories. In such instances, as in all others, the Committee have to consider and judge upon the facts brought before them.

By Section 6 (3) (*b*) of, and the First Schedule to, the Medical Act, 1950, the disciplinary jurisdiction exercised by the Committee is made applicable to persons who are provisionally registered by virtue of that section; and where the term 'registered medical practitioner' is used in this Notice it is intended to include, unless the context indicates otherwise, practitioners who are provisionally registered.

1. Certificates, Notifications, Reports, etc.

Registered medical practitioners are in certain cases bound by law to give, or may be from time to time called upon or requested to give, certificates, notifications, reports, and other documents of a kindred character, signed by them in their professional capacity, for subsequent use either in the Courts or for administrative purposes.

Such documents include, among others, Certificates, Notifications, Reports, etc.

(*a*) Under the Acts relating to births, deaths, or disposal of the dead;
(*b*) Under the Acts relating to Lunacy and Mental Treatment, and Mental Deficiency, and the Rules made thereunder;
(*c*) Under the Factory Acts and the Regulations made thereunder;
(*d*) Under the Education Acts;
(*e*) Under the Public Health Acts and the Orders made thereunder;
(*f*) Under the Acts and the Orders relating to the notification of infectious diseases;
(*g*) Under the Family Allowances Acts, National Insurance (Industrial Injuries) Acts, National Insurance Acts, and National Health Service Acts, and the Regulations made thereunder;
(*h*) Under the Old Age Pensions Acts and the Regulations made thereunder;
(*i*) Under the Merchant Shipping Acts;
(*j*) For procuring the issue of Foreign Office passports;
(*k*) For excusing attendance in the Courts, in the public services, in public offices, or in ordinary employments;
(*l*) Under the National Service Acts, or in connexion with persons serving in Her Majesty's Forces;
(*m*) In connexion with matters under the control of the Ministry of Pensions; and
(*n*) Of vaccination required for purposes of international travel.

Any registered medical practitioner who shall be proved to the satisfaction of the Committee to have signed or given under his name and authority any such certificate, notification, report, or document of a kindred character, which is untrue, misleading, or improper, whether relating to the several matters above specified or otherwise, will be liable to have his name erased from the Register.

2. Unqualified or Unregistered Assistants and Covering

The employment by any registered medical practitioner in connexion with his professional practice of an assistant who is not duly qualified or registered, and the permitting of such unqualified or unregistered person to attend, treat, or perform operations upon patients in respect of matters requiring professional discretion or skill, is in the opinion of the Committee in its nature fraudulent and dangerous to the public health; and any registered medical practitioner who shall be proved to the satisfaction of the Committee to have so employed an unqualified or unregistered assistant will be liable to have his name erased from the Register.

Any registered medical practitioner who by his presence, countenance, advice, assistance, or co-operation, knowingly enables an unqualified or unregistered person, whether described as an assistant or otherwise, to attend, treat, or perform any operation upon a patient in respect of any matter requiring professional discretion or skill, to issue or procure the issue of any certificate, notification, report, or other document of a kindred character (as more particularly specified in section 1 hereof), or otherwise to engage in professional practice as if the said person were duly qualified and registered, will be liable on proof of the facts to the satisfaction of the Committee to have his name erased from the Register.

The foregoing part of this paragraph does not purport to restrict the proper training and instruction of bona-fide medical students, or the legitimate employment of dressers, midwives, dispensers, surgery attendants, and skilled mechanical or technical assistants, under the immediate personal supervision of a registered medical practitioner.

3. Sale of Poisons

The employment for his own profit and under cover of his own qualifications, by any registered medical practitioner who keeps a medical hall, open shop, or other place in which scheduled poisons or preparations containing scheduled poisons are sold to the public, of assistants who are left in charge but are not legally qualified to sell scheduled poisons to the public, is in the opinion of the Committee a practice professionally discreditable and fraught with danger to the public, and any registered medical practitioner who is proved to the satisfaction of the Committee to have so offended will be liable to have his name erased from the Register.

4. Dangerous Drugs

The contravention by a registered medical practitioner of the provisions of the Dangerous Drugs Act and the Regulations made thereunder may be the subject of criminal proceedings, and any conviction resulting therefrom may be dealt with as such by the Committee in exercise of their powers under Section 33 of the Medical Act, 1956. But any contravention of the Acts or the Regulations, involving an abuse of the privileges conferred thereunder upon registered medical practitioners, whether such contravention has been the subject of criminal proceedings or not, will, if proved to the satisfaction of the Committee, render a registered medical practitioner liable to have his name erased from the Register.

5. Association with Unqualified or Unregistered Persons

Any registered medical practitioner who, either by administering anaesthetics or otherwise, assists an unqualified or unregistered person to attend, treat, or perform an operation upon any other person in respect of matters requiring professional discretion or skill, will be liable on proof of the facts to the satisfaction of the Committee to have his name erased from the Register.

6. Advertising and Canvassing

The practices by a registered medical practitioner:

(*a*) Of advertising, whether directly or indirectly, for the purpose of obtaining patients or promoting his own professional advantage; or, for any such purpose, of procuring or sanctioning, or acquiescing in, the publication of notices commending or directing attention to the practitioner's professional skill, knowledge, services, or qualifications, or depreciating those of others; or of being associated with, or employed by, those who procure or sanction such advertising or publication: and

(*b*) Of canvassing, or employing any agent or canvasser, for the purpose of obtaining patients; or of sanctioning, or of being associated with or employed by those who sanction, such employment,

are in the opinion of the Committee contrary to the public interest and discreditable to the profession of Medicine, and any registered medical practitioner who resorts to any such practice renders himself liable, on proof of the facts to the satisfaction of the Committee, to have his name erased from the Register.

7. Association with Uncertified Women Practising as Midwives

Whereas it has been made to appear to the Council that certain registered medical practitioners have from time to time, by their countenance or assistance, or by issuing certificates, notifications, reports, or other documents of a kindred character, enabled uncertified persons to attend women in childbirth otherwise than under the direction and personal supervision of a duly qualified and registered medical practitioner, as required by law;

And whereas such conduct is in the opinion of the Council and of the Committee discreditable to the profession of Medicine, and calculated to defeat the purpose of the statutes made in the public interest for the protection of mothers and infants;

Notice is hereby given that any registered medical practitioner who is proved to the satisfaction of the Committee to have so offended will be liable to have his name erased from the Register.

By Order of the Disciplinary Committee,

W. K. PYKE-LEES,

Registrar,
General Medical Council.

November, 1957.

APPENDIX C

ETHICAL CODE

(reproduced by permission of the British Medical Association)

MEDICAL CONSULTATIONS IN PRACTICE

1. A practitioner consulted is a practitioner who, with the acquiescence of the practitioner already in attendance, examines a patient under this practitioner's care and, either at a meeting of the two practitioners or by correspondence, co-operates in the formulation of diagnosis, prognosis, and treatment of the case. The term 'consultation' means such a co-operation between practitioners. In domiciliary consultations it is desirable that both practitioners should meet and in other circumstances similar arrangements should obtain wherever practicable.

2. It is the duty of an Attending Practitioner to propose a consultation where indicated, or to acquiesce in any reasonable request for consultation expressed by the patient or his representatives.

3. The Attending Practitioner should nominate the practitioner to be consulted, and should advise accordingly, but he should not unreasonably refuse to meet a registered medical practitioner selected by the patient or by the patient's representatives, although he is entitled, if such is his opinion, to urge that the practitioner selected has not the qualifications or the experience demanded by the particular requirements of the case.

4. The arrangements for consultation should be made or initiated by the Attending Practitioner. The Attending Practitioner should ascertain in advance the amount of the fee, if any, to be paid to the practitioner consulted, and should inform the patient or his representatives that this should be paid at the time of the consultation.

5. In cases where the Consultant and the Attending Practitioner meet and personally examine the patient together, the following procedure is generally adopted and should be observed, unless in any particular instance there is substantial reason for departing from it.

(*a*) All parties meeting in consultation should be punctual, and if the Attending Practitioner fails to keep the appointment the practitioner consulted, after a reasonable time, may examine the patient, and should communicate his conclusions to the Attending Practitioner in writing and in a sealed envelope.

(*b*) If the consultation takes place at the patient's residence, the Attending Practitioner should, on entering the room of the patient, precede the practitioner consulted, and after the examination the Attending Practitioner should be the last to to leave the room.

(*c*) The diagnosis, prognosis, and treatment should be discussed by the practitioner consulted and the Attending Practitioner in private.

(*d*) The opinion on the case and the treatment as agreed should be communicated to the patient or the patient's representatives where practicable by the practitioner consulted in the presence of the Attending Practitioner.

(*e*) It is the duty of the Attending Practitioner loyally to carry out the measures agreed at or after the consultation. He should refrain from making any radical alteration in these measures except upon urgent grounds or after adequate trial.

6. If for any reason the practitioner consulted and the Attending Practitioner cannot examine the patient together, the Attending Practitioner should send to the practitioner consulted a brief history of the case. After examining the patient, the practitioner consulted should forward his opinion, together with any advice as to treatment, in a sealed envelope addressed to the Attending Practitioner. He should exercise great discretion as to the information he gives to the patient or the patient's representatives and, in particular, he should not disclose to the patient any details of any medicaments which he has advised.

In cases where the Attending Practitioner accepts the opinion and advice of the practitioner consulted he should carry out the measures which have been agreed between them; where, however, the Attending Practitioner finds he is in disagreement with the opinion and advice of the practitioner consulted he should by suitable means communicate his disagreement to the practitioner consulted.

7. Should the practitioner consulted and the Attending Practitioner hold divergent views, either on the diagnosis or on the treatment of the case, and should the Attending Practitioner be unwilling to pursue the course of action advised by the practitioner consulted, this difference of opinion should be communicated to the patient or his representatives by the practitioner consulted and the Attending

Practitioner jointly, and the patient or his representatives should then be advised either to choose one or other of the suggested alternatives or to obtain further professional advice.

Note: In the following circumstances it is especially desirable that the Attending Practitioner should endeavour to secure consultation with a colleague:

(*a*) When the propriety has to be considered of performing an operation or of adopting some course of treatment which may involve considerable risk to the life of the patient or may permanently prejudice his activities or capacities and particularly when the condition which it is sought to relieve by this treatment is not itself dangerous to life;
(*b*) When any procedure likely to result in death of a foetus or of an unborn child is contemplated, especially if labour has not commenced;
(*c*) When continued administration of any drug of addiction is deemed desirable for the relief of symptoms of addiction;
(*d*) When there is reason to suspect that the patient (i) has been subjected to an illegal operation, or (ii) is the victim of criminal poisoning or criminal assault.

8. Arrangements for any future consultation or additional investigation should be effected only with the foreknowledge and co-operation of the Attending Practitioner.

9. The practitioner consulted shall not attempt to secure for himself the care of a patient seen in consultation. It is his duty to avoid any word or action which might disturb the confidence of the patient in the Attending Practitioner. The practitioner consulted should not communicate with the patient or the patient's representatives subsequent to the consultation except with the consent of the Attending Practitioner.

10. The Attending Practitioner should carefully avoid any remark disparaging the skill or judgment of the practitioner consulted.

11. Except by mutual consent the practitioner consulted shall not supersede the Attending Practitioner during the illness with which the consultation was concerned.

OTHER INTRA-PROFESSIONAL OBLIGATIONS

Under the code of ethics of the profession a practitioner ought not to accept as his patient (except with the consent of the colleague concerned),

1. Any patient or member of a patient's household whom he has previously attended either as a consulting practitioner or as a deputy for a colleague.

2. Any patient or member of the patient's household whom he has attended within the previous two years in the capacity of assistant or locum tenens.

3. Any patient who at the time of the application is under active treatment by a colleague, unless he is personally satisfied that the colleague concerned has been notified by the patient or his representatives that his services are no longer required.

4. Any patient who so applies because his regular medical attendant is temporarily unavailable. In such case he should render whatever treatment may for the time be required, and should subsequently notify the patient's regular attendant of the steps he has taken.

5. Notwithstanding Paragraph 3 above, when a practitioner in whatever form of practice is asked for advice or treatment by a patient and has reason to believe that the patient is already under medical care and that the request is made without the knowledge of the attending practitioner, it is the duty of the practitioner so approached to urge the patient to permit him to communicate with the attending practitioner. Should the patient refuse this proposal and *if the circumstances are exceptional* the practitioner is at liberty to examine the patient and to tell the patient his findings and conclusions, but, save for any emergency which exists, he shall not accept the patient for treatment.

EXAMINING MEDICAL OFFICERS

For the purpose of this code an examining medical officer is a practitioner undertaking the examination of a patient of another practitioner at the request of a third party with the exception of examinations under statutory requirements. Paragraphs 2 and 3 below do not apply to examinations in connexion with superannuation, pre-employment, or proposals for life or sickness assurance.

(1) An Examining Practitioner must be satisfied that the individual to be examined consents, personally or through his legal representative, to submit to medical examination and understands the reason for it.

(2) When the individual to be examined is under medical care, the Examining Practitioner shall cause the Attending Practitioner to be given such notice of the time, place, and purpose of his examination as will enable the Attending Practitioner to be present should he or the patient so desire.

(Preferably such notice should be sent to the Attending Practitioner through the post, or by telephone, but in certain circumstances a communication might properly be conveyed by the patient.)

Exceptions to this are:

(*a*) When circumstances justify a surprise visit.
(*b*) When circumstances necessitate a visit within a period which does not afford time for notification.

Where the Examining Practitioner has acted under (*a*) or (*b*) he shall promptly inform the Attending Practitioner of the fact of his visit and the reason for his action.

(3) If the Attending Practitioner fails to attend at the time arranged the Examining Practitioner shall be at liberty to proceed with the examination.

(4) An Examining Practitioner must avoid any word or action which might disturb the confidence of the patient in the Attending Practitioner and must not, without the consent of the Attending Practitioner, do anything which involves interference with the treatment of the patient.

(5) An Examining Practitioner shall confine himself strictly to such investigation and examination as are necessary for the purpose of submitting an adequate report.

(6) Any proposal or suggestion which an Examining Practitioner may wish to put forward regarding treatment shall be first discussed with the Attending Practitioner either personally or by correspondence.

(7) When in the course of an examination there come to light material clinical findings, of which the Attending Practitioner is believed to be unaware, the Examining Practitioner shall, with the consent of the patient, inform the Attending Practitioner of the relevant details.

(8) An Examining Practitioner shall not utilize his position to influence the person examined to choose him as his medical attendant.

(9) When the terms of contract with his employing body interfere with the free application of this code, an examining Medical Officer shall make honest endeavour to obtain the necessary amendment of his contract either himself or through the British Medical Association.

INDUSTRIAL MEDICAL OFFICERS

Subject to statutory requirements these rules shall, where existing ethical rules or custom fail to cover the circumstances, govern the professional relationships of industrial medical officers with their medical colleagues in other branches of medical practice, with those employees under their professional care, and with managements. The rules apply not only to whole-time officers but also to those employed part-time or in any other capacity.

1. (i) When an industrial medical officer renders advice or treatment to an employee at the place of employment, and when in the employee's own interests he deems it advisable, he shall inform the employee's own doctor of the material facts.
(ii) When an industrial medical officer finds on examination that an employee is unfit for work he shall advise the employee to consult his own doctor or he may, in emergency, send him direct to hospital.
(iii) If an employee is under the care of his own doctor or of a hospital and if at the place of employment there are special facilities and equipment for continuing treatment, the industrial medical officer may arrange for such treatment with the approval of the doctor or hospital concerned.

2. When in the course of an examination of an employee for superannuation purposes, retirement or special duty, material clinical findings come to light, the industrial medical officer should with the consent of the person examined inform his doctor of the relevant details.

3. Except in emergency, an industrial medical officer shall not undertake any treatment that is normally the responsibility of the employee's own doctor, unless it be with his agreement.

4. In his capacity as industrial medical officer he shall not undertake treatment of any member of an employee's family who is not employed at the same place of work.

5. A part-time industrial medical officer shall not utilize his position to influence an employee to choose him as his medical attendant.

6. An industrial medical officer shall not, except in emergency, or where a prior understanding with local practitioners exists, send any employee direct to hospital. When he considers that attendance at hospital is necessary or advisable, he shall refer the employee to his own doctor, to whom he may make a suggestion to this effect. When, in an emergency, an industrial medical officer sends an employee to hospital, he shall inform the relatives (if the patient is likely to be detained) and also the employee's own doctor, where known.

7. When an industrial medical officer is asked by his management to report on the condition of an employee who is absent from work for health reasons and under the care of his own doctor, the industrial medical officer, before examining the patient, shall first communicate with the employee's doctor, informing him of the time and place of his intended examination.

8. An industrial medical officer should, whenever possible, respond to an invitation for consultation with an employee's own doctor.

9. An industrial medical officer shall not carry out any personal preventive measure which is purely experimental without the consent of the employee, and where desirable, the consent of the employee's own doctor.

10. The personal medical records of employees maintained by an industrial medical officer for his professional use are confidential documents. Access to them must not be allowed to any other person except with the consent of the industrial medical officer or with the consent of the employee concerned.

An industrial medical officer shall at all times be responsible for the safe custody of his records. On the termination of his appointment he shall hand over his records only to the industrial medical officer who shall succeed him in the appointment.

If there is no successor to his appointment, the industrial medical officer retains his responsibility for the safe custody of his records or for their destruction.

11. An industrial medical officer shall not disclose his knowledge of industrial processes acquired by virtue of his appointment except with the permission of his management or when so required in Courts of Law.

12. When an industrial medical officer has examined an applicant for employment, and as a result of the examination employment is subsequently refused, the industrial medical officer may disclose his decision to the applicant and, when authorized, may disclose the findings to his own doctor.

ADVISORY NOTES

(1) When an industrial medical officer addresses a communication to the employee's own doctor and receives no reply within a reasonable time, he shall be at liberty to assume that the employee's own doctor takes no exception to the contents of his communication. It is important in the employee's interest that no opportunity of useful co-operation between the employee's doctor and the industrial medical officer should be neglected. Such co-operation may be

of particular value when an employee is under treatment for an occupational disease of which the industrial medical officer has special experience.

(2) Industrial medical officers should not make statements as to liability in the case of accidents at the place of work except when so required in Courts of Law.

GUIDANCE FOR PROFESSIONAL CONDUCT IN RELATION TO DENTISTS

(As agreed between the British Medical Association and the British Dental Association)

CONSULTATIONS

(1) Where a patient, in the opinion of his medical attendant, needs dental treatment, the patient should be referred in all but exceptional circumstances to his own dentist. In the event of the patient having no regular dentist, there is no objection to a doctor recommending a dentist of his own choice.

(2) When on behalf of one of his patients a doctor wishes to consult a dentist, the doctor should communicate in the first instance with the patient's own dentist. In the event of the patient having no regular dentist there is no objection to the doctor consulting the dentist of his own choice.

(3) Where the dentist has reason to believe that the patient has some constitutional disorder and considers some major dental procedure is necessary he should consult the patient's doctor before carrying out such treatment.

(4) Where there is a conflict of opinion between a doctor and a dentist concerning the diagnosis and/or treatment of the condition of a patient, they should consult with each other to reach an agreement which is satisfactory to both.

Where the conflict of opinion remains unresolved, the patient should be so informed and invited to choose one of the alternatives or assisted to obtain other professional advice.

ANAESTHETICS

When an anaesthetic is advised by the dentist, it is competent for him to select the anaesthetist, but, if such anaesthetist is not the patient's doctor, no objection should be taken to the patient inviting his doctor to be present. Where the operation proposed is a major one, or if it is known to the dentist that the patient is under medical care, the dentist should consult the patient's doctor upon the operation proposed and should invite him to be present if the patient so desires. Similarly, where the patient is under dental care and the doctor advises operative or other major treatment arising from the patient's dental condition, the dentist should be consulted.

On the completion of any dental operation, and especially if there is any reason to think that post-operative complications may ensue, the patient should be advised to consult the dentist immediately if such complications arise and the dentist should take all reasonable steps to facilitate such consultation.

APPENDIX D

ACTS AND REGULATIONS

(In this Appendix are listed Acts and Regulations relating to the subject matter of the Chapters of the book. Where reference to this Appendix is made in the text, see below under the appropriate Chapter.)

CHAPTERS 1 TO 6

The Privy Council, the General Medical Council—Medical Registration and Discipline

The Medical Act, 1858.
The Medical Act, 1886.
The Medical Act, 1950.
The Medical Act, 1956.
The Medical Practitioners Act, 1951 (Republic of Ireland).

Certificate of Incapacity from Unregistered Persons

The National Insurance (Medical Certification) Regulations, 1948, S.I.1175.

These Regulations refer to certificates 'from registered medical practitioners or by such other means as the authority may accept in a particular case'.

CHAPTER 10

Medical Auxiliaries

The National Health Service (Medical Auxiliaries) Regulations, 1954, S.I.55.
The National Health Service (Medical Auxiliaries) (Scotland) Regulations, 1954, S.I.77.

CHAPTER 13

Fees for Witnesses

Criminal Procedure, England.
The Witnesses Allowances Regulations, 1955, S.I.1655.

CHAPTER 14

The Coroner

The Coroners Act, 1954.

The Coroners Rules, 1953, S.I.205; 1956, S.I.1991.
The Coroners (Fees and Allowances) Rules, 1955, S.I.1668.

CHAPTER 16, *Births*

CHAPTER 17, *Deaths*

The Births and Deaths Registration Act, 1953.
The Registration of Births, Deaths and Marriages (Scotland) Acts, 1854–1938.
The National Insurance (Maternity Benefit and Miscellaneous Provisions) Regulations, 1954.
The Anatomy Acts, 1832 and 1871.
The Cremation Act, 1952.
The Corneal Grafting Act, 1952.

CHAPTER 18

Notification of Infectious Diseases

The Public Health Act, 1936.
The Public Health (Scotland) Act, 1945.
The Public Health (London) Act, 1936.

Notification of Industrial Diseases

The Factories Acts, 1937 and 1948.
Pneumoconiosis and Byssinosis Benefit Act, 1951.
The Industrial Diseases (Benefit) Act, 1954.
The Pneumoconiosis and Byssinosis Benefit Scheme, 1952, S.I.373 and 1301.
The Pneumoconiosis and Byssinosis Benefit Amendment Scheme, 1954, S.I.1444.

CHAPTER 19

Mental Disorders and Deficiency

The National Health Service Act, 1946 (Part V and Eighth Schedule).
The National Health Service (Scotland) Act, 1947 (Part V and Ninth Schedule).

(In the Schedules to these Acts are to be found reference to relevant sections of other enactments on these subjects.)

The National Health Service (Emergency Mental Treatment) Regulations, 1948 (S.I.1075) and 1950 (S.I.1224).

CHAPTER 20

Divorce and Nullity

The Matrimonial Causes Act, 1937.

The Divorce (Scotland) Act, 1938.

CHAPTER 21

Drugs

The Pharmacy and Poisons Act, 1933.

The Poisons Rules, 1952, S.I.2086 and 2260; 1953, S.I.1301; 1954, S.I.267 and 1096; 1955, S.I.1135 and 1978.

The Poisons List Order, 1953, S.I.1300 (amended by S.I.266 and 1095 of 1954; S.I.1134 and 1977 of 1955).

The Dangerous Drugs Act, 1951.

The Dangerous Drugs Regulations, 1953, S.I.499; 1954, S.I. 1047; 1957, S.I.704.

The Dangerous Drugs (Application) Orders, 1952, S.I.347 and 2106; 1954, S.I.1029 and 1367; 1955, S.I.872; 1956, S.I.817.

The Dangerous Drugs (Relaxation) Orders, 1952, S.I.1861; 1953, S.I.397; 1954, S.I.1030.

The Export of Goods (Control) (Consolidated) Order, 1954, S.I.118.

The Radioactive Substances Act, 1956.

The Therapeutic Substances Act, 1956.

The Therapeutic Substances (Sale and Supply) Regulations, 1956, S.I.346; Amendment Regulations, 1957, S.I.550.

CHAPTER 22

Abortion

The Offences against the Person Act, 1861.

The Infant Life (Preservation) Act, 1929.

CHAPTER 24

Adoption

The Adoption of Children Acts, 1926 and 1949.

The Adoption of Children (Scotland) Act, 1930.

The Adoption Act, 1950.

The Adoption Societies Regulations, 1943, S.R. and O. 1306.

The Adoption of Children Rules, 1949, S.I.2396.

The Adoption of Children Rules, 1950, S.I.80.

Boarded out Children

The Children's Act, 1948 (Section 14 and 33 (3) and Second Schedule, para. 44)).

The Boarding out of Children Regulations, 1955, S.I.1377.

Habitual Drunkards

The Habitual Drunkards Act, 1879.

Fees

The Road Traffic Act, 1934, Section 16.

Veterinary Work and Vivisection

The Cruelty to Animals Act, 1876.

CHAPTERS 26 TO 33

The General Practitioner in the National Health Service

The National Health Service Act, 1946.
The National Health Service (Scotland) Acts, 1947 and 1951.
The National Health Service (Amendment) Act, 1949.
The National Health Service Act, 1951.
The National Health Service Act, 1952.
The Public Health Act, 1936 (of which the following sections were repeated by the N.H.S. Act, 1946—171, 173–178, 180–186, 197, 200-202, 203 (4) and 204.
The Public Health (London) Act, 1936 (of which the following sections were repeated by the N.H.S. Act, 1946—13, 219–223, 225–233, 250–254, 255 (5), 256).

Regulations and Terms of Service for General Practitioners

National Health Service (General Medical and Pharmaceutical Services) Regulations, 1954, S.I.669.
National Health Service (General Medical and Pharmaceutical Services) (Amendment) Regulations, 1956, S.I.1076.
National Health Service (General Medical and Pharmaceutical Services) (Scotland) Regulations, 1955, S.I.1942.

Certification

The National Insurance (Medical Certification) Regulations, 1948, S.I.1175.

Executive Councils (Chapter 29)

National Health Service Act, 1946, Section 31 and Fifth Schedule (as amended by the National Health Service (Amendment) Act, 1949).
National Health Service (Scotland) Act, 1947, Section 32 and Sixth Schedule (as amended by the National Health Service (Amendment) Act, 1949).

National Health Service (Executive Councils) Regulations, 1954, S.I.224.

The National Health Service (Executive Councils) (Constitution) (Scotland) Order, 1947, S.I.1358.

The National Health Service (Executive Councils) (Variation of Constitution) Order, 1947, S.I.610.

The Isles of Scilly (National Health Service) Order, 1948, S.I.167.

The Isles of Scilly (National Health Service) Order, 1950, S.I.1835.

Medical Practices Committees (*Chapter* 30)

National Health Service Act, 1946, Section 34 and Sixth Schedule.

National Health Service (Scotland) Act, 1947, Section 35 and Seventh Schedule.

National Health Service (Amendment) Act, 1949, Section 15.

Service Committees and Tribunals (*Chapter* 31)

National Health Service (Service Committees and Tribunal) Regulations, 1956, S.I.1077.

(N.B. The constitution of Service Committees is different in the Scilly Isles and some of the clauses do not apply to that area—see Regulation 48.)

National Health Service Act, 1946, Section 42 and Seventh Schedule.

National Health Service (Scotland) Act, 1947, Section 43 and Eighth Schedule.

Supplementary Ophthalmic Services (*Chapter* 33)

National Health Service (Supplementary Ophthalmic Services) Regulations, 1956, S.I.1078.

National Health Service (Supplementary Ophthalmic Services) (Scotland) Regulations, 1948, S.I.1450; 1956, S.I.41.

Medical Practitioners called in by Midwives (*Chapter* 33)

The Medical Practitioners (Fees) (No. 2) Regulations, 1948, S.I.695.

The Medical Practitioners (Fees) (Scotland) Regulations, 1948, S.I.1431.

(For details of fees see *The Medical Practitioners' Handbook* or Appendix VII of the *Scottish Handbook for General Medical Practitioners*.)

CHAPTER 34

Superannuation

National Health Service (Superannuation) Regulations, 1955, S.I.1084.

National Health Service (Superannuation) (Scotland) Regulations, 1955, S.I.1143.

National Health Service (Superannuation) (England and Scotland) (Amendment) Regulations, 1957, S.I.788.

APPENDIX E

CERTIFICATES UNDER THE NATIONAL HEALTH SERVICE ACT

The certificates which must be issued free of charge are laid down in a Schedule to the Terms of Service and are listed below.

In addition a practitioner must issue free of charge any certificate required for the purposes of the National Insurance Acts, 1946, in accordance with any Regulations made under those Acts.

CERTIFICATES UNDER THE NATIONAL HEALTH SERVICE ACT

Practitioners who provide general medical services under this Act are required to issue free of charge to persons on their list only those certificates which are prescribed by the Regulations. The certificates are:

Medical Certificate	*Short Title of Enactment Under or for the Purpose of which Certificate Required*
To support a claim or obtain a payment either personally or by proxy under the enactments specified	Family Allowances Act, 1945. National Insurance (Industrial Injuries Act, 1946. National Insurance Act, 1946.
To prove inability to work or incapacity for self-support for the purposes of an award by the Minister of Pensions and National Insurance. To enable proxy to draw pensions, etc.	Pensions (Navy, Army, Air Force and Mercantile Marine) Act, 1939. Pensions (Mercantile Marine) Act, 1942. Naval and Marine Pay and Pensions Act, 1856. Air Force (Constitution) Act, 1917. Personal Injuries (Emergency Provisions) Act, 1939. Polish Resettlement Act, 1947.

Medical Certificate	*Short Title of Enactment Under or for the Purpose of which Certificate Required*
To establish pregnancy or other medical grounds for the purpose of obtaining extra coal or welfare foods	Emergency Powers (Defence) Acts, 1939–45, as having effect by virtue of the Supplies and Services (Transitional Powers) Act, 1945, and Supplies and Services (Extended Purposes) Act, 1947.
To obtain permission to import foreign drugs and appliances. To obtain permission to export special foods with sick traveller or with infant of two years of age or under	Import, Export and Customs Powers (Defence) Act, 1939.
To enable patient to have his sight tested under the Supplementary Opthalmic Services	National Health Service Act, 1946. National Health Service (Scotland) Act, 1947.
To establish fitness to receive nitrous oxide and air analgesia in childbirth	Midwives Act, 1951. Midwives (Scotland) Acts, 1915 and 1927.
To secure registration of stillbirth	Births and Deaths Registration Act, 1953. Registration of Stillbirths (Scotland) Act, 1938.
To enable payment to be made to another person in case of mental disability of person entitled to payment from public funds. To justify release of patient from detention after absence on trial	Lunacy Act, 1890. Superannuation Act, 1887.
To establish unfitness for jury service	Juries Act, 1922. Jurors (Scotland) Act, 1825. Jurors (Enrolment of Women) (Scotland) Act, 1920.

Medical Certificate	*Short Title of Enactment Under or for the Purpose of which Certificate Required*
To establish unfitness to attend for medical examination	National Service Act, 1948.
To support late application for reinstatement in civil employment or notification of non-availability to take up employment, owing to sickness	National Service Act, 1948. Reinstatement in Civil Employment Act, 1944. Reinstatement in Civil Employment Act, 1950. Reserve and Auxiliary Forces (Training) Act, 1951.
To enable disabled persons to be registered as an absent voter	Representation of the People Act, 1949.

APPENDIX F

FEES

CHAPTER 1

	£	s.	d.
For provisional registration	5	5	0
For full registration:			
After provisional registration	6	6	0
For any other person	11	11	0
Alteration of name in Register	0	5	0
Certified copy of entry in Register	0	2	6

CHAPTER 14

	£	s.	d.
Fees under the Coroners (Fees and Allowances) Rules, 1955, S.I.1668:			
Post-mortem examination	4	4	0
Post-mortem examination and attending inquest as witness	6	6	0
Each subsequent day of attendance at inquest ..	3	3	0
Attendance at inquest other than in connexion with a post-mortem examination	3	3	0

CHAPTER 17

	£	s.	d.
For Cremation Certificate, Form B or Form C, plus a mileage allowance of 1*s.* a mile or part of a mile each way outside a radius of two miles. (Fees recommended by the British Medical Association)	2	2	0

CHAPTER 18

	£	s.	d.
For notification of Infectious Disease	0	2	6
For notification of Industrial Disease	0	2	6

CHAPTER 24

	£	s.	d.
Road Traffic Act:			
Fee for each victim of accident attended ..	0	12	6
Mileage fee: per mile travelled less four miles ..	0	0	6

CHAPTER 25

	£	s.	d.
Boarded out Children:			
Fee for initial examination..	1	5	0
Fee for subsequent examination	0	12	6
National Insurance Contributions (weekly) as from July 1, 1958:			
Self-employed person (Class 2), male	0	12	0
female	0	10	0
Employed person (Class 1):			
Male—Employer's contribution	0	8	3
Employee's contribution	0	9	11
Female—Employer's contribution	0	6	9
Employee's contribution	0	8	0
For Insurance Examination and Report (as agreed between the British Medical Association and the Life Offices Association):			
'Short' form (policy not above £300)	0	15	0
More comprehensive report	2	2	0
Report without examination, no fee laid down (usually 10*s*. 6*d*. to £1 1*s*. 0*d*.)			

CHAPTER 26

	£	s.	d.
Temporary Resident Fee	0	17	0
Special Temporary Resident Fee (convalescent homes, camps, etc.)	0	8	6
Emergency Treatment, in areas where a scheme operates, normally:			
1. Emergency consultation (at any place or time)	0	8	6
2. Minor surgical operation requiring general anaesthetic, treatment of fracture; reduction of dislocation or administration of nitrous oxide of ethyl chloride	0	15	0
3. Administration of general anaesthetic other than nitrous oxide of ethyl chloride	1	15	0
Services of a second practitioner to administer an anaesthetic	1	15	0
Or in the case of nitrous oxide or ethyl chloride	0	15	0

CHAPTER 27

Trainee Assistants:

Training grant to trainer, £150 p.a.

Grant for salary and boarding of trainee, not more than £850 p.a.

Car allowance, £200 p.a.

Fee for Arresting Dental Haemorrhage in Emergency:

12*s.* 6*d.* for each visit or attendance. Fee to be claimed from the dentist.

General Practitioners in the Hospital Service:

Terms and Conditions of Service of Hospital Medical and Dental Staff.

Para. 10 (*a*), Payment per bed p.a., £26 5*s.*

Para. 10 (*b*), Payment p.a. to practitioner for each weekly half-day, £183 15*s.*

Maximum remuneration p.a., £1,653 15*s.*

CHAPTER 32

National Health Service (General Medical Services):

Capitation fee, 17*s.* 6*d.* Loading (501–1,500) 11*s.* 6*d.* per capita.

CHAPTER 33

For notification of vaccination or immunization, 5*s.*

APPENDIX G

THE POISONS RULES, 1952

(See Chapter 21)

Fourth Schedule

(as amended by S.I.1301 of 1953, 267 of 1954, 1978 of 1955)

Substances required to be sold by retail only upon a prescription given by a duly qualified medical practitioner, registered dentist, registered veterinary surgeon or registered veterinary practitioner.

Allylisopropylacetylurea.
Amidopyrine; its salts; amidopyrine sulphonates; their salts.
Anti-histamine substances, the following; their salts, their molecular compounds.

Antazoline.
Bromazine.
Chlorcyclizine.
Diphenhydramine.
3-Di-n-butylaminomethyl-4 : 5 : 6-trihydroxyphthalide.
Phenindamine.
Promethazine.
Substances being tetra-substituted N derivatives of ethylenediamine or propylenediamine.
Barbituric acid; its salts; derivatives of barbituric acid; their salts; compounds of barbituric acid, its salts, its derivatives, their salts, with any other substance.

Beta-aminopropylbenzene, its salts; its N-alkyl derivatives; their salts; beta-aminoisopropylbenzene; its salts; its N-alkyl derivatives; their salts.
Chlorpromazine; its salts.
1 : 4-Dimethanesulphonoxybutane; its salts.
Dinitrocresols (DNC); their compounds with a metal or a base, except preparations for use in agriculture or horticulture.
Dinitronaphthols; dinitrophenols; dinitrothymols.
Disulfiram.
Dithienylallylamine compounds; their salts, except diethylthiambutene, dimethylthiambutene and ethylmethylthiambutene.
Fallamine; its salts; its quaternary compounds.
6-Mercaptopurine Mustine; its salts.

Para-aminobenzenesulphonamide; its salts; derivatives of para-aminobenzenesulphonamide having any of the hydrogen atoms of the para-amino group or of the sulphonamide group substituted by another radical; their salts, except when contained in ointments or surgical dressings or in preparations for the treatment of coccidiosis in poultry.
Paramethadione.
Phenylacetylurea.
Phenylbutazone; its salts.
Phenylcinchoninic acid; salicylcinchoninic acid; their salts; their esters.
Polymethylenebistrimethylammonium salts.
Sulphonal; alkyl sulphonals.
Tri-(2-Chloroethyl)amine; its salts.
Triethanomelamine; its salts.
Troxidone.

THE DANGEROUS DRUGS ACT

(See Chapter 21)

The following appendices, containing lists of drugs, are to be found in the Memorandum issued by the Home Office, 'The Duties of Doctors and Dentists under the Dangerous Drugs Act and Regulations,' D.D. 101, 6th edition, February 1956, H.M.S.O., price 9*d*.

Appendix II

List of drugs whose prescription and supply by doctors and dentists is controlled under the Dangerous Drugs Act, 1951, and the Dangerous Drugs Regulations, 1953.

N.B.—To this list the following were added by the Dangerous Drugs Act, 1951 (Application) Order, 1956, S.I.817:

1 : 3-Dimethyl-4-phenyl-4-propionyloxyhexamethyleneimine, its salts and any preparation, admixture, extract or other substance containing any proportion of 1 : 3-dimethyl-4-phenyl-4-propionyloxyhexamethyleneimine.

3-Hydroxy-N-phenethylmorphinan, its salts and any preparation, admixture, extract or other substance containing any proportion of 3-hydroxy-N-phenethylmorphinan.

4-Morpholino-2 : 2-diphenyl ethyl butyrate, its salts and any preparation, admixture, extract or other substance containing any proportion of 4-morpholino-2 : 2-diphenyl ethyl butyrate.

4-Dimethylamino-1 : 2-diphenyl-3-methyl-2-propionyloxybutane, its salts and any preparation, admixture, extract or other substance containing any proportion of 4-dimethylamino-1 : 2-diphenyl-3-methyl-2-propionyloxybutane.

Appendix III b

Preparations which are exempted from the provisions of the Dangerous Drugs Regulations, 1953.

APPENDIX H

LIST OF NOTIFIABLE DISEASES

Infectious Diseases

The following infectious diseases are notifiable:

ENGLAND AND WALES

Smallpox.
Cholera.
Diphtheria.
Membranous croup.
Paratyphoid.
Erysipelas.
Scarlatina or scarlet fever.
Fevers known by the name typhus, typhoid, enteric or relapsing.
Whooping cough.
Plague.
Acute poliomyelitis (including polio-encephalitis).
Acute encephalitis.
Meningococcal infection.
Malaria.
Dysentery (includes amoebic and bacillary dysentery).
Acute primary pneumonia.
Acute influenzal pneumonia.
Ophthalmia neonatorum (to M.O.H. of Maternity and Child Welfare Authority).
Measles.
Leprosy (direct to Chief Medical Officer, Ministry of Health).
Food poisoning.
Tuberculosis (*a*).
Puerperal pyrexia (*b*).

SCOTLAND

Acute poliomyelitis (including acute polio-encephalitis).
Acute influenzal pneumonia.
Acute primary pneumonia.
Cerebro-spinal fever.
Cholera.
Continuing fever or puerperal fever.

Diphtheria.
Dysentery.
Encephalitis lethargica.
Erysipelas.
Infective jaundice.
Leprosy.
Malaria.
Membranous croup.
Ophthalmia neonatorum.
Plague.
Puerperal pyrexia.
Relapsing fever.
Scarlet fever.
Smallpox.
Tuberculosis.
Typhoid or enteric fever.
Typhus fever.
Whooping cough.

The Regulations require every medical practitioner who diagnoses tuberculosis from evidence other than that of a tuberculin test to notify the Medical Officer of Health on a special form. The notification must be sent so that its contents cannot be observed during transmission.

(*a*) Paragraph 5 of the relevant Regulations (S.I.704 of 1952) explains that the notification by a hospital of a case of tuberculosis should be sent to the Medical Officer of Health of the district in which the patient normally lives. Notification to the Medical Officer of Health of the district in which the hospital is situate is only necessary when, with long-stay patients, the hospital itself may reasonably be regarded as the place of residence of the patient.

(*b*) The new form of certificate introduced by the 1954 Regulations to be used for notification of Puerperal Pyrexia (S.I.1169) includes a statement of the cause, if known, as well as the age, date of confinement or miscarriage and date of onset of the disease. If the patient is an inmate of a hospital the place from which she was admitted is to be stated, and whether the case occurred in general practice or in an institution.

List of Notifiable Industrial Diseases

The following is a list of diseases notifiable:

Poisoning by lead, phosphorus, mercury, arsenic, manganese, carbon bisulphide, aniline.

Chronic benzene poisoning.
Toxic jaundice.
Toxic anaemia.
Compressed-air illness.
Anthrax.
Epitheliomatous ulceration through pitch, tar or mineral oils.
Chrome ulceration.

INDEX